D1488401

LES NUITS DE PARIS

"THE NOCTURNAL SPECTATOR"

Based on the frontispiece of
the original 1788–1794 edition of *Les Nuits de Paris*

LES

NUITS

DE

PARIS

or

THE NOCTURNAL SPECTATOR

by

Nicolas-Edme RESTIF de la Bretonne

A SELECTION

Translated from the French by
LINDA ASHER *and* ELLEN FERTIG

With an introduction by
JACQUES BARZUN

Random House
NEW YORK

RESTIF DE LA BRETONNE

by Jacques Barzun

In France, where literary passions equal in intensity
and organization the American love of sports and hob-
bies, there are Balzacians and Proustians, Beylists (who
worship Stendhal) and Flaubertists. These people
know the works of their idols, their lives, and their
connections, to the remotest cousin. Among the recognized clans of this sort there is a growing body of
Restivists, devotees of the strange character and writer
who called himself Restif de la Bretonne.

I am not a Restivist. Even if I had the requisite
enthusiasm for the man and also the collector's lust for
facts distantly related to a subject of interest, I should
not pass the first trial of strength, which is to read and
reread all the works: Restif managed in seventy-two
years of life to produce some two hundred and forty
volumes. Of this output, one work is a minor masterpiece—the *Life of My Father*. Another is an autobiography in sixteen volumes, dedicated by the author to
the author, whose purpose explicitly derives from Rousseau's *Confessions*. We have it on record that Valéry

thought Restif "far superior" to Rousseau. But that is the sally of an often perverse critic. Restif was not so much original as (to transliterate the French idiom) "*an* original," that is, an eccentric whose singularity did not end with himself but left ideas and writings to which we return with curiosity and pleasure.

These pleasurable writings are found scattered through the hundreds of volumes, and it is from one of them, conceived as a supplement to the Autobiography, that the present selection of *Les Nuits de Paris* has been made. The first version, published in 1788, contained three hundred and eighty-one nights, but it was added to during the Revolution and was completed by 1794. The way in which the *Nights* were supposed to supplement Restif's confessions appears when we know that his intention in the former book was to "unveil the human heart." The *Nights* disclose new aspects of life that the author came upon in later years and extend the unveiling to an enlarged number of fellow citizens.

It is thanks to this aim and its persistence that Restif finds himself unwittingly in tune with our modern sensibility. Writers have always sought to unveil the heart. That is literature's business; and despite the psychologists it has remained virtually a monopoly. In the disrobement each generation of writers believes that all previous revelings have been incomplete or illusory, a belief which is perhaps the strongest urge to writing. If one can measure that urge by its quantitative product, Restif was moved by a colossal force. Yet, as I say, his particular desire is in no way unusual. What brings him close to us is, first, the similarity between certain features of his time and ours and, second, the mixture of rationality and wild instinct with which his intermittent genius seized upon reality and transferred it to the written page. In that encounter he even acquired some of our poses and fashioned some of our tricks of style.

Restif was born in a village of Lower Burgundy in 1734. Though he had remote forebears in the judiciary he came of peasant stock, his name being simply Nicolas Restif. La Bretonne was the name of a farm, added later—eighteenth-century fashion—to enhance the sound and importance of the literary trademark he wished to establish. Restif pretended that he was descended from the Roman Emperor Pertinax, whose name means the same as *restif*, that is to say, stubborn. This was not his only quality. Restif was precocious besides, and in more ways than one. He was taught at a good Jansenist grammar school, but certainly did not receive there the knowledge that enabled him to have had twelve love affairs by the age of fifteen and twenty illegitimate children by the time of his majority. This roster was of course compiled by the performer himself, who half a century later wound up that part of his life's activity with a recapitulation in successive paragraphs of seven hundred amours—a sort of Who's Who, which the author and beneficiary put into his memoirs under the engaging rubric of "My Calendar."

Apprenticed as a youth to a printer in Auxerre, Restif promptly made love to his master's wife while reading one of Voltaire's plays aloud to her. She was apparently the great passion of his life, a fact that he memorialized by falling in love with every woman who resembled her; he was especially susceptible to the distinction of small feet.

So far, we are still in the eighteenth century: I mean that the mixture of literature and love-making, like the tolerance for private acts which today would lead to dismissal and a bad employment record, takes us back to an age of social and emotional latitude. We are quite sure that Restif did not feel compunction, or regret his mistress's compliance, until she showed the untimely trait of sincere repentance. She is said to have sickened and died over her transgression. Her husband, meanwhile, knew all and sought a mild revenge. He found it by arranging that Nicolas should marry a certain Agnès Lebègue, whose reputation in the town was not of the best. That she was attractive and kind seems borne out by the fact that the fastidious philosopher Joubert (one of Matthew Arnold's favorites) loved her in his youth. But Agnès and her husband did not get on, the chief cause being that she was also a writer. He complained of her extravagant outlay for pen, ink, and paper, and very likely the sense of competition on both sides soured their forty years of married life: this scrimmage over careers is where we enter the atmosphere of the twentieth century.

Restif was modern also in the ease with which he let his literary work combine utility and the satisfaction of his wrongs. He made a book out of Agnès: *The Unfaithful Wife.* When she died, he promptly married an Englishwoman whom he had met a few days before at the zoo. A few days more and she ran away with his furniture. Yet again a few days and she was laid out in a new book, aptly entitled: *National Prejudices.*

The readiness with which women yielded to Restif has made critics liken him to Casanova, whom indeed he resembles in his voluminous preoccupation with himself. One should note that these self-centered beings are still eighteenth-century writers; which should dispose once and for all of the tedious cliché about Rousseau and Romanticism having introduced the ego into literature. Neither Rousseau nor any other Romanticist rivals these two relentless recorders of their own intimate vicissitudes. It may in fact have been that quality of self-absorption that made Restif attractive to women:

the trait is childlike. And it is also generally true that a person who finds himself entrancing is likely to entrance others, if only out of curiosity. At any rate, it was not a handsome physique or the charm of conversation that captivated the women of Restif's acquaintance. He was short, thick, very dark of face, with a hooked nose and burning black eyes; oddly dressed and not very clean; at once nervous, restless, and self-confident; uttering foolish or confused ideas, making vain or obscene remarks, falling into a rage or a tearful apostrophe to conventional sentiment: Restif was undoubtedly a spectacle as well as the "Spectator" we find in the *Nights*. He might even pass for Rameau's Nephew as Diderot portrays him, were it not that the nephew is a more calculating character, more critical because more imaginative.

Restif indeed boasted that he had no imagination. What he hoped to catch the ear of posterity with was his truthfulness, his factuality—what some would call today his "valuable material." Of the fifteen or sixteen hundred stories that he concocted, all (according to him) were the truth. The reader of the *Nights* shall judge, but truthfulness is not the point. The point is the democratic and scientific attitude, the sociological stance. Restif is a pedant and a fact-grubber like modern man. On one occasion he called on the Comte de Tilly to ask him for anecdotes of his erotic past, anticipating both Dr. Kinsey and the technique of "oral history," though without a tape recorder. The forty-two volumes of Restif's *Contemporaines* were gathered in the same way. And though he undoubtedly embellished, his devotion to the reality principle marks the advent of the common man in the history of art. In the midst of, or as a prologue to his most storylike adventures, Restif will discuss the right term to denote a certain kind of rain gutter at the edge of a roof, or the political and social origins of the traffic problems created by the rich when they use their carriages on city and country roads.

These passages of preaching or analysis would be digressions if they resulted from mere incoherence of mind. They proceed in fact from literary principle. In his memoirs, to which the *Nights* are an Appendix of facts, he means to give the "moral anatomy" of mankind. He differentiates himself from Rousseau by saying that Rousseau depicted the man of genius; whereas he, Restif, will dissect the ordinary man. The upshot will be "natural history" and will thus form "a useful complement to Buffon," words which suggest Balzac's Preface to the *Comédie Humaine* sixty years later, where the novelist professes to give a "zoology of society," not after Buffon this time, but after the evolutionist Geoffroy St. Hilaire.

Restif's *Contemporaines or The Adventures of the Prettiest Women of Paris* is akin to Balzac's Scenes of City Life. The first half of Restif's *Monsieur Nicolas* supplies the Scenes of Rural Life. Many lesser works in only six, eight, or ten volumes, such as *The Perverted Peasant* (male and female, in different series), complete the panorama. But fiction is not the only form Restif adopts to satisfy his sense of mission. In dozens of other works he employs direct discourse. He is an indefatigable Utopian who diagnoses social ills and proposes remedies in education, law, language, the theater, the nature and social position of women, the science of man and society. These works constitute the series entitled *Singular Ideas* and comprising: *The Educographer, The Thesmographer, The Glossographer, The Mimographer, The Gynographers, The Andrographer,* and, with a disarming literalism that makes Henry Miller seem bashful, *The Pornographer.*

In this mass of notions ranging from the prohibition of inheritance and the regulation of prostitutes to a kind of communist exchange of labor and goods according to need and without money, one finds many ideas no longer singular; they are commonplace whether as proposals or as reforms long since adopted. To say this is only to say that Restif was a child of the Enlightenment, in which the desire to repair and remold man and society brought forth every scheme and fancy we know today. We have not gone beyond, except insofar as realization goes beyond conception. For many who were *philosophes*, or on the fringe of the movement, the Revolution seemed at first the embodiment of utopia. Restif, who boasted that "he knew the people," had predicted the outbreak, but he was soon disenchanted with its effects.

He did know the people, their worst side especially, and during the feverish two years before 1789, there began for him a period of fear for his life and suppressed rage at what he saw, of living upon dreams and memories and yielding to old neurotic habits, which quite in the modern manner led to his best art. Suffering from anxiety in our sense, reaching often a paranoid state which sharpened his awareness of reality while decking it out with imaginary terrors, he began to write the book which, as usual, he called by different names—*The French Thousand and One Nights, The Night Owl, The Philosopher Owl*—and which finally became *Les Nuits de Paris* or *The Nocturnal Spectator*.

What holds together the anecdotes of the *Nights* is the fiction, based on slender fact, that Restif had promised a compassionate Marquise to bring to her notice all cases worthy of her succor, especially those of young girls in danger of mistreatment or already victims of it. As a scheme for literary construction, this is probably the flimsiest ever devised; but as an envelope for Restif's own observations and egotistical-libidinous dreams, it is perfect. For twenty years he had been a night prowler, haunting particularly the Île Saint-Louis in the middle of the Seine next to the Cité, the core of the oldest Paris, in the shadow of Notre Dame, the Palais de Justice, and the Sainte-Chapelle. There Restif used to wander in the dusk, inscribing on walls and quays the initials, dates, and Latin phrases for his cherished "anniversaries." "The future," he tells us, "is to me a great gulf, which frightens me and which I dare not plumb, but I do what people do who are afraid of the water—I throw a stone into it. An event happens to me; I write it down, then I add, 'What shall I think of this a year from now, to the day, to the hour?' The thought tickles and nags me; I follow its development the whole year long, and since nearly every day is the anniversary of some event I have noted, every day brings me some new enjoyment. I say to myself: 'Here I am at this future time whose veil I should never have dared to lift before.'"

Restif's feeling for these anniversaries makes us think of Stendhal, who might have written like his elder: ". . . it is for me a delicious emotion to find a date beneath which I have expressed the state of my soul as it was two, three, or four years ago. If that state was sad, even horrible, I thrill with joy like a man saved from shipwreck. If it was happy, I draw comparisons and my soul melts. If it was melting then, I feel it anew, the strength of my emotion grows, it intoxicates me, and I weep again."

Whether Restif's contemporaries understood the man in their midst who had furnished them with a libraryful of gallant, even salacious, adventure stories, may be questioned. When they went to his pages they were going slumming. On one occasion indeed, a dinner was given for a choice group of high-placed ladies and gentlemen, including Talleyrand, all wearing masks, that they might freely enjoy the singular writer's company. He spoke to them of his old-fashioned tastes, and why he clung to them. He amused the company by telling them how he wanted his engraver to draw women in tight waists to make them svelte, and in very high heels, which "sylphidize the leg." But Restif's fantasies were more than old-fashioned, just as the aristocrats' slumming was more than a fad: both were signs of an approaching dissolution. When dreams and realities are in violent contrast and the contrast becomes an obsession, it means that the world and the inner life are locked in a death struggle. And it is always the dream that conquers, though seldom in the shape it first wore.

The *Nights* is an endless depiction of those dreams and realities of decay. We can feel as well as see them, for they are out of our experience too. The "Spectator" is an incipient *voyeur* of horrors, as his own titles suggest: "The Den of Iniquity," "The Graverobbers," "The Drunkard's Rebuke," "The Ragwoman," "The Dance Hall" (where transvestites abound)—and so on down the moral sewers of the town. On his own island, the juvenile delinquents persecute the elderly Owl, rub out his anniversary inscriptions and jeer and throw stones at him. These youths are the raw material for the gang of bandits—looters, pimps, white slavers, sadists—who will enliven the Revolutionary mob and whom Restif tilts against like a second Don Quixote. Before violence broke out, were they real or merely divined, then exaggerated and multiplied by the fancy of a man whose erotic oestrus cloaked itself as benevolence and indignation? They were real; we have independent proof. But they live in words as a personification of the evil that Restif apprehended and wanted to overcome by goodness. This is the fantasy of all revolutions—to put down evil in a bloodbath and fraternal embraces.

But the abstract evil is only the shadow of the

concrete evil, which is the city. The streets, the night of Dickens and Baudelaire are prefigured in Restif's pages; which is one reason why Gérard de Nerval wrote of him as one of the *Illuminés*. Lonely and nameless, the small, unimportant city ghosts move in the dark, friend indistinguishable from enemy; so that when Restif plays the archangel to some victim of lust or violence he is suspected and disbelieved. The city is assumed to be necessarily evil because everyone is an unknown, is lost, and soon loses himself. On the land, as Restif shows in his rural tales, strangers do not exist, and the peasant must be *perverted* to be evil. Hence Restif's indignation against the revolutionaries, whose measures increase urban individualism and selfishness, instead of ushering in the brotherhood of man. The final *Nights* were added after the close of the book, to deal with the failure of the dream of redemption, one year after the taking of the Bastille: "Take up your darkling flight again, Night Owl; utter a few more funereal cries as you roam the lonely streets of this vast city, in the hope of striking terror in the hearts of the criminal and the perverse!"

The true revolution, Restif believed, was the one he had effected himself in the twin realms of morality and style. It will always seem absurd to readers of English literature that a man with seven hundred mistresses should consider himself a moralist. And to Philistines it will always seem comical that a man should think he has done something when he has reformed style. Take it or leave it, Restif wagered with posterity that he would hold its attention on these two grounds, and we are reprinting him—translating him, what's more—for readers of English who of course are other than Philistine. How should they receive his claim?

On the morals question, Restif is a great echo and amplifier rather than an original dissenter. Rousseau

was before him; Rousseau was the man who sold his
fine shirts and who depicted in *The New Heloïse* how
modern society was to live—without servants, without
gambling and philandering, without wigs and tight corsets, without tyrannizing the children. The plain, in-
expensive life, with outdoor sports, marriage for love,
and the hygiene of natural simplicity was his imaginative creation. Others had lived such a life and still
others had praised it in an unthinking pastoral mood,
but Rousseau made it seem practicable and right.
What Restif contributed to the revolution in manners
was an abundance of touches, observations, and traits
of character, drawn from his peregrinations through
the back streets. When he theorizes about uprightness
and the good life, he rants like the hero of a sentimental drama; but when he is moved by what someone
said or did and he simply reports it, he achieves at once
a new morality and a new style.

Already in Rousseau's *Confessions* the language
expressed a changed quality of feeling. The sentences
are of an exquisite simplicity—but they are still exquisite. Art had not yet reached the point of being
deliberate counter-art. That point Restif attained in the
name of democratic fervor, as we do today out of anti-
social animus. Having "caught nature red-handed,"
Restif is sure that he has made the language "dare to
speak of everything." But this is a dubious claim compared with his negative art, his obvious impatience
with phrase-making. In this regard, he is at one with
Stendhal and suggests Hemingway, as almost any passage from the *Nights* will show, provided one abstracts
the intermittent filler of rhetoric:

"I was walking along rue Dauphine. [Then come
three lines of sentimental cant.] A man was knocked
down. People shouted "Stop!" The coachman, a heartless brute—the guilty coachman cracked his detestable
whip to get away. . . . The wheel rolled over the poor

wretch's chest! [Here three more lines of rant.] A gush
of blood. The carriage vanished. My former agility is
gone; I could not catch up with it. . . . When I got
back I tried to enter the Café Montmayeux, where
they had put the injured man. The idle and inquisitive
crowd blocked my way. A tall young girl, with the sweetest face, and dressed with the respectable neatness that
bespeaks a decent family, came near, tried to see, to
learn what had happened. They told her about the
accident. 'Good heavens! But are they taking care of
the poor man? All they do is stand there, staring at
him!' Just then the door opened. Someone pushed his
way through the crowd. The girl saw the victim. 'It's
my father!' she cried. She tottered. I tried to hold her
up. 'Let me go, I'll be twice as strong.' The crowd let
her through. She called for a surgeon, for stretcher
bearers. I was the only one who listened to her. I
brought a surgeon. I ran to find bearers. They took the
poor man home. Oh, God—what a sight! His daughter
was pale; her lips were white as death, but she did what
she could. The mother, who had been ill, fainted and
could not be revived. I took care of her. The man died
at midnight."

How much this snapshot style owes to Restif's
mode of composition, which was to set his sentences
directly into type, the reader who is looking for clues
will decide for himself. Restif was evidently able to
compose long sentences in this way as well as short.
His dot-and-dash system was deliberate and could not
be improved upon for the effect of drama and trans-
parency which he intended. When the subject is not
of the moralistic kind that I chose, the absence of any
commentary, almost of any conclusion—as in, say,
"The Molested Woman"—leaves an impression unlike
any other in our western literary experience. The prose
gives us those *aperçus* one obtains from a train at night
when moving past a tenement window behind which

some domestic drama is being enacted. The *Nights,* in so many ways a book congenial to our temper—offbeat, factual, anti-social, and anti-literary—is in that respect something more: a foreshadowing of the surrealism that comes naturally out of realism and that accompanies just as naturally the discordant endings of great periods.

CONTENTS

SUPERNUMERARY NIGHTS

THE
NOCTURNAL
SPECTATOR

THE POOR FOLKS' POCKETBOOK

I had some business to attend to at six o'clock; I rose;
I left the house. The streets were still quiet and
empty, for the useless people[1] were not yet out of
bed. At the corner of rue de la Monnaie I found a
purse. It held two louis d'or and ten smaller coins;
it was made of leather, and it was soiled. "Oh, you unhappy man or woman who have lost this purse!" I exclaimed. "How I pity you!" And within my heart I
felt a pain like the one I had known when I myself
lost the only six-livre coin I had ever owned as I was
buying a mackerel at the entry to the New Market.[2]

A man's own misfortune makes him sensitive to another's. I set off at a run toward the market place, for I reckoned thus: "This man—or woman—was on his way to use this money for the purchase of provisions. If he had been on his way back the purse would be empty, but it is full." When I reached the stands, I saw a man and a woman leaving in tears; the man especially was in despair.

"What's wrong?" I asked him.

"He has nothing left!" his wife said. "He has lost . . . all we had, two louis d'or and ten three-livre coins. . . ."

At that moment a lady passed followed by two servants; she was apparently on her way to the Saint-Eustache church. She stopped, drew from her purse three louis and six francs, gave them to the man, and moved on. I followed her, and presenting the pocketbook I told her, "Since you have restored the loss this money belongs to you, for I found it. I was about to return it when you anticipated me." The lady listened to my words, glanced at me, took the purse, tucked it away, and continued on. And I went about my business.

※ 2 ※

THE HOLE IN THE WALL

On my way home (. . .) I entered the Place Saint-Michel. I was walking lightly and soundlessly in the shadow of the houses, like the night watch.[1] A muffled noise reached my ears. I drew closer: three men were cutting a hole in the wall, near the door of a house. I grasped the knocker and I sounded a tremendous blow, saying, "My friends, why make a hole? The door is right here; they will open it for you. . . ." They never heard the last words; the reverberations of the knocker shook them to their very bones, their legs especially; they fled, leaving their tools behind. The door opened, and I showed the doorkeeper what labors had been undertaken to lighten his task.

. . . .

I went out. It was two o'clock. I crossed the Pont Marie. The loveliness of the night drew me to the tip of the Île Saint-Louis, and I followed the Quai d'Anjou. As I gazed at the Île Louvier, I happened to see three wretches floating stolen lumber[2] on the water and piling it into boats at mooring (the jetty had not yet been built). One of them lashed the wood to a line; another drew it up onto the Île Saint-Louis. They were dreadfully frightened at the sight of me. "Why do you do something that terrifies you so?" I asked them. They did not answer, and vanished. I continued on my way, and I came across another wretch carrying off the clamps that hold the stones of the parapet together. I turned away, with a lament for the misery of mankind!

🎄 3 🎄

THE DRUNKEN MAN

I was turning out of rue Culture-Sainte-Catherine, when my foot struck something limp. I stooped and I felt it: it was a man! . . . I tried to rouse him; he was cold; I pulled him a short distance, into the light of the street lamp. He was drenched with blood. I shuddered with horror. The notion that I might be risking danger myself did not occur to me. I cannot look at blood without fainting, and yet I felt myself strong. I hoped a patrol might pass by, but at three o'clock the patrols are asleep.

Just then I heard a carriage approaching and ran toward the sound. I reached it and begged the coachman to turn a few steps out of his way to succor someone in need. The master consented; the lackeys' torches lighted the scene: it was a man in his cups, who had injured his head; he was dead drunk. The owner of the carriage was a young nobleman of the court, the C.D.C.T.[1] His young wife was riding by his side; both of them climbed down; we put the moribund man in the carriage, the lackeys and I. He was carried to the Hôtel-Dieu while the master and his gentle spouse followed on foot. This is a wonderful story! However, it is not unique; the aristocracy in France is replete with delicate sensibilities. When I reached my house I wrote a description of this splendid act. (. . .)

The next day I inquired after the drunkard. He was a family man who had become ill from drinking wine. His wound was not very serious, and he was expected to recover enough to leave in a day or two. I wrote this happy news to the young and virtuous nobleman, thanking him in the name of all humanity.

. . . .

❧ 4 ❧

THE BROKEN MAN

. . . I went home by way of rue Saint-Antoine and
the Place de Grève.[1] Three murderers had been broken
on the wheel there, the day before. I had not expected
to see any such spectacle, one that I had never dared
to witness. But as I crossed the square I caught sight
of a poor wretch, pale, half dead, wracked by the pains
of the interrogation[2] inflicted on him twenty hours
earlier; he was stumbling down from the Hôtel de
Ville supported by the executioner and the confessor.
These two men, so completely different, inspired an
inexpressible emotion in me! I watched the latter embrace a miserable man consumed by fever, filthy as
the dungeons he came from, swarming with vermin!
And I said to myself, "O Religion, here is your greatest
glory! . . ." I saw the other as the wrathful arm of the
law. . . . But I wondered: "Have men the right to
impose death . . . even on the murderer who has
himself treacherously taken life?" I seemed to hear
Nature reply with a woeful no! . . . "But robbery?"
"No, no!" cried Nature. "The savage rich have never
felt they devised enough harsh safeguards; instead of
being friends and brothers, as their religion commands,
they prefer the gallows. . . ." This was what Nature
said to me. . . .

I saw a horrible sight, even though the torture had
been mitigated. . . . The wretch had revealed his accomplices. He was garroted before he was put to the
wheel. A winch set under the scaffold tightened a

noose around the victim's neck and he was strangled;
for a long while the confessor and the hangman felt his
heart to see whether the artery still pulsed, and the
hideous blows[3] were dealt only after it beat no longer.
. . . I left, with my hair standing on end in horror. . . .

❦ 5 ❦

THE MOLESTED WOMAN

I was walking, deep in thought, and was passing a
house whose entryway was open when I heard shrill
cries from the stairway. Puzzled, I climbed it swiftly.
"Who's that coming up?" cried a man's voice. At that
same moment someone plunged down the stairs; I
darted into the toilet. The man passed me, his naked
sword in hand. I climbed on then, and found a disheveled young woman on her knees and in tears.

"I have come to help you," I told her. "Who is
that madman?"

"Ah, save me, save my life!"

At these words from the young woman I was no
longer frightened of anything. I closed the door and
shot the bolts; then I opened a window. I saw the
madman returning, the sword in his hand. When he
reached the door and found it locked, his rage passed
all bounds; the young woman trembled. The whole
house having awakened, people talked to me through
the windows and I asked for help; they came after
deftly disarming the madman. He was led off to a police
commissioner, who sent him to prison. Later I shall

write the story of the young woman, who entered a convent the following morning. I spent the night on a mattress in her room; two women shared her bed.

❧ 6 ❧

THE IMPRUDENT GIRL

In the evening, before my walk and before my visit to the Marquise,[1] I wrote down the story of the molested woman. (. . .) Then I went out, and crossed to the Île Saint-Louis; it was half past eleven. I was strolling slowly toward the dark eastern tip of the island, when I heard the voices of two persons seated on the stone at the foot of the forward wing of the Bretonvilliers[2] building. I stopped to listen.

"What will become of me? Tomorrow they will know I didn't return to my mistresses' house! I'm ruined. . . . Oh! Why did I . . . have to . . . listen to you!"

The man spoke very harshly, and threatened to leave the poor girl if she did not hold her tongue. "We'll spend the night at the market place, and early tomorrow morning you'll go back to your mistresses' house."

It was not yet midnight. I simply followed my impulse: I stepped forward. "Come, my . . . lady" (when I saw her clothing I said "my lady" instead of "my girl"). "It's not too late. . . . Come along, come with me; I'll find some excuse for your tardiness." The girl rose and came toward me. . . . "If you save me," she said, "I shall venerate you like my own father!" I took her hand and led her back to rue des Rats, where her mistresses lived; I devised the excuse that she had had the misfortune to be attacked. . . .

The young man had followed us; he heard the girl protesting her innocence to me; he waited in order to set me straight (according to *his* story). I listened to him as I proceeded to the Marquise's house.

"That little lady," he told me, "is the daughter of a tapestry-weaver on rue Galande. Two years ago she lost her mother, and since then her father allows her too much freedom; this was what gave me the notion to court her. What I did anyone would have tried to do; whenever you see a girl who is too free, you assume she probably abuses her freedom. My guess was correct; I got everything I wanted. Today she walked out with a pretty blonde who had a clandestine meeting with a secret lover. I took them by surprise and pretended to be jealous. The blonde caressed me to calm me down, and I saw it would be possible to make her unfaithful to her sweetheart. I let her go, though, and kept the weaver's daughter with me, to exercise my power. She was heartbroken over my threats to leave her unless she came and spent the night with me at the market place. She was on the point of yielding when you approached us; but I think she is angry with me. Actually it doesn't concern me much; I know she prefers her mistresses' house to her father's, because the ladies are lace menders and every day she sees young men there. She scarcely deserves tender treatment, and right now I like the blonde better. The blonde is the daughter of a very disreputable Flemish woman, and I believe the girl is being kept; but she's a new item, and it will be an easy victory."

I found this young man a gabbler, a liar, a boor and a coward all at once. . . . When I reached rue Payenne, I dismissed him with a wave of my hand (. . .).

THE MOLESTED WOMAN, (*continued*)

As I went out in the evening I hoped that chance, which had served me so well in the case of the weaver's young daughter, would be equally helpful with the molested woman. I took the Pont Neuf, and reached her house in the Place de l'École. Just next door lived a foundryman with six daughters; the eldest was lovely, and although she was very young I had often noticed her the preceding summer as she strolled in the evening on the Quai de l'École with her neighbor, the pretty young daughter of a chandler. I stepped into that house, and I asked whether they had heard of the incident the night before.

"Yes," the foundryman replied, "do you know something about it?"

"It was I who rescued the young lady."

"Really? Tell us, then, how you did it!"

I recounted what I had seen. "Now," I added, "can you throw some light on the matter for me?"

"Certainly! We'll tell you who the young woman is, and about the man who was molesting her. Despite her youth, the lady has been married for a year; her husband is a skillful musician who, having won little recognition in Paris, went to try his fortune in London. When he left, he asked one of his friends, a painter, to come each day to call on his young wife, to offer his arm for a stroll, and to escort her to the theater. This last request would cost nothing, because of the musician's many acquaintances among actors. At first everything went as the husband had wished. The young lady was happy; she showed frank and genuine delight when her husband's friend appeared. That is to say, she was very sweet; add to this the fact that she is very pretty. The painter is younger than the husband; he is a good-looking man; he was confident of an easy victory. His first attempts were gently turned aside; he grew impudent to a degree which cannot be described. The young woman was most distressed, but she objected only half-heartedly. Thus it was that the treacherous friend's passion became uncontrollable.

"At first he utilized every possible means to conquer her; meeting with no success, he dropped his mask. Against her will he stayed in her room all night; he threatened to dishonor her by writing to her husband and telling everyone else that he had caught her with the servant. However, it was all to no avail; the young woman wept but she did not yield. Here in the neighborhood we sometimes heard a noise; but no one knew what it meant. Finally, the day before yesterday, he decided to satisfy his obsession, as he put it to her. He hung about playing piquet until midnight, disguising his evil intentions. The young woman mistrusted him; she tried to send him away. The painter chatted until one o'clock. She begged him to leave. "No," he said, "today I take the plunge!" The young woman was firm in the face of his threats; he grew furious. He drew his sword and told her this would be her last hour if she did not yield. At first she tried friendly remonstrance and pleading; a violent attack was the cruel man's reply. The poor woman cried out. It was about two o'clock; everyone was asleep. We woke up, but we could not tell whether the screams came from the street or from one of the apartments. Yet, someone must have opened the door to the entryway, and then not dared to go up. You were more courageous.

"This morning the young lady decided to enter a

convent where a kinswoman lives, until her husband's
return. The wicked man denied everything before
the police commissioner, but the witnesses' testimony sent him to prison. The young woman is determined to exonerate him, to the best of her ability—
unless her husband should want revenge, which she
does not expect to be the case."

This is what he told me, before his whole family—
the father of the lovely Charlotte, whom I shall do a
favor one day. When I had left that house, I proceeded
to the Marquise's; I told her the story of the musician's
young wife (. . .).

❧ 8 ❧

THE VICIOUS GIRLS

When I went out I happened to turn into rue Saint-
Martin. It was nine o'clock in the evening. Three girls
were walking ahead of me, discussing a fourth whom
they had just been tormenting (that was their expression). They were working girls, and they bore great ill
will toward one of their colleagues who was probably
much nicer. They claimed she thought she was pretty,
that she was putting on airs, and that she did not want
to be friendly, and they determined to humiliate
her as soon as they had an opportunity. Their plans
toward this end were vicious as could be! They would
persuade her that she was admired and adored by a
libertine, famous in his own circle but unknown to
a decent girl; they would prepare her to hear him out,
only to plunge her subsequently into all the shame,
the misery of having been deceived and humiliated.

Laughing all the while, they devised the methods they would use: first the rake would be introduced as a relative of one of them; next, an excursion party would be arranged during which, after an insidious lunch, poor Manette would be left completely alone with him. Considering the trouble they took with the meal, they never doubted that she would commit a serious transgression; she would be discovered at it and become the laughingstock of her cruel enemies. However, if she did not submit, they planned to make her seem ridiculous by her preparations for an imaginary wedding which would end in a hideous farce.

When I had learned enough, I decided to speak to them, and I confronted them. One of the girls was tall, well built and pretty—she was the least spiteful; I told her how astonished I was at what I had heard! She remained silent. But the plainest of them spoke up sharply, asking me why I was interfering. "I heard everything," I told her, "I know the young woman in question; I shall warn her of your intentions." Alarmed, the tall one said, "Don't do that, sir! She is under the protection of someone important!" "Then abandon your evil schemes against her; for I shall know who you are and I shall find you again." I spoke firmly. They mollified me, and I pretended to leave them. I walked for a while in the shadow, and taking advantage of their delay when a carriage obstructed their path, I drew ahead of them. They turned into their lodgings. With enough to go on, I went to call on their victim. With some difficulty I succeeded in speaking to her, and even then she would receive me only in the presence of a neighbor. I warned her of the conspiracy against her.

I have learned since that the three spiteful girls did not abandon their plot of vengeance at all; they had only postponed it. But it turned against them; the young man whose aid they enlisted, the lover of one of them, was struck by Manette's worth; he came to prefer her, and married her recently.

At eleven o'clock I left the house where Manette lived, and went to call on the Marquise. I reported what I had just witnessed (. . .).

🎕 9 🎕

THE STREETWALKER

It was late when I went out the following night; I took a shorter route. At the corner of rues Saint-Martin and Grenier-Saint-Lazare I was accosted by a rather pretty girl with a voluptuous languor in her manner. She took my hands, and made me the most beguiling promises to persuade me to go up to her room. I declined gently, touched by compassion for the unfortunate young girl, and I had begun to make certain remarks as to the perils of her trade, when the girl, who had seemed so sweet and almost affectionate, suddenly altered her tone and her language.

"Get out of here, you Savoyard,[1] you murderer! . . . Help! Stop thief!" She then gave vent to a stream of invectives.

"I did not yield," I said to the crowd that gathered, "but if I had gone with her you may be sure she would have called me worse yet, after I had paid her! . . . Let it be a lesson to you, young men— these deceiving sirens entice men by spurious sweetness!"

I went on my way. As I walked toward rue

Payenne, I meditated on the women of the streets, and one night I shall tell the Marquise of my conclusions (. . .).

☙ 10 ❧

THE LAUNDRESSES' SECRETS

I proceeded home, with no encounter save one with two girls burdened with laundry on their way to the boat before daybreak. One said to the other, "How you were showing off last Sunday, in your fancy white gown! Well, I must say it looked good on you."

"I should think so! It belongs to a fine lady, and Mlle. Raguidon of rue Guillaume made it with her own fine hand. . . . I'd be a fool to buy my own clothes. I have something white every Sunday, and always something different. These women don't really dirty their clothes. When I get hold of them, on they go, and I shine! Stockings, chemises, petticoats—nothing is mine. And what about you, my dear?"

"Me? Don't say a word, or I'll tell on you, like you would me. I do the same. And I lend handkerchiefs, shirts, collars, stockings to grenadier Latereur."

"And I to Lamerluche in the night patrol."

"Bonnets to little Manon."

"Chemises to Javote."

"And then I rent them out, too."

"So do I."

"Beware, my good ladies, or I'll tell your clients," I said to them, and, laughing, passed on ahead. They were pretty and did not yet seem twenty. They squealed, and instead of going down to the boat at the Pont de la Tournelle, passed it by. I hid, and as soon as they no longer heard my steps they turned back to it.

❧ 11 ❧

THE RAGWOMAN

I was walking homeward, deep in thought, as was my habit. On rue Pavée, almost at the Lamoignon mansion, I noticed something dark stirring on the ground; it resembled a large dog. I dread those animals since the time I was bitten by one in my childhood. I gave a start. A cry that was deep and plaintive but less chilling to me than a dog's bark lead me to believe it was a human creature; I went closer, my hair standing on end with terror. It was an old ragwoman, drunk from too much brandy; she lay sprawled on the ground, her head resting on a sack that held a few dogs and cats which she had killed for their meat and hides. I woke her.

"Come along, mother, get up! Your nap must have refreshed you. Where do you live?"

She stirred a little. . . . "Not a penny under twelve sous for the big tom! Three nights now I've been waiting to get him—he belongs to a very pious lady; he's fat as a pig—got a fine hide on him . . ." She pulled it from the sack; it was still moving!

"Get up!"

"The two pups? They're only six months old; tender as dewdrops! They gave me some to eat Sunday at Maison-Blanche[1]—passed it off for wild rabbit: the pastry maker in the faubourg makes his mincemeat out of it. . . . The pork butcher out in the district dresses up his sausage with it." She spread them out for inspection.

"Lady! I'm no roadhouse-keeper, nor a pastry cook, nor a pork merchant."

"Then what are you, pumping me like that? Get out of here!" And she swung her crook at me. I was forced to retreat.

🎄 12 🎄

THE DEAF MAN'S ACCIDENT

When I went out in the evening about ten, I walked along the Quai Saint-Bernard, and had the pleasure of performing a useful act. On the steep slope of the Pont Marie I saw a deaf man knocked down by a carriage. The drivers of these vehicles are almost all scoundrels. This particular one, without any regard for the poor man whom he had caught unawares, whipped up his sorry nags, certain that he had not been seen. "Stop!" I cried, throwing myself on the horses' necks. I was just in time. One wheel was already pressing on the man's ribs, and he cried out. The coachman's malice was so apparent that he was frightened; he jumped from the seat and ran off. One should never presume ill of people, but I know enough drivers and have often heard their conversations; one could bet ten to one that this barbarian was wittingly indulging himself in the pleasure of running over a man.

Seeing the carriage abandoned, I helped the deaf man to climb into it. I did not know if he was badly hurt or not. I obtained his address from him, mounted the box, and delivered the man home. He was the head of a large family; I told them I believed him seriously injured, and I returned the carriage to the Place Maubert; next I told them in the guardhouse of all that I had done.

❧ 13 ❧

NIGHT IN LES HALLES

I went to visit the cabarets at Les Halles, about which I had heard a great deal. I expected to find some fascinating sights there, but I saw nothing but debauchery: people smoking, or sleeping; lewd women with billiard or card sharks, brawling and swearing at one another; a few sad rakes who had come there looking for amusement and who were bored instead.

I was about to leave, greatly displeased with this den of squalid carousing—a place set aside for provisioners, who make no use of it—when I caught sight of a very pretty young blonde led by a kind of female monster. She bought the girl brandy and I saw that she intended to intoxicate her. I blessed the Supreme Being that I was present. The young girl could not swallow the brandy. I approached her. The female monster thereupon made me certain lewd propositions, pointing out that this was a brand-new article. The girl tried to behave like a wanton and was not successful at it. I suggested leaving. This was accepted. "Take us to your lodgings," the monster said to me.

I held the girl's hand as I walked, and I turned in the direction of rue Payenne, certain that I would bring great pleasure to the generous Marquise. I was not mistaken. She was finishing her letters when I knocked. The chambermaid appeared on the balcony; I gave the signal, and the door was opened for me. I presented the blonde to the Marquise, in my parlor (. . .); I had left the monster at the door. A bed was set up for the girl in the parlor itself, and I left. The old woman was waiting for me.

"Off with you," I told her, "or the Marquise de M***, who lives in this house, will have you arrested!"

The stout monster vanished with unimaginable dispatch.

❦ 14 ❦

THE RAID

I went several nights without seeing the Marquise, for she was well enough to attend some supper parties. (. . .) I made some observations, which I shall read to her when she sends me word she is free. Of course, though the thread of these *Nights* seems unbroken, they did not actually occur in close sequence; it is now January, 1768.

I had often seen unfortunate girls being led off to the Saint-Martin[1] prison; the next night, I visited the Saint-Honoré quarter at an early hour. I was surprised to meet no one at all; I went on. Then I saw two or three of those vile men known as informers, warning some of the women, reassuring others; all of them, mistrustful, fled hastily to other parts. I had no leisure to follow them, but I learned since then that almost all of these hapless girls kept little rooms some distance away, where they slept. Only the inex-

perienced, or those languishing in poverty, were in
danger. As I watched I noticed a crowd of people; it
was ten girls and four old women, escorted by the foot
patrol. The young ones were frantic; they were scan-
tily clothed and disheveled. I was revolted by the
shameful behavior of the commissioner, who did not
permit—did not command—the wretched girls to
dress. . . .

I followed behind them. They were taken into the
office of the man who had ordered the raid. I attempted to enter with them, but to no avail; I was
turned back by the guard, and I waited some two
hours. After that time, the group of hapless women
emerged, desolate. I was especially affected by the
tears of a child thirteen or fourteen years old. I went
as close as possible, and I called to her: "Take heart,
my child! If you want to change your way of life, I
shall take you out of Saint-Martin tomorrow." I was
thinking of the Marquise, and I felt no qualms about
imposing on her; the unfortunate require little to
supply their needs; and then, I knew that philanthropy
is an excellent remedy for the vapors! . . .

At my words, an aging woman garbed in satin
exclaimed, "I wouldn't give Maret what he wanted—
that's why I'm here—but I have protection!"

"It's a pity," I replied, "that you have special protection! You would do better to have only the government's, with conditions that would lessen the disadvantages of your profession."

Meanwhile the wretched women were moving
forward. At the gate to Saint-Martin, someone told
me, "If you feel any concern for that girl, the one you
spoke to, don't let her sleep in that accursed place;
claim that she is your sister, and take her away."

I heeded the advice. I stepped forward when she
entered, and I asked for her as being my sister whom
I had just recognized, and whom I wished to return

to her family. The gatekeeper took my name and address; I signed the register, and young Aglaé was turned over to me. She was wild with joy. As I took her to my sister's home, she told me about her parents. They were respectable drygoods merchants on rue Galande. She had been seduced by a married man who, to escape the consequences of his crime, had offered to put her into a boarding house. And place her he did for thirty sous a day, in a boarding house run by the woman in satin. He saw her there several times; eventually she was asked to visit with one friend of the house, then with another; she had come to the sixth and she still did not fully recognize the ignominy of her fate until the raid took place in which she had just found herself.

We reached her house in the course of this tale. It was locked. I pulled at the bell she indicated; a window opened on the floor above, and someone asked what I wanted. I replied, "Open the door; I have an important message to deliver."

The merchant came down. I told the girl, "Let's keep your unhappy situation secret; we shall mention only a boarding house and an ordinary seduction in order not to break your parents' hearts." She agreed. And when her father came to the door, I told him that I had found his daughter as she was escaping from a pension where her seducer had lodged her. I talked for some time in the girl's presence to show her exactly what she should say. We were kept a long while. The mother appeared, and wept as she kissed her daughter. I was pleased to see that she loved her, and I felt all would be well.

It was late; I was close to my house; I went home.

❧ 15 ❧

THE RAID, *(continued)*

Toward seven in the evening I went out, for as I had
gone to bed before two and hence had arisen in the
morning, I had done a great deal of work. I called on
the young girl's parents. I discovered that she had
revealed everything to her mother, but that they had
arranged between them to use discretion with the father. His wife thanked me profusely, and young Aglaé
described the raid:

"It was nine o'clock; two men, who looked like
spies, had come to see the madam (this term is not
Aglaé's), to tell her the minor police inspection was
on, and not to let her girls go out. The madam had
asked, "You're sure it's not a major inspection instead?
Tell me! I've got three new ones here, and it would be
a shame if they went and picked up a case of g*** in
the workhouse at such an early age." I did not hear
that; it was one of the young beginners she mentioned
who went out; she came back and told us, the other
young one and me. The two of them left the house
right away, and since they knew more than I, they
must surely have escaped, for they were not among us
after the raid. A moment later I heard a shout in the
big drawing room downstairs, then cries and moans
from all the girls. Out of curiosity I went down. Usually I was not allowed downstairs; but meeting no
obstacles this time I reached the drawing room. Seeing
me enter, a man in a robe laughed and rubbed his hands
together, saying, "Ah, here's another one! She's real

pretty too!" I listened, with my mouth agape. A man dressed in blue put his hand under my chin. I pushed him away. "Well, look who's playing the vestal virgin!" He said some other foul things and tore my shawl off. The man in the robe called me over to him. Since he was old and disgusting, I refused. One of his lackeys kicked me forward. I began to cry. I was pawed by three or four hooligans who had come in with the man in the robe. Meantime the madam was talking a great deal; she said she had authorization; that she would lodge a complaint and that she would get redress. They laughed in her face. They kept on writing and writing. When they had finished, they made us go outside. She asked for a carriage. 'No,' the man in the robe answered her, 'you'll walk, as an example.' I was mauled again by the hooligans. Finally we left. I was not a bit unhappy at being taken from that cursed house, where I had been held like a prisoner. You saw us, monsieur, and you spoke to me. That is the whole story."

I refrain from comment on this tale; but I shall return to it in the *Nights* to come, which I shall devote to a discussion of that area of public administration. Aware now of the nature of the house where her seducer had lodged her, the young woman shuddered in horror! She is protected forever from dalliance and libertinage.

Her account and the advice I gave her occupied the evening until eleven o'clock. As I strolled, I passed under the Marquise's windows; from there I went on to rue Saintonge. I sang a song under the window of the apartment Victoire[1] had lived in; then I completed my excursion, absorbed in a plan for reform that would lessen the abomination of prostitution. I went around by the boulevards.

❧ 16 ❧

THE DISMEMBERED CORPSES

Returning home, I took rue Saint-Martin, rue de
Gèvres, the Pont au Change and the Pont Saint-Michel.
At the corner of rue de la Huchette, at the point called
the Cagnard,[1] I saw some young men hurrying up
rue de la Harpe. I went to see what they had been doing
at the Cagnard, and I found—the limbs of a dismembered child. I shuddered. . . . But there was nothing
for me to do there; I left.

The following morning I visited the apothecary
there, to tell him what I had found under his windows. He laughed: "That's what's left from a class in
anatomy; medical students[2] are not allowed to use
corpses and they are obliged to steal them or buy
them; they don't know how to dispose of them when
they are through with the dissecting. Four students
take up the segmented body; two walk ahead, and two
follow to be on the alert; they know of the secret
spring latches at a few entryways along their route,
and are careful to keep them open—they take refuge there in case of danger. They finally reach this
spot to discard the remains, and they run off."

"Why are bodies not given the surgeons legally?"

"Everyone with any sense asks that question;
they should be given the bodies of criminals and the
corpses of convicts who die in prison, and those who
die of unusual diseases in the hospitals. Once, in a little
article of mine, I even made a proposal for donating
certain still-living criminals to the public dissecting

room, for experiments to be carried out on them, which would make their deaths doubly useful to society whose scourge they had been; but I was denounced in horror, as a cannibal." Satisfied with this explanation I left the apothecary, assuring him that I shared his opinion.

❧ 17 ❧

THE GRAVEROBBERS

In the evening, on my way to visit the Marquise, I intended to walk through the Saint-Séverin graveyard; it was closed. I took the little ruelle des Prêtres and I listened at the gate. I heard some sounds. I sat down to wait in the doorway of the presbytery. After an hour the cemetery gate opened and four youths went out, carrying a corpse in its shroud. They went off along rue île des Prêtres, rue Boutebrie, and rue du Foin, and darted into a dark little house on rue de la Harpe, three or four doors from the corner.

I went on to see the Marquise, and I gave her an account of the morning's and evening's events.

❧ 18 ❧

THE GRAVEROBBERS, (continued)

As I returned, the idea occurred to me to go to the apprentice surgeons' house to see what they were doing with the body they had just stolen. I reached the downstairs door to their amphitheater and I pushed it; it yielded, and I climbed to the third floor where I had seen a light. I stepped quietly to the doorway, and I saw . . . on a large table, the body . . . of a girl of eighteen, buried the day before. They had already opened the chest . . . I knew the girl's parents; I withdrew in deep sorrow, but I kept silent. Would that criminals were given to the students!

🏵 19 🏵

THE FESTIVITIES

On Monday I decided to continue watching the excesses perpetrated in Paris on feast days.[1] In the course of a daytime outing, my indignation had been sharply aroused by the absence of police, which allows children and streetcorner Savoyards to soil women's clothing with dirt! We find out, to our great astonishment, that in the very capital of France the fair sex is insulted, drenched with filth! It is an outrage, and of great significance, for it bears on morality. In any land where women are not honored in public, like sacred objects, even more than priests, there can be no morals. . . .

Such were my thoughts as I walked along, when at the corner of rue du Petit Pont I saw a boy of fifteen smearing mud on a young woman's dress! The husband, or a relative, or perhaps a stranger, was behind her; he struck the boy on the head with his cane, knocking him down. I hastened to him. He lay motionless, with a wound at his temple. I called for help. He was carried to the Hôtel-Dieu; he was dead; all efforts were futile. The punishment was too severe; but does not the police administration have itself to blame for this accident, like a hundred others before and since? (. . .)

⁂ 20 ⁂

THE DANCE HALL

. . . .

It was carnival time: masqueraders appeared in the streets on their way to balls, or coming from them. I did not yet know persons who offered such entertainment in their homes, and I had never seen the Opéra Ball: the only one I had ever attended was the one given by the young folk in Auxerre, which I described in *Monsieur Nicolas*. [1]

I studied everything that met my gaze and I moved on gradually, without thinking of where I was going. I found myself at the Buci circle. There I saw a young and pretty girl, whose mother I knew, alone with two young men; they slipped into Coulon's where, at a price, the public was offered supper and dancing. I entered like everyone else and proceeded to a seat on a bench in the darkest corner. I watched from there.

Since coming to Paris I had heard much talk of effeminate men, but either those people never go out, like the drones in a beehive, or they go in disguise. It was at the ball that I saw them, for the first time, in all their depravity. Five or six gallants came to the ball at Coulon's, ten times more womanly than women.

They were immediately surrounded but they made the most of themselves: the swarm of brazen coquettes sought them out, teased them, even pursued them, while the dandies drew away, not shyly, but in a fashion a hundred times more arrogant than if they themselves had been the aggressors. Next I watched the girls; they gorged their eyes on the fops, who often paid them some insolent compliment. When that occurred, the foolish girls flushed with delight and depravity. I was astonished—or rather, infuriated!

The two elegant young men escorting the girl I knew seemed not to be fops of the first order—they might be classed only as second degree, or perhaps third; accordingly, the little flirt appeared to treat them with indifference, turning all her attention to the effeminate youths. The suitor was injured by his lady's behavior and grew angry; the effeminates, who were fluttering about, noticed this, and as the pretty Virginie was a novelty, they clustered around her. She was ecstatic, the little fool! Thereupon the sweetheart, a Saint-Côme student,[2] grew wild with jealousy and plunged into the midst of these female men like another Aeneas amid the squealing Shades; he hurled them left and right as easily as if their bodies were merely thin mist. They did not grow angry; they laughed smugly, and so mirthlessly that I felt my heart chill. Meanwhile the young sawbones had seized his lady's hand and tried to lead her away; she resisted, and voiced her refusal with a certain dignity. Seconded by his companion, the young man attempted to use force.

At that point I approached them. At the sight of me Virginie was disconcerted; she told the young men she did not know them, and that she had come to the dance hall with her uncle (she pointed to me). I felt I should not contradict this lie; the young surgeon, intimidated, withdrew quietly with his companion to another corner of the hall. I then told Virginie that

she had to leave with me at once lest she disgrace herself completely. She begged for just one more contre-
danse, which I permitted her. But meanwhile I sent
for her mother, who was having supper in town quite
nearby, on rue Mazarine. She appeared as Virginie was
finishing. She flushed and then paled on seeing her
daughter. Full of verve, Virginie returned to my side
and thanked me in the most flattering terms for my
kindness in bringing her to the ball. "I had come out
on the doorstep," she said, "to see the masqueraders.
Monsieur was passing by; I walked a few steps with
him, for a better view, and we followed the masqueraders here." We went out directly, but on the way I
told the mother the truth, and the poor woman shed
tears (. . .).

❦ 21 ❧

THE BOY IN GIRL'S CLOTHING

The following evening was Mardi Gras. I was to have
supper with the Marquise at her apartment, in the presence of her chambermaid and the two Demerup girls,
who had a little table for the three of them. I intended
to arrive early, but chance willed it otherwise.

I was walking on rue Saint-Honoré. At the corner
of rue Champ-Fleuri I saw a small gathering of people;
I approached them. There stood what seemed to be a
girl of about sixteen, whose sweet demeanor they were
admiring. I was struck by her gentle, innocent beauty.
I spoke to her, asking how she had drawn this attention to her. She smiled at me, and nothing in the
world was so enchanting as her smile. I was puzzled

until, without a word, the child raised her skirts and exhibited her breeches. Then I understood that this was a boy, who was amusing himself in a scarcely suitable fashion; this should certainly bring our police to prohibit masquerades of all kinds, including the delirium of the carnival. I expressed my disapproval to the child. As I spoke a private carriage stopped; the man inside put his head out of the window to find out what was going on; the boy was brought forward.

"It can't be!" he cried. "It's a girl! . . . Good heavens! I have to make sure."

The boy tried to make off. Two lackeys stopped him: he was put inside the carriage. . . . I draw a veil over the rest of this horrid tale. . . . Suffice it to say that this child is an effeminate today; that he occupies a place in the ***; that this fateful adventure brought about not only the collapse of his morals, but his parents' despair as well. . . .

. . . .

❧ 22 ❧

THE RAGE FOR PLEASURE

Four men were dragging a fifth along the little rue Tiron: two of them held his arms; another walked ahead, pulling him; the fourth pushed from behind as he stifled him with a kerchief over his mouth. Their victim uttered muffled and inarticulate cries. At first, not sure of what was happening, I followed them instead of going to call the police from the Saint-Paul market place. They took their victim into a kind of

deceptive cul-de-sac behind rue des Juifs. There, because the spot is isolated, the one who had stifled
him with a kerchief removed it.

"Say, you boys! What do you want of me?"

"We have no money left, and we need some; or
else this is your last day . . . you old . . ."

"You're mad!" said the old man. "What you're
doing will cost you dear!"

"No threats, or we'll disgrace you, by getting ourselves hanged; that is what we have decided. We have
no more money; the whole city is celebrating and we're
the only ones . . ."

"I'll give you some . . . Ha! . . . I'll give you
some . . . only don't come up with me! . . . You
frighten me!"

I went up to them then, without a word, and I
went straight toward the old man, who took me for
one of his nephews' friends. "Monsieur," he said, "you
are a stranger to me; you run a greater risk than they do!
You, a grown man, how can you go along with these
reckless youngsters!"

"I am no accomplice of theirs," I said to him
under my breath. "I have come to help you."

He did not believe me; I saw that he was an old
man in second childhood. I stood aside, ready to help
him if it became necessary. He went up to his rooms;
two of his nephews stayed at the gate and the two others, their partners in crime, went up with the old man.
Impelled by some sense or instinct, I ran to seek
aid—not from the police, they were too far off; besides, they would not have been effective, however
little the youths might resist.

Near the old rue du Temple I found two men, one
of whom I knew; I told them what was happening, and
we returned to the old man's house. The two nephews were still at the gate; we walked through like residents of the house. We reached the uncle's apartment

on the third floor; the two hooligans had bound him up and we heard him plead for mercy. We entered abruptly; first we untied his housekeeper, who let us into her master's room; then we set the two hooligans to flight, after forcing them to leave all the money they were about to carry off. We unbound the old man, and we advised his old housekeeper to be sure and lock the doors, and we left.

It was just in time; the two nephews and their friends had vanished, but in order to go and call the police and have us arrested as thieves. We saw the guard go by. We observed the whole affair. The old housekeeper answered through the window, telling the true story; other tenants corroborated it, and the guard withdrew. The nephews were not indicted: they had fled at the first words of the explanation, and according to what I learned later, they left the country believing they were under secret indictment and close to arrest.

As I turned toward home I thought: "O administrators! Abolish the carnival, and don't ever allow three feast days to fall in succession—not even two, or even one on a weekday! Sunday is enough."

❦ 23 ❦

THE ESCAPING PRISONER

Upon my return, I was deeply preoccupied. I passed a prison which no longer exists. I stopped, my mind filled with black thoughts; I was standing still when I heard a faint noise. I saw a poor wretch who, using a rope, was slipping down the side of a high tower overlooking the river. My hair stood on end. "What is this," I said to myself. "Is he a murderer? . . . I'll report him. Is he a hapless soul fleeing the tyranny of an unjust family or a powerful enemy? . . . Ah, let him escape! . . ." So I kept silent, and walked to the spot the prisoner had to pass. He didn't come. I saw him swim upstream. Again I went to wait for him, somewhat on my guard. He came out of the water near the Grands-Degrés[1] steps. "You are bathing in rather cold weather," I said to him.

"Bathing? I fell into the water!"

"May I help you?"

"Yes, kindly give me your hat. I have lost mine."

I could not refuse: I gave it to him. He put it on, and went off so quickly that I lost sight of him. I learned the next day that he was a notorious sneak thief, and I will admit that I was sorry to have lost my hat; I would have done better to alert the inattentive sentry. . . . But who, without being duty-bound, would take it upon himself to drive back into the pit of misfortune a luckless soul who so clings to the tree of liberty? Compassion is always praiseworthy, though it be occasionally misplaced.

🎄 24 🎄

THE MURDERED MAN

On my return I stepped along briskly, wrapped in a handsome cloak with braid at the collar. A man came up beside me, hit me in the side, grasped the edge of the cloak, pulled it from my shoulders, put it over his own, and fled. I was taken by surprise, but as I am

swift on my feet, I quickly overtook my man; a blow
of the fist on his shoulder turned him about in a pirou-
ette. I took an edge of the cloak, I lifted it from the
thief's shoulders, and put it over my own; then I told
him never to bother me again! He seemed to take
stock of me with his eyes, and seeing determination
in mine, he moved away. I turned home much pleased
with myself.

I am uncertain how it happened that I went
through rue Saint-Séverin. Across from the church, it
seemed to me I heard someone running off up the little rue des Prêtres; I moved closer; then I caught sight
of something on the steps of the church. I wanted
to know what it was. I touched it. . . . It was a man
drenched in his own blood. He was already cold and
still. I did not know what to think: horror and fear
made my hair stand on end. The man was dead; his
heart was no longer beating; where should I turn?
What to do? I was deliberating when I heard footsteps.
I drew off to one side, and I heard: "He got what he
deserves. But we can't leave him here. . . . Everything would be discovered—we'll have to throw him
into the water, or else take him to the dissecting
room. We'll knock, and then leave before they come
down to answer the door."

They did indeed lift the body and carry it to the
dissecting room on rue de la Harpe. They knocked
loudly four times and darted away. The surgery students came down, and carried the man up to their
rooms. What shall I say? It was a stroke of fortune:
they found a breath of life still in him. And those good
young men—who stole bodies that sometimes deserved greater respect—made a different, more useful
study instead of dissecting him: that of recalling to
life a man who had reached his lowest ebb through
loss of blood. I learned since that they each contributed to buy him broth when he needed it, and that

they sustained the man until he could identify himself. This was not until after a week in a kind of coma. The murderer was a famous artist, extremely brutal and violent when in his cups. Because of his talent he found some protectors, but they intimidated him and this latest crime reformed his vicious character, or at least restrained him from killing.

❦ 25 ❦

THE "WELL-LIGHTED" BLIND MAN

Before visiting the Marquise I always made an expedition in order to replenish my supply of anecdotes. I was not in love with the Marquise, but I was attached to her—as to a superior being—by her virtues and by her charm; and I feared, more than she herself did, a relapse into the unhappy condition in which I had found her.[1]

I went to the neighborhood which is in a sense the quintessence of French urbanity. It is not the court, but it is perhaps more significant, for its tone is often better. This district curbs the court; it conveys to it the imperious law of national custom and compels it to conform to that law. If the court displeases the section, the latter calls a halt and compels it to change. This section, in a way the nerve center of the capital, comprises rue Saint-Honoré and the adjoining Palais-Royal quarter. Rue Saint-Honoré seems filled with nothing but shopkeepers, but there is an enormous number of people of taste in the upper stories, and especially in the adjacent streets. There are even outsiders who spend their lives nowhere else, without residing there. They leave their own homes in the morning—in the Faubourg Saint-Germain, in the Marais,[2] at Chaussée-d'Antin, and the rest—and come to eat, play and stroll in the good section; they return to their own homes only at night, and they know nothing about the Marais, the Faubourg Saint-Germain or the Montmartre sections beyond their own apartments.

I stayed until half past ten, watching things which I must see and tell more fully as these *Nights* progress. From the end of rue de Richelieu on my way back I saw a soldier with a lantern at the corner of rue Saint-Nicaise; his light fell on a blind man seated at the other side of rue Saint-Honoré. I thought it was a coincidence, when I heard the blind man cry, "Am I well lighted?"

"Oh, yes," answered the soldier, "you stand out clear as a sun."

"Good, good! . . . Have the truck-gardeners begun to arrive?"

"Yes, I've already seen two horses go by, with two saddlebags each."

"Did they give anything?"

"No."

"You wretch! It's because you haven't turned the light on me! Who do you think will find me here if you don't shine the light on me? . . . I'll pay close attention; I'll sniff out whatever goes on, and for every farmer who gives nothing I will deduct his missing alms from what I'm to give you."

"I'll point you out to them!"

"Don't you dare! Once our arrangement is discovered, no one will give anything."

The sentry, who had come nearer, went back and directed the light toward the blind man. I waited to see what would happen.

Since after a while I saw no one appear, I stepped

over to contribute a small sum. I noticed that the
blind man sniffed at me. He began to recite a few prayers. I went past but I turned back.

"Who is the man that just gave me something?"

"I didn't see him," the soldier answered.

"It was a man who works at a printing press, or
who handles a good deal of printed paper. . . . He
gave me two liards."

A moment later, two streetwalkers approached
and gave their alms without a word. When they had
disappeared the blind man said, "That was two of
those ladies! I smelled them. . . . They're from the
big house, I suppose? I was going to ask them if they
aren't allowed to use water. I wouldn't want them,
poor blind man that I am, no matter how young and
accommodating they are! I like cleanliness. . . . Here
comes a truck-gardener— Back where you belong!"

I had neither seen nor heard the farmer yet: he
appeared and gave his alms of one liard, for which he
had prayers said for him.

Wrapped in a blue cloak, probably because of the
coolness of the night, a lone girl appeared unexpectedly from a nearby entry: "Pinolet, do send me someone; you'll get your share; you know I never forget a
favor."

"I will, my good miss, if I smell someone with
gold or silver on him. . . ."

She left. Gamblers came out of the door of the
card room at the corner of rue des Bons-Enfants;
one of them approached the blind man and gave him
a coin. Instead of saying a prayer, the blind man called
him back: "Monsieur, have you somewhere to stay? Is
it far from here? I am a poor blind man who can't see,
but I feel some concern for you."

"My friend, I am going back to my furnished rooms
in the Faubourg Saint-Honoré."

"It's so far away! Right here, just next door to the

gambling-house, there's a young brunette—so pretty, so sweet, so good. . . . I wouldn't tell you about her if I didn't know how nice and sweet she is. Go there and use my name; the first entryway after the café, with the grillwork gate, third floor; go on, go on. . . ."

The young man, who had won a large sum, went off in that direction, and I watched him enter; then I returned to the blind man.

"I'm very glad," he was saying to the sentry, who often crossed over to him, "that I sent that young man to Eustoquie; she's a good girl, and so reliable! . . . I sensed that that young man was gentle and generous, and partial to women; besides, I have noticed that the only good people are men who like women, and women who like men."

"You are lucky to be able to scent things that way, *père* Pinolet—a face, clothing, cleanliness, virtues, faults! I would give my two eyes and my lamp to be like you."

"Oh, my poor Aurillac! Long live sight! I would rather be a bootblack and able to see than be what you know I am and blind—and after all, you know I'm well paid. The other day I smelled that murderer who had just killed his brother. I was talking to him; the family was on his tail but I didn't know it. I sent him to Eustoquie; and when I smelled some very excited people, all in a sweat, I asked them what they were looking for. They told me. 'You'll have him within a half-hour.' I sent someone to warn Eustoquie about the situation. She made the man pay, of course, but she didn't turn him in; she took no chances—a man who kills his brother can kill a prostitute. But at a certain signal she told him, 'Here comes the night patrol; go out that door. . . .' He left by the stairway down to rue Saint-Honoré; he had taken no more than four steps when his family seized him. They did what they set out to do, but people think they never man-

aged to capture him. That's a laugh! You can catch anyone you want. . . . Here come the farmers."

The blind man immediately set about loudly reciting the usual prayers which brought him a few liards.
Day would break soon; the time for nocturnal adventures was past. I retired to my house. But I shall see
that blind man again.

✣ 26 ✣

THE SAINT JOHN'S DAY BONFIRE[1]

Provided they are not harmful, I sometimes like the
wildness of the old customs, or their good-hearted simplicity, as much as I do the restraint of the new.

It was Saint John's Eve. Everyone was going to the
Place de Grève to watch a meager bonfire; at least that
was the purpose of most of them. But certain persons
had another intent: the pickpockets considered that
festival an annual windfall; others saw it as an opportunity to indulge in savage dissipation. All occasions
for large gatherings, whatever they may be, should be
banned because of their dangers. Although I did not
know it, the original,[2] Du Hameauneuf, was joining
me; I noticed him at the entrance to the Quai de
Gèvres. We walked on together. "If you want to see
something," Du Hameauneuf told me, "you must take
some risks; nothing goes on at the edge of the mob.
Let's go in." I knew he was right, and though I felt
some reluctance I made my way into the crowd on the
heels of my guide.

It seemed rather uneventful to me at first. But as
I listened to the conversation, I realized that a group of

jewelers and clockmakers from the Place Dauphine were forming a ring and cleverly maneuvering some quite pretty young women into its center, simply in order to subject their victims to the brazen inquisitiveness that obsessed them. "Watch out!" M. du Hameauneuf said to me. Thus, I observed the action that developed, and turned my attention to another group. This one worked differently: it closed around all those persons who seemed likely to have money and watches. They pushed them by a subtle wavelike motion, of which they were scarcely aware; and the one who was forcing them on most roughly was the one who complained loudest of the crush. This riffraff stayed honest until the final fireworks.

"Watch out!" Du Hameauneuf repeated. "Without me you would have been carried along, but together we provide support for one another." I noticed that the undulations were quickening. I never looked at the rockets and neither did the pickpockets; they seemed to slip their hands into the pockets or the moneybags as the rockets shot up, and to pull the hook out during the shouting and excitement caused by each falling empty rocket. But I soon turned from that scene back to the other.

As for the journeyman goldsmiths, they were still at it. Some of those heedless women who were caught in the different circles they had formed seemed to be lifted two feet from the ground, others lying horizontally across many arms; some of them were caught in the center of a double circle and all of them were being treated in the most degrading, and sometimes cruel, fashion. No one heard their cries because the hoodlums chose the moments when the empty rocket tubes were falling, and at other times they themselves shouted to drown out the cries of their victims. Du Hameauneuf cut through the various rings like a knife and took me with him. "Don't say a word!"

he warned me. "We would be smothered." We saw some hideous things: in one instance, a young girl in the center of a triple circle, with her mother who was forced to be a witness and accomplice to the indignities perpetrated on her daughter. The hapless girl fainted. . . .

The rest of this tale cannot be told. Fortunately, the fireworks stopped and were not resumed. We told the merchant provost of what we had seen, and our statement, together with another, put an end to the perilous pranks. The pickpockets and the hoodlums vanished in an instant, and the outraged girls found themselves surrounded by different people entirely, who imagined only that the girls had perhaps been too tightly crushed. The original observed to me: "Whenever they find themselves mixed up with a mob, clerks and those who are what is known as skilled workers indulge in atrocious behavior, and the reason for it is a simple one: the work these young men do is not fatiguing, and it leaves the body with all its energy intact. And so, they corrupt each other, first, by talking about it, and then, the moment they find themselves near women they can touch, by giving vent to all the excesses of an unbridled imagination."

. . . .

At this point, I told the original that I was leaving, for I had business to attend to. He reminded me that we were to see each other the following evening, and we said goodbye. I was outraged by what I had just seen, and by the depravity of the human race. Among the offenders I had recognized a Fleming named Calkus, whom I determined to frighten by threatening to report him.[3] He ran off, and left the capital.

. . . .

❧ 27 ❧

THE HARE

. . . .

I returned along rue Saint-Honoré: I passed the to-
bacconist's shop; I saw the blind man in a good beam
of light; I took rue des Poulies, and for some reason I
turned into the little rue Jean-Tison. About a third of
the way along that street, I heard something in the
air above me. I raised my head, and I saw a long pole
stretching from one window to another across the
street. I had no idea what it meant; finally, after a
few twitches, a huge hare fell right at my feet! . . . I
picked it up, taking careful note of the door of the
house from which it had been knocked down, and I
took cover under a portico.

Three minutes later a young man appeared,
searching for the hare: it was one of the pole-wielders.
I let him search. Two of them returned with a light.
Nothing! . . . When they withdrew I felt for a secret
catch to the victims' door. I found it and I climbed to
the fourth floor; it was the apartment of an old tailor
who had a very pretty daughter and a still fetching
wife. I knocked until the answer came: "Who is it?"

"Your hare."

"What do you mean, my hare?"

"Your hare that jumped from your window into
the street."

"Ah . . . !"

The mistress said something then, and the
daughter too. Before opening for me, they went to look

at the window. Nothing. The husband drew the bolts, turned the key slowly; then I heard the girl say, "Papa! Light the candle! Suppose it's burglars!"

"You're right!" said the father.

I waited rather a long while. Eventually the door opened a bit and I saw the pretty daughter on one side, the mother on the other: the first with a cleaver in her hand, the latter with a coal shovel. Laughing, I presented the hare: "I have had the pleasure of rescuing your hare! Fortunately I saw where it fell from, otherwise I would have been forced to keep it." They thanked me with some hesitation, and closed the door again. I heard them saying, "Yes! This is the one! It's ours! . . ."

"Husband!" said the woman. "Look and see whether it's not just the hide with stuffing inside."

"No, no, it's our hare, in the flesh. . . . Good Lord, what an honest man! If it had been me who found it, I wouldn't have given it back."

"Monsieur," I called in to him, "that is not good! But don't put it back at your window."

I departed. Reaching the street, I saw the old tailor hanging up the hare again on a new nail, by the light of a candle his daughter held. I remained at a short distance. No sooner was the light extinguished, than the three fellows from across the way began their game again. I hoped to spirit the hare away from them again and carry it back to the tailor: that would have been most agreeable! But he was punished for the notion of keeping it if he had been the one to find it. Instead of falling, the hare slid the length of the pole and fell into the pilferers' deft hands. I had planned to carry the hare back again, but even without it, I thought it would be amusing to go back up. I knocked noisily.

"This time your hare is gone for good; look at your window."

The tailor jumped out of bed while I went downstairs: he opened his window as I reached the street; he uttered a mournful "Oh!" A moment later I saw his wife and his daughter with candles: their gestures and their expressions were truly ludicrous. For such a petty theft I did not feel I ought to start a great commotion by reporting the poachers. I held my tongue. The tailor and his family came down, but they stepped into the street only after the most elaborate precautions. They searched all around, and at the slightest sound the two women especially darted into the entryway calling for the tailor. Almost the whole neighborhood stuck their heads out of the windows; they were informed of what was happening, and thought it most extraordinary that the hare had vanished twice! They advised the tailor to go back to bed, assuring him that when he woke the next morning, he would find his hare again.

28

THE HARE, (continued)

At eight o'clock I was on my way toward the Palais-Royal, when at the corner of rue Jean-Tison I was accosted by a clockmaker from Charité-sur-Loire, but whom I had lodged with some time earlier in Paris, on rue des Poulies. He seemed delighted with the encounter. "It's really a coincidence that I should run into you now; I am off to have supper with three of our compatriots who live very near here, on rue des Poulies," he told me. "They'll be happy to see you, they have often spoken of you. But you are never at home! Come! Come with me!"

. . . .

I found the clockmaker with three of my compatriots—young men who lived together. Supper was being served. I declined to join them, but there is a way of tendering an invitation to which one always yields. That is when people accuse you of haughtiness, of indifference toward your homeland. So I stayed. They served a roast of half a hare; the other half had been stewed, with a fowl, probably prompted by my invitation. The hare from the night before crossed my mind and I looked out of the casement window. I recognized the tailor's, and the tailor himself with his daughter. Without any explanation I said, "I see a man I know—I beg you, my dear compatriots, let me invite him, with his wife and daughter, to share our meal." My request seemed to disconcert them greatly. I declared that I could not, in all conscience, sup with them without those good people. So they agreed. I went down, and over to the tailor's house, and I invited him to come and take his supper with his neighbors across the way. He was as surprised by the invitation as they had been to whom I had suggested it. I urged him earnestly and politely. The tailor finally gave in; the girl put on a bonnet and a very becoming little cloak; she slipped into her shoes and followed her mother, who was elegantly groomed at all times.

We arrived just as we were about to go looking for me. The young lady was enough to make her parents welcome. Her hosts were delighted to have her. Supper was gay. They realized that I did not know the tailor, who did not recognize me, having caught no more than a glimpse of me; and they were more mystified than ever. Explanations were given back and forth: the tailor said he had come because he thought I was one of his old customers, whom he named. I told him I was not that man. My compatriots questioned me in their turn: I told them I would explain everything before I left. Meanwhile, one of them was devoting the most delicate attention to the young Cécile: he told her how delighted he was to have met her; and the parents believed that I had invited them at my friend's request. They were satisfied with that notion. When supper was over I escorted the tailor home; the young admirer accompanied us.

When we returned to the other two, I told them, "Yesterday you took the hare from those good people; it fell the first time, and I carried it back to them. I informed them the second time, and today, by chance, you invited me to eat my share of it. I could not accept in good conscience unless the true owners ate of it as well. And this was the reason for my behavior this evening. Now you are righteous; before supper you were not." This made them laugh. However, the clockmaker scolded the young men. Subsequently, the one who had shown interest in Cécile married her, for the girl had two houses in Paris as dowry.

I reached the Marquise's house early, and I told her the story of my supper, which she seemed to find highly entertaining.

❦ 29 ❦

THE PLACE LOUIS-XV

. . . .

On the fourteenth of May I was convalescing. At eight o'clock in the evening I felt strong enough to venture out, and I went as far as the Tuileries.[1] A bonfire had been set for a great celebration, but I saw nothing of

it, seated as I was on the palace steps, which lead
down to the flower beds. The frightful uproar I heard
next did not startle me; it is the usual thing in such
disorderly celebrations. I left, leaning on the first cane
I had carried since my arrival in Paris, and alone I went
out through the gate to the Pont Royal, which I crossed
alone. But soon an immense crowd was following me.
I heard weeping and moaning. Never had there been
such a disastrous evening! The havoc was ascribed to a
thousand imaginary causes. There could only be two—
the sneak thieves and the libertines—and I was convinced of this the next day. The last Saint John's
Day fireworks come to mind: the same thing occurred
then at the Place Louis-XV. The sneak thieves were determined to steal—they pushed and crowded; the libertines to have certain women—and they caused their
deaths, and died with them. The thieves did the greater
harm, and started it; the libertines, however, caused
much of it, because in attempting to crouch down they
fell and were crushed underfoot. A third element, the
hooligans, contributed their own share to the chaos;
its character must be made clear.

In Paris the townspeople and the naturalized outsiders have a harsh, self-centered pattern of thinking.
They look with contempt on everything around them;
they are all of them without compassion. If something
interests them, they shove and push to reach it; to
them men and women are inanimate bulks whom they
throw to the ground, whom they tread underfoot, and
the more harm they do the greater their pride and
pleasure; it is a feat they boast of the next day. The
thieves and the libertines wanted the crowding and
disorder, but not what did occur; the hoodlums, on
the other hand, seeing the situation, aggravated it at
the risk of dying themselves. They increased the disaster by climbing onto the stacks of bodies, by trampling them ruthlessly. Except for them, perhaps no one

would have succumbed. . . . That evening I saw a desolate lover who had taken his mistress to the bonfire return to search for her, not find her, imagine her terrible fate, and die of grief. She reached him just as he gave up the ghost. . . .

There was much praise for the action of those foot soldiers who lifted and carried their colonel. They deserve great blame instead. By waiting a short time the colonel would have risked nothing, while by carrying him, by forcing a path through the crowd, who can tell how many wretched victims they caused to die the cruelest death! . . . O rulers of the world, hear me, grant none but private celebrations; it is for God alone to bring all of nature together in rejoicing!

I was too weak to visit the Marquise.

☸ 30 ☸

THE SOUBISE GARDEN

. . . .

It was early June: the time when nature is garbed in her fine flowery gown. I walked toward the Marais when I first went out, and awaiting the hour when I was to see Mme. de M***, I turned into the garden of the Soubise mansion. It was as though I had come upon a haven of innocence and purity. A throng of children with their nursemaids frolicked around the pond; girls who were somewhat older, but with that touching artlessness of adolescence, walked about under the chestnut trees; and on the lawn, planted with vegetables and fruit trees, I found a whole tribe:—all the Jewish little shopkeepers observing the Sabbath:

fathers, mothers, children, and maids—all of them mingled together.[1] They spoke German among themselves, and did not mix with the rest of the crowd. They probably took me for one of their own; I was walking about slowly, and I listened. From what I saw and heard, it appears to me that sincerity and patriarchal customs still reign among them. The maid addressed her master and her mistress like a sister or a daughter, depending on her age; the children were respectful and loving; the fathers and the mothers seemed to live for them alone. I found the feeling of these poorer Jews edifying, for when it comes to the rich ones, we are well aware that it is another thing entirely. The scene was the same everywhere; in any case, they were preparing to leave, so I went to the other side, where the young Christian girls were strolling.

They were all charming, and some of them were quite lovely. They thought I was a Jew, and I heard them saying to one another: "He is a Jew, but there is no need to be afraid—those people are very obedient to their law. They are all right, and they are very close." They sat down on the bench. I took a seat behind them, below the terrace. They lost sight of me, and I heard a conversation then which was fascinating for its frankness and naïvité.

"Well, I would really like these Jews if only they weren't Jewish!" said one girl.

"What does that mean?"

"Oh, I know what she means, she needn't explain! She means she would like to have a husband like that someday—don't you?"

"That's what I meant; it would be wrong to lie."

"I, for one, don't want to marry ever: my aunt says all men are wicked; and, in fact, I see it in many families—all wives are more or less unhappy."

"Dear friend," said one of the biggest, "hasn't it occurred to you that maybe it's the woman's fault sometimes? I assure you that my own mama is very happy with my father! And every day she tells us: 'My children, you must respect your father! He is such a good man, so upright, he works so hard, he is so well thought of, so capable, that we all owe him our well-being. . . .' I only hope I shall have the same good fortune, especially if I leave the choice to my mother and father, who are very prudent and sensible, and who love me—oh! as no child has ever been loved—and I return the feeling."

"I feel quite differently from Sophie! We are the same age—I'm fifteen, and so is she—but I see nothing in our home that would tempt me to marry. My mother was beautiful and my father adored her; and ever since they were married she has never been able to do as she likes. Always objections at the smallest expense! And so my mother tells me that the best of men—my father—is no good."

An alert little girl spoke up then: "That's certainly an example of faulty reasoning! Because Mademoiselle's father is the best of the pests, it follows that all men are worse than he! But you can certainly see, ma'm'selle, that a man who would never say the things *he* says would be better than he is, don't you?"

"That is not the point!" another cried. "Don't you know that my friend's mother is a silly woman, and that if Victoire becomes rich one day, as she will, she will owe her fortune to her father's prudence? She is right to say that he is a fine man, for I have heard my father—who according to my mother is the wisest and cleverest of men—say that except for the strong will of my good friend's father, his whole fortune would be squandered because her mother is a feather-brain—and still, she is a good wife and a good mother."
"Then she is not like Madame . . . her daughter isn't here, is she? . . . that poor Irène. . . . Oh, how unhappy she is! Her mother doesn't love her, and she

makes her suffer terribly! So much so that my mother says, when a person has a mother like that, she is under no obligation to love her."

"No, ma'm'selle!" said the girl who had been the third to speak. "Nothing can excuse you for not loving your mother! When you become a mother—if God grants you that happiness—how would you feel about having your child hate you?"

"If I were unfortunate enough to be a nasty mother, it would be quite unimportant to me!"

"But my friend," the other girl continued, "it would not be unimportant to your daughter! Irène loves her mother, who does not love her, and Mama says, in that way she has found a means of turning her mother's hatred to her advantage: for it is very noble to love a mother who does not love you—to love her solely because she has given you life, and because she is your mother!"

"Oh, yes—yes!" exclaimed ten of those sweet girls at once. I saw that they were about to get up, for one of them remarked that it was getting late. I approached them.

"Young ladies," I said to them, "I have just heard your conversation, and I can't tell you how much respect it has inspired in me for you! At your age, the fair sex has all the finest qualities. Try to retain throughout your life that priceless sincerity which is your great charm, and which has brought tears to my eyes!"

They listened to me, amazed, without a word. I felt I ought to spare them from embarrassment, so I walked away. All of them left, and I heard them say: "He is kindhearted, that Jew! He almost had tears in his eyes as he spoke to us."

"They were once God's chosen people."

"They will be that again one day."

"Yes, sometime before the end of the world. But

that one there—will he be damned meanwhile?"

"No, no!" said one of the youngest. The others did not dare to decide whether I would be damned, but they trembled at the thought! . . . I remained for a while after the departure of these kind girls. Then I went to visit the Marquise earlier than usual.

I waited alone about half an hour for her to appear at her gate. I was asked if I wished someone to keep me company. I declined with thanks, for I meant to write down what I had just seen and heard in order to read it to Mme. de M***. She appeared as I was writing. She was delighted: "You make use of everything!" she said to me. (. . .)

❧ 31 ❧

THE REAL MAGUELONE

I made certain not to miss the Boulevard and the nocturnal entertainment! (. . .) I chose the Café Caussin as the most fertile ground for activity because of its proximity to the traveling players. I had just entered when I saw a beautiful harlot go by beyond the front canopy. She was dressed in a most provocative fashion, and her shoes were white with very high heels. Someone said, "Yesterday you mentioned Maguelone —there she is, that's her for sure!" I was struck by these words, not because I did not know what it was about the lovely lady that had caught my eye the day before, but I wanted to meet the girl for whom she had been mistaken. I rose and followed the girl, admired her pretty waist, and across from the Nicolet Theater[1] I addressed her.

"You are the lovely Maguelone, aren't you?" I said. She looked at me with a smile: "Who told you my name?"

"Everyone—you are so well known! A beautiful woman like you causes quite a stir." The remark pleased her. "Would you like to buy me a *bavaroise?*" [2] she asked. "I feel short of breath; it would do me good."

This I could not refuse. I led her to Café Alexandre, since I did not want to become the focus of attention with her at Caussin's. I wanted to study the girl, and to understand her. I thought her face had something noble in it, a certain fineness; her manner was easy, and at first seemed pleasant. I thought she was highly alluring, though that was scarcely consistent with her profession. At the outset, her whole behavior seemed that of a most charming girl. Yet, I said to myself, based on past experience: "It is impossible that this girl, apparently so delightful, should have anything but a deceitful spirit and a depraved heart."

After the *bavaroise,* which she took with a bun, she asked for some coffee; she poured a little milk into it to make it less strong, and I did the same, having ordered nothing at first. Wine and coffee have a favorable influence on some people; that is to say, the more these liquids take effect, the more gentle, gay and affectionate they become. It follows then that such persons are naturally gay, good and tender, and that by heightening their spirits, stimulants activate these qualities. But I noticed that, conversely, Maguelone became temperamental and insolent after the coffee. An idea had occurred to me concerning her: while by myself I am nothing, there was much I could do through the Marquise! This was my notion: it is an excellent deed to retrieve a lovely girl from a life of vice, and to endeavor to return her to a normal existence, to society! Ah, if that lovely woman wanted to become a wife and a mother, what man would she fail to make happy? She might be married in the country, after her heart had been purified. . . . Say, is there a man or a woman whose heart would not be purified by that of the divine Marquise? . . .

But when I began to notice the excessive capriciousness I determined to sound Maguelone's character. She asked for brandy. Despite my aversion to that despicable liquor, I ordered some, and let her have all of it. She became animated, and as it developed, her character turned out to be the most outlandish, the most bizarre I had ever encountered. She would smile at me, then cut me short and insult me, which is worse than offending. I tried to muster all my patience. But it is impossible to relate how far she taxed it! She considered me a miser, a nobody, and she acted accordingly. When I had let her go quite far, I still restrained myself. She thought I was the very image of foolishness, a real Colas.[3] She rinsed her mouth with the last of the brandy and water, and spat it all in my face. One might think that, however irascible my character, I had no right to become angry with a woman I was experimenting with, but it was the last straw. She gloried in the laughter of all the customers around us. I have a strong grip and I seized her roughly by the arm: "All right, Maguelone, wipe it off . . . and . . . don't force me to tell you twice. . . . I wanted to test you to see how far you would go. . . . Obey me, or by God . . ."

All eyes were fixed on us; all mouths hung open. I shook Maguelone so forcefully that I bent her to the floor. She attempted to laugh, but I said, "No, no! No more joking! Wipe it off with your napkin! Do it! I command you!" I bent her down again. My strength terrified her and she changed her tone. I insisted; she wiped me clean, resuming the charming manner she had started with.

Now I knew how to handle her and was no longer

at a loss. When she had finished, and had kissed me, without a word from me, I said, "You have treated me abominably, in front of all these people; you must ask my forgiveness—forgiveness, on your knees. Do it; I command you!" She stared at me, astonished. I seized her again: "Do it, and at once!" She smiled, so . . . No, there is no way to describe the charm of that smile! If I had not taken an interest in her I would have let her off, disarmed. "On your knees!" I cried, pretending to grow furious—something which was quite easy for me, as my face flushes readily. Then, with one hand resting lightly on me, she went down on one knee. "Both of them!" She got down on both.

"What do you want me to say?"

" 'Monsieur, I ask your pardon for my obnoxious behavior; you had done nothing to provoke it; I am stupid, and an impossible person.' "

"Repeat that to me word for word—I never could learn anything by heart."

I repeated it; she recited after me. My mien was dreadful; hers, sweet and gentle. I saw some people weep. When she had finished she asked whether she might rise. I offered her my hands. She rose painfully, looked at me, and sat down when I gave the nod. I hardly spoke to her again. As a final crushing blow I should have taken a pipe, and smoked it slowly, but that was not possible. I ordered an ice and told her to eat it. She used the most seductive tricks to get me to accept a few spoonfuls: I remained unbending. When she had finished I indicated for her to leave, and to follow me. She obeyed meekly, leaning on me. The whole room echoed with applause. It could not have been for her. . . . Maguelone departed with regal dignity.

When we were outside I said to her: "Maguelone, I am taking you with me."

"I shall do whatever you want," she replied. "I have never met a man who dominated me as you have!" I did not answer; I offered her my arm, and she leaned on it with the greatest amiability in the world. I led her to the Marquise's house. She thought it was mine, and this increased her respect for me.

I left her with the chambermaid and the Demoiselles de Merup[4] in order to give the Marquise a more unrestricted account of all that had occurred. Then I told her that the girl would have to be vanquished through fear, and that without identifying myself I would, from time to time, come to the parlor of the house where she was to be sent, to keep her in hand and to direct her training. The adorable Marquise agreed to everything, and reserved to herself only the right to pay for the care I asked for the poor girl.

A hackney was sent for; I climbed into it with Maguelone, who said, "Then this isn't your place?" I did not answer. She became sweet and affectionate. I rejected her feebly. Finally we reached a courtyard. We stepped down. I gave the Marquise's orders in a loud voice, as if they were my own, and I withdrew, leaving Maguelone quite astonished at the outcome! . . .

She has had many temper tantrums since she came to that house. She is treated with great kindness, but I am the only one who reprimands her, and I listen intently to her complaints. It is a sizeable task to educate this girl, whose extraordinary story I shall tell one night. For the moment, suffice it to say that she was the illegitimate daughter of a nobleman, and that at the end of two months she would have been heartsick at leaving her refuge (. . .).

✺ 32 ✺

THE SAINT-LAURENT FAIR[1]

For some time I had felt a great desire to see the tightrope dancers perform again. I could have chosen no
better night. The Boulevard shows were playing at the
Saint-Laurent Fair. I walked along the beautiful boulevards, continued to the Porte Saint-Martin and came
to the Fair, which is held on the Lazarist[2] convent
grounds. All the traveling players (and formerly the
comic opera) are required to appear there, apparently to put some life into this useless fair, which is so
totally useless that it has been necessary to send the
players there to revive it. It is commerce alone which
should attract both the public and the players, but
there is no country which knows less of commerce, and
the methods of promoting it, than France. The tax administration destroys the nation's industry, frustrates
its every spurt of new energy, and will end by demolish-
ing it. Exemptions are needed but the administration
will not hear of them. It dreams only of enormous
profits, but enormous profits cannot be made from
poor men; it draws little from everyone and exhausts
them all in order to grow fat on their blood and then
display a mad and criminal extravagance. But exemptions granted to the two fairs—the Saint-Laurent and
the Saint-Germain, both of which would then be taken
out of the hands of the monks who cannot properly
continue to manage them—would draw foreigners to
France, and would above all give the merchants of
Paris an opportunity to exhibit and sell all their old

stock. The administration itself would gain, through greater circulation and consumption of the other products, but the financial mentality is the slow poison of the state. When will people be asked to contribute directly to the public treasury? . . . This is what I was thinking about from the Porte Saint-Martin to the Saint-Laurent enclosure.

In the bazaar I saw a few niggardly shops with scanty wares, shopgirls spreading fashionable gowns for display as spiders stretch their webs, billiard halls, cafés, smoking-rooms, and a great many clowns. The entertainments were beginning, amid a dreadful racket, and they left even the billiard halls empty; I felt as though I were in Spain. I joined the throng, and I watched what was going on at the performance, in an area much smaller and more concentrated than the street outside. First, I noticed that the crowd consisted mostly of three kinds of people: sneak thieves; novice apprentices, who did not even earn the price of their candles,[3] and a few of whom were no more reliable than the first group; and lastly, youngsters who had slipped away from their families. Then there were underemployed workmen, or those who cannot work by lamplight, and there were foreigners. The women were mostly young shopgirls, seamstresses, scrubwomen, embroiderers and craftsmen's daughters.

It was impossible to start any kind of trouble here, like in a huge crowd, but some tried. They took advantage of the smutty quips in the spectacle to explain the obscene clowning to the girls. From time to time there was a slight movement in the crowd, during which the sneak thieves attempted to operate. Hooligans played practical jokes on the girls at the most absorbing moments, and after some particularly indecent behavior they absconded when the young woman screamed, while the upstart's companions would stand around her with feigned aloofness on their faces, their

eyes fixed on the platform. I saw a young girl, with
her mother, who was abused so seriously at a moment
when she was laughing with all her heart that she
fainted. She even suffered some injury. I rebuked the
mother for having brought her daughter to such a place.
A doctor had to be called. . . . I turn my eyes from
this vile episode. A young man from the country lost
his watch, his tobacco case, his purse and his handkerchief. In fact, I believe that those who stripped him
were not professional thieves but cruel practical jokers
who were highly amused by his green manner and awed
expression.

The subject of the play was Cassandre, shamefully betrayed by Léandre, who was of course aided by
Columbine and Pierrot. The brazen hussy used the
most nefarious methods, in an outrageous manner, to
deceive Cassandre while forcing him to pay her dowry.
She caressed him and cajoled him, and thus gave a
most instructive lesson to the uninitiated. The Columbine was pretty; and contrary to the custom among
players, she was even dressed with a kind of sensuous
taste! Therefore, what she said and what she did became only the more intriguing. At one point, as she
caressed Cassandre, pressing his head to her bosom, the
handsome Léandre tickled the palm of the old man's
hand; and the latter, thinking it was Columbine, went
through a pantomime like that in a dance of savages. It
was during this farce that the young girl was molested,
and she was not the only one; the lascivious old codger
stirred up a general frenzy among the excited young
men, and many of the women and girls were forced to
walk elsewhere or to leave.

A wise police administration abolished these bur-
lesques, which ended completely in 1777, at the last
Saint-Ovide Fair in the Place Louis-XV. I did not go
into Nicolet's as I had intended. I postponed my visit
to the following night. I helped to bring the molested

girl home. Four of us carried her gently; that is, we relieved one another every fifty paces. She was seriously injured and stayed in bed for six weeks. I need make myself no clearer. She was young, blond, and very pretty (. . .).

🏵 33 🏵

THE MAN WHO LEAPED FROM
THE WINDOW

I returned along the Boulevard, and followed it until rue de Richelieu, by which I went back to the city. In the road across from rue Saint-Marc I noticed something about the height of a dog. I went closer—it was a man. I said nothing to him, since I felt it would be improper to intrude. I was puzzled, though, that he should be huddling almost in the center of the street. However, I remained at a distance, mystified at his immobility. As I hesitated about what to do, a girl who seemed to be a chambermaid came out with a little lantern in her hand. She went over to the man, touched him, gave out a cry, and darted back inside. I was walking toward him in my turn, when some people came over from the house where the girl had disappeared. She was accompanied by a young woman, who appeared to be her mistress, and by the doorkeeper. The man gathered up the huddled figure, who gave up a kind of howl, and carried him into the house, and the door closed behind them.

I was extremely curious to know the meaning of all this. I wondered whether to knock or to find some pretext to make inquiries. I decided on the latter course.

I knocked, and the door opened. "What an extraordinary occurrence! It could cause some talk! Let us come to some agreement on what I should say, as a witness. It might be worth your while." At my words, at my kindly expression, I was invited to enter: I was ushered in to the lady and her maid. I found them in great distress. Before we talked, I helped them to lay the man carefully in a good warm bed. I saw that the attentions of a surgeon were necessary; the poor man had suffered some dislocation. I offered to go for one, but my proposal was not accepted; the doorkeeper was sent out. While we waited, I asked once again what it would be best for me to say, for everyone's sake, in case what had happened were to cause talk. Here is the story told by the young chambermaid, whose mistress told her to speak:

"Since you have seen everything, and since you may say what you please, I prefer to put myself at your discretion. He is my lover. I have been rash enough to receive him several times at night, but nothing untoward has ever happened. Tonight, as he entered, he was seen by Monsieur, my dear mistress's husband. When he noticed the circumspection with which such a respectable gentleman tried to gain entrance, he thought the man was a lover coming to see his wife. He went to Madame's door, knocked with all his might, and forced her to open it. My lover, who was in my room, feared that he would compromise both my mistress and myself if he were discovered, so he gauged the window with his eyes, and over my protests, he risked a leap. I closed the window immediately after him, and thought he was well on his way. Monsieur looked everywhere and, finding nothing, decided he was mistaken; he begged Madame's forgiveness, and persuaded himself that he had only seen one of the house servants. He went out and left immediately for Versailles, where he had been called on urgent orders. When everything was quiet again I opened the window to show Madame how my lover had gone out through it. Imagine my astonishment when I saw him, still in the same place where he had landed! We ran to him, Madame and I; and the doorkeeper, whom we trust, lent us a hand. There you have it."

I am not like those evil minds who always probe beyond what people are willing to let them see: I simply took the pretty servant's word for it. The surgeon arrived: he found the man to be in critical condition! He applied ointment to all his limbs and then, since he felt that the man would be up to being carried, he asked whether I could help them. I agreed; the doorkeeper and I carried the man across our arms, and when I grew weary, the surgeon took my place. I relieved him in turn, and as the man lived not far from rue de Richelieu, we reached his home and entrusted him to his doorkeeper. The surgeon stayed with him: the doorkeeper and I returned together. I had noticed that the doorkeeper did not show himself to the victim's porter. I have learned since then that the injured man recovered, but only after a long confinement, and sufferings which drastically tempered his gallant ideas. I passed Pinolet;[1] I entered the Den on rue Jean-Saint-Denis, but I was recognized. I reached my house at three o'clock.

❧ 34 ❧

THE BRUTE

On rue du Figuier, I heard a scream and a window flew open. It was on the fifth floor. "Help me! Help me!" a woman was crying in a choked voice. No one inside the house seemed to hear her. I tried the door to the entryway, and opened it. I hurried up. I always went out armed with a hooked stick, like a porter's. Reaching the fifth-floor door I knocked loudly. "Oh, you wretch!" the woman said. "Someone has come to help me!" Just then the door opened. The man rushed out and tried to throw me down, but I stood firm. "Get out," I said to him, "you can see I'm not holding you!" He fled. I entered the woman's room. She was a dressmaker of about thirty, but with a pretty face. She dressed, for she was in the nude. I asked her what had happened.

"Monsieur," she told me, "the scoundrel is my water carrier,[1] my errand boy—well, he was employed to do odd things around the house. I work, as you can see; I dress with a degree of taste and above all I like to be clean. He fell in love with me. At first he indicated it to me only by a very ardent zeal to serve me; I wanted to pay him despite his protests, but he refused my money. Taken aback by this behavior, and suspecting his motives, I wanted to dismiss him, but he threw himself at my feet, and implored me to such an extent that I yielded and kept him on. I did not know that the neighbors suspected me. . . . Then, three days ago, I heard two women talking about me: "With her face and clothes, she must be really common, to be using her water carrier!" I wanted an explanation, and I asked for it. I was given the coarse reply that I must certainly know it, and that when a woman slept with her water carrier, she had really hit bottom. That gave me a jolt! I paid Jean, and forbade him ever to set foot in my house again. He didn't return. But today, using my extra key which he had stolen from me, he slipped in while I was sleeping. He was aware of the rumors about me and was going to attack me, since he was certain that the neighbors wouldn't come and help me. That's my story."

I was puzzled; I determined to learn the real truth, either to corroborate the woman's word, or to make her marry the Auvergnat if she had behaved badly. . . . I discovered that she was innocent: the water carrier was sent back to Auvergne, and the spiteful neighbors were intimidated.

❧ 35 ❧

THE DOORSTEPS

There is a practice in Paris whereby the capital resembles the provincial cities—a practice which is in evidence only when the evenings begin to grow longer, in late July, in August, and into mid-September: the women sit outside their doors in order to get a breath of fresh air and chatter among themselves. Often a lone woman on the important streets like rues Saint-Honoré, Dauphine, Saint-Denis, and the rest, finds it pleasant enough to come out onto her doorstep to watch the passers-by and enjoy the various sights, which she cannot see in wintertime. The streets of Paris are indeed like its opera house; the scene changes every moment. In an enormous city, this practice gives rise to various incidents. Lovers and sneak thieves both have taken advantage of it: the former to make off nimbly with a woman's shoe[1] and turn it into an object of worship; the latter to steal a pendant earring, a cross on a velvet ribbon around the neck, or even a slipper, for the sake of the buckle. The thieves have been known to feign a brawl among themselves, tumble into a group of seated women, and rob them. Love may play a parlor game, and with eyes blindfolded, head pressed between the knees of some fair lady, arrange a tryst under Argus' very nose.[2]

❦ 36 ❦

THE HOLY VIATICUM

In rue de l'Égyptienne, known as rue de la Jussienne, I heard the sound of the small bell; a priest, an altar boy and the bearers of the blessed sacrament were walking without a procession.

I took off my hat, and accompanied the minister of consolation for the sick, responding with the altar boy to the psalms he was reciting.

We climbed to a sixth floor in the little rue Verdet. It was the home of a firewood-cutter. The minister pronounced a short exhortation, but how inspiring! "My brother—your life has been blameless and difficult; have faith in the goodness of God! You have known only sorrow in this life; the good awaits you in the next. When a man shows resignation in the face of such misery . . ."

"What! Misery?" the dying man broke in, raising himself on the bed. "You're mistaken! I've been the happiest of men! I've had a wonderful wife and good children; work, good health, the good opinion of my customers and my neighbors, who thought too highly of the small services I liked doing for them. . . . Ah, monsieur! I have been happy in this world!"

"Well!" the priest said, embracing him with tears

in his eyes. "Then you will be even more so in the next." He spoke no more to this good man, but taking up the holy Viaticum, he cried enthusiastically: "My Lord, behold a temple worthy of you!"

He gave communion to the ailing man, genuflected, and began the *Te Deum*, which he completed as he made his way back. I accompanied him to the church, then I returned to the sick man's house to ask about his condition: he was better.

. . . .

🕸 37 🕸

THE TWO WORKMEN

As I returned I came across two rather amusing drunken men: they were workmen. One of them asked the other for a pinch of tobacco.

"No! I don't want to have anything to do with a sot like you: a wineskin, a good-for-nothing, who pours everything down his gullet—his wife's and children's bread, their clothes, their hats, their shoes; the spoons, the forks, the bedclothes, and even the andirons and the tongs off his own hearth."

"But you're the one who did that."

"If it was me, I refuse to drink with me anymore. I'm no good and I despise myself . . . like a glass of water. . . . Did you drink with me? . . . Did you?"

"Sure, you know I did; we just left La Courtille." [1]

"You drank . . . with me? . . ."

"Yes, yes."

"Well then, here's a good punch in the mouth,

and here's a kick too. . . . You're a terrible man,
drinking with a lowlife like me, with no character, no
manners."

"What! You hit me! . . . All right, I'll give it right
back to you."

They struggled, and I separated them. I took the
drunker one home, and tried to make him listen to
reason. He paid attention to me. When we reached
his door he opened it, and we went up. There I found
a desolate woman, and some half-naked children.

"Monsieur," said the poor woman, "while we were
out, three days ago, he sold everything so he could go
off and get drunk. He works at a trade in which wages
were almost doubled some time ago, but damn that
increase! With the excuse that now he can earn as
much in three days as in six before, he carouses for
three days, and besides what he earns, he uses up what
little we had."

I realized how right she was! I tried to console her,
and promised to enlist the help of a distinguished
lady who would see to it that her husband was restrained. I left her, deeply pensive, and these were
my thoughts:

Among all our men of letters, I am perhaps the
only one who knows the common people and mingles
with them. I want to describe them; I want to be the
sentinel of orderly conditions. I have gone down into
the lowest classes in order to see everything that is
vile. Beware, philosophers! Love for humanity may
lead you astray! What you call the best may be the
worst! The people must not earn too much; they are
like stomachs swollen and rendered sluggish by too
much food. In the belief that you do good—listen to
the words of experience—you may bring on total
ruin! . . .

And you, statesmen, beware still more! A fateful
revolution is approaching! The spirit of defiance is

spreading, growing! It festers silently in the lowest class! I declare this to you publicly, and if you deign to investigate, you will be shown overwhelming evidence! Even the wives of the workers themselves know that the insane increase in salaries is wrong, that it turns coarse men's heads! O statesmen! I have seen proof that such a degree of good living, of comfort, cannot be absorbed by people in the cities, though those in the countryside make the adjustment. Furthermore, the present earnings of certain workers entail the terrible drawback that they deny our arts and crafts the possibility of competing with those of other countries. . . . I shall stop, lest certain blind zealots accuse me of a kind of Machiavellianism, or of supporting that brazen writer who speaks out for slavery. But I hold certain principles counter to those of Machiavelli and of Nero's apologist;[2] and if the latter does certain things with which I am unfamiliar, I have seen some and felt some which he will never know.

❧ 38 ☙

THE MAD DOG

I returned once again through the New Market and the Pont Neuf. Across from the Place Dauphine, a huge collared dog, who looked diseased, came running to leap at me. I climbed the Henry IV grill so nimbly that the dog could not reach me. He butted his head against the bars; then he threw himself upon the orange vendors' old empty crates. I shouted to the sentry to take cover, which he did. The sergeant emerged and ordered the dog killed, but the animal ran off, and no matter what I said they did not pursue him. I asked the night watchman to warn the orangewomen to burn the cases the dog had bitten, and I pointed them out. I was terribly alarmed! If it were up to me, there would be no dogs in the city. Imagine! People make a diversion, a pastime, of raising and sheltering an animal who can turn more poisonous than the most dangerous serpent! This is one of the follies of the human race. I hate dogs and I love people.

❊ 39 ❊

THE STREETLAMPS

In earlier days, there was a moment of the evening when the city dwellers were plunged into deep darkness. It was the moment of nightfall, and a time when the streets were extremely busy. Besides the fact that the time for lighting up was apparently set too late, there were so many of the poor lanterns with their single candles and they emitted so little light that all of them had to be lit before one could see even faintly. Nowadays the service is provided much earlier, by a smaller number, and when a lamp is lighted, it throws a brilliant shine for a good distance. We are better off, and this improvement has come about in our time. Occasionally, in fact, there is a tendency to the other extreme: at certain times of the year the lanterns burn in daylight—an error simple enough to prevent by setting the hours not by seasons but by days, with the schedules set back a few minutes for open spaces like bridges, quays, and such.

Hooligans used to break the lanterns in their nightly rounds, for their slight elevation set them within reach of a stick. This vandalism no longer occurs, nor could it. Coachmen of all sorts respect the lamplighter and the lamp. A dandy in a cabriolet will stop—and even a prim young lady's driver, always a shade more insolent than a young fop's chauffeur.

. . . .

🕸 40 🕸

THE BILLBOARD STRIPPER

Some nights later I encountered the man who had told me the way to eke out a living in *Lazy Man's Labor*[1], and he pointed out the man in question to me. We were just saying goodbye, when he tugged at my arm: "There's one of another kind," he told me, "even more extraordinary, and one that will astound you, it's so niggardly—and yet, it has kept that man alive for thirty years! You would never guess. . . . Well then, he pulls posters off the billboards at street 'corners, and that provides for all his needs. . . . Watch him. . . . He sells the single ones to the grocer at three sous a pound; those that are stuck, one on top of the other, he sells to the cardboardmaker; and whatever is absolutely filthy and ruined he collects in his little room, and keeps himself warm with it during the winter. The wretch is absolutely incapable of any work; not that he is physically handicapped, but from indolence. He denies himself all pleasures; he eats the most revolting things, which he buys on street corners from women who sell scraps. He goes out at night to take down the posters; but as he wants to avoid giving cause for complaint, he reads the dates and lets them stay as long as the day mentioned has not yet passed. He never touches the permanent notices, like advertisements for books, medicines, and such. Every single evening he strips the walls of theater playbills, and that item alone brings him twelve or fifteen sous a day. He sleeps from eight in the morning until three or four in the afternoon. The rest of the day he sorts his papers, and carries them off to sell. As the rejects would not be enough for his fuel, during his daily rounds he picks up small bits of wood and charcoal, vegetable peels, straw and chair-stuffing that have been thrown into the streets, and the summer supplies him enough to heat his room during the worst cold spells in winter."

. . . .

🎇 41 🎇

ACCOUNT OF A FIRE

As I went out in the evening at nine o'clock I saw a woman run by, screaming. She had been visiting, a few hundred feet from her home, when someone came to tell her that her house had caught fire. It was only in the chimney, which fortunately was built of brick, so that, despite its violence, it caused no damage. While I watched I was addressed by a stranger, who said to me: "It's nothing—nothing! No cause for alarm! I've seen plenty of fires in Paris! I've seen some terrible ones! The Opéra, in 1763[1]; the one at the Saint-Ger-

main Fair; but the most horrible of all was the time
the Pont au Change burned." [2]

"You were there?"

"I was very young, but I can still see it. I'll tell
you how it was. The fire started in the daytime, at
three in the afternoon. On the fourth floor there was
a dressmaker, who had girls of good family entrusted
to her as pupils because of her reliability. When lunch
was over, this woman went out to an appointment
she had, but as she wanted to be sure of things at
home, she left her pupils under lock and key, as was
her custom. The fire started, not in her apartment but
in the one below it. The girls were singing and talking; they were making so much noise that they heard
nothing. It was only when the flames were visible that
one of them noticed them, from the smoke. She put
her head out of the window, saying, 'My good friends
—something is burning!'

" 'Yes, yes!' came the answering cries. 'We've been
calling you for the last half-hour! It's in your house!
Come down quickly!'

"At these words, they had all come to the window,
and they began to scream.

" 'We're locked in!'

" 'Jump from the window! We'll catch you!'—and
a few blankets appeared. But given the timidity natural
to their age and sex, none of them dared to do it.

"When the fire had penetrated their room, we
could see them clinging to the windows, and their
wails were heartbreaking. People don't think clearly in
such situations, for they could have been rescued. But
the police controlling the crowd hold off the volunteers, and those who are kept there only want to
break away. The poor girls fell, suffocated by the
smoke. It was a horrible sight!"

"I've heard enough!" I told him. And I moved off
to catch my breath.

I went to the Marquise's, meditating on what harm an impulsive person can cause in a big city by an ill-conceived idea, like the notion of forcing people to fight fires. Call the neighbors; let them alone have the privilege of helping, and you will have enough hands, together with the fire brigade; and above all, see to it that the latter are quick to get underway! Punish them if they are not ready at the first alarm! . . .

As I left Mme. de M***, I met the philanthropist. I told him of the fire.

"I was present at one of those terrible accidents," he told me, "in the middle of the night. I saw a soldier from the Paris guard go into the flames to bring out a woman in childbed and her infant. She was in a room the fire had not yet reached, but he had to cross through the flames.

"Another time I saw a Capuchin risk death to save a man hanging over the flames. I saw a man I shall not name save five children locked in a garret. I have seen that impassioned mankind fears nothing, and that thus armed it works miracles!"

🕸 42 🕸

THE DEN OF INIQUITY

For a long while I saw nothing happen. Working hard during the day on a difficult task, I would leave the house later and return earlier. Various experiments in literature, which the Marquise was urging me to try and which filled my nights, kept me from seeking other diversion. Part of all that was published in *Le Paysan-Paysanne*[1] and in *Les Françaises;*[2] *Oribeau* was one of those experiments, and if that work is not better, that is because it was not produced under the auspices of my good fairy, but there are a few scattered passages with which I am satisfied, though I am very rarely so with my pen's output. We revised a translation of Quevedo's *Tacaño,* which was published two years later under the title *Le fin matois.* It is a poor work in both languages; the last seven chapters are entirely mine, as Quevedo never finished this work in the French manner. But what occupied most our time was the *Paysan,* and many of the *Contemporaines* stories! . . . This is enough of an account.

I have said that I went out at nine o'clock for the sake of amusement and relaxation. I wandered into a street of whores near the Maubuée fountain. I heard some muffled sounds from a suspicious-looking house. I am very shy but not cowardly—that is, I would be afraid to walk by a group of ladies, and I willingly brave a band of villains. In the first case, it is a question of pride—I fear comparison; in the second it is courage—I am no poltroon.

I went up quickly, but found the doors closed. However, as these places are never tightly shut and the girls usually have no individual locks, one can easily see what goes on in their rooms through the orifice of the missing mechanism. I saw a young man, who seemed to be a bumpkin from the provinces, being shorn of his valuables in the roughest fashion by three women—two trollops and the procuress. I was puzzled to see him put up such feeble resistance against three women, one of whom was an old crone, another a child; even the strongest was no match for him. And yet, he was behaving in a most frightened, submissive manner. The fact is that what I saw was not the whole scene.

When he had nothing left, I heard a male voice say,
"There now, my friend, now you'll sign your contract.
Completely voluntary, isn't it, since you're the one
who's begging me for it?"

"Yes, sir, it's voluntary."

"Excellent! Otherwise I wouldn't take you. . . ."

The tall youth signed. The door opened; I stepped
to one side. The young man emerged with the recruiting agent.[3] The door closed again. I let the recruiting
agent go—I knew him by sight, he was from the Quai
de la Ferraille—and I listened to the trollops. They
were laughing: "Ha! He got a real going-over!" A
man's hoarse voice responded: "They're a godsend,
those bumpkins, and we shouldn't let a single one slip
by. . . . All right, now let's see the money."

"Hey, leave something for us!"

"Each one gets an écu."

"That's not enough!"

His reply was a slap for the middle girl, the only
one who had spoken up. They gave him everything,
but not without shouting, cursing, weeping. I could
not understand how so much uproar was tolerated in
the other apartments! But I soon realized that the
whole house was inhabited by such prostitutes. The
scoundrel opened the door and came out. . . . Ah,
Lavater![4] You would have seen him for what he was!
He was crime incarnate—by the ugliness and cruelty
of his gaze and his brow, by the hideous, involuntary
movements of his odious features.

After his departure the girls fell to quarreling
among themselves and came to blows. The old one ac-
caused the middle one of laying them open to imprisonment for the rest of their days by letting that bad
character in on the job. She declared that she and the
young one were going to leave her. The middle one
swore and cursed; she was not ugly by nature, but at

that moment there had never been such a hideous monster. They went out, however, the middle one and the crone leaving the girl behind, for she was combed, dressed and shod too well to go out into the mire. No sooner had they gone down than I entered. I was moved with compassion for the child, whose scarcely begun life could still be salvaged.

"My girl," I told her, "you are ruined! Everything that happened was overheard. The villain who left will be punished; you will be arrested and put into the Hôpital⁵ for the rest of your life, because of your youth; your two companions will be flogged and branded. Come with me; I shall save you if you want to become a virtuous girl!"

The child was dumbfounded at first; but then she gave me her hand, for me to take her away. She was tiny; I caught her up under my arm and covered her with my cloak. I went down the stairs; at the door I met the two furies, who moved aside to let me pass. I heard them say, "What's he carrying off, that fellow?" At the same time they accosted an old man, singing him the praises of the child. I saw him follow them. But I had no time to observe that new episode. I carried the little one to the Marquise's purifying house; I gave instructions on handling the terror and I returned to where I had found her.

I had not been long. The old man was still there. The two women were behaving quite differently with him than with the country lout! They seemed to fear him; they assured him and swore that they had not meant to cheat him. They called to Françoise; they searched for her through the whole house. They called on their neighbors to bear them out. The old man insisted, though; he wanted them to show him the little girl. He accused the two women of having whisked her away, of keeping her locked up and hidden out of fear of her being recognized. I realized then that this might be a decent man. He spoke of sending for the police; thereupon I made my appearance.

"Monsieur," I said, "you will not find the little one here; she is gone! She is in a safe place, under the protection of Madame la Marquise de M***, who pays the pupils' keep; I can show you proof of this whenever you like."

"Ah! Since when?"

"About ten minutes ago."

"Well! That's another matter! . . . Are you sure?"

"Come!"

"I shall. How did it happen?"

I recounted all I had seen, heard, and done. He smiled when I told him that I had had the girl under my cloak while he himself was being solicited. The old man revealed himself to be the police commissioner***, who had just been informed that those two miserable women had got hold of an orphan who was somewhat neglected by her guardian, a drunkard; he told me he had wanted to look into the situation for himself before taking action. He opened a window, and wiped his nose. Immediately, five or six persons were heard climbing the stairs: his lieutenants. The two women threw themselves to their knees, terrified. I remarked to the commissioner that these two miserable women were lost to society; that it was as well they be left to ply their low trade, since it was tolerated to a certain degree, as hand their place over to others; that such monsters were useful for frightening witless libertines and turning them away from vice forever; but that as far as the man with the hideous face was concerned, every effort should be made to take him, as well as Monsieur Such-and-Such, the recruiting agent, whom I had recognized.

The commissioner replied that they must be punished first; and that, as to the other rascal, they knew

where he could be found. And indeed, he was brought
in a moment later. He denied everything brazenly, but
I testified against him: I described the whole affair.
Then I inquired whether it would be necessary for the
young girl to testify. The commissioner said that he
would take her deposition where she was. Ah, what
wrath the ugly man showed toward me! He nearly
stabbed me. I dodged the blow; he was held very
tightly, and garroted so that he could scarcely crawl.
He was led off to prison; and I went to see the Marquise.

I returned along the same route. I learned then
that the commissioner had released the two women,
with an admonition to report to him whatever they
should discover about the activities of their colleagues.
Apparently, after questioning them he had had good
reasons for dealing with them thus, and it was more
important to quell the worst offenses. Indeed, crimes
of every sort are committed in vile places, and the
stench they give off was beginning to permeate society;
its baleful effects have since been seen.

❧ 43 ❧

THE RAINSPOUTS

The term *échené*[1] (spout) should be used for the
protruding gutters which collect the water from roofs
into a cascade, and simply *gouttière* (*gutter*) for the
roof edges which pour it drop by drop. A hundred
examples could be listed to illustrate the degree to
which the people of Paris corrupt the language, and
impoverish it. I am proud of the words with which

I enrich the French tongue, for they are good ones; however, I have not yet introduced the word "forability," as the *Mercure* of October 6, 1787, accuses me of doing; and to this end I beg the distinguished newspaper editors to read the original proof when they criticize, and not to depend on the malice of obscure printers or on the wicked stupidity of the usual run of proofreaders. I said the "*favorability* of the premises", and I respectfully inform my compatriots in general that as the French language is a dialect of Latin, and a language only insofar as it is a part of Latin, all words may be drawn from that ancient tongue, and that all those derived from it either directly or by analogy are clear, and are, above all, French. I submit further that it is not French to take a word from a language not derived from Latin, not even from the Spanish tongue, sister of our own, if that word came from Arabic; with the exception, however, of certain names of things which exist only in the country where the foreign language is spoken. *Almanach* will always be a foreign term, however colloquial it has become, for it is intrinsically unintelligible to us by reason of the great difference between Arabic and our language. The Arabic word *maxi* or *macsi* (eunuch), which came to France at the time of the Crusades, did not take hold here—our authors have never used it, and I have heard it uttered only as an insult in my youth.

I have used a great many felicitous expressions in these *Nights*. Not that I believe this to show genius —genius is quite another thing, truly! Neither I myself have it, nor those gentlemen who accuse me of committing a crime in so doing, thank God! Genius such as Corneille had cannot exist in a century of wit like ours unless it be a bit mad, like the genius of J.-J. Rousseau; neither Pascal, nor Racine, nor Boileau, nor Voltaire had genius, but a great deal of wit,

an excellent wit which we would be very happy to have
except for the disadvantages which counterbalance it,
and more! Oh, all of you who, like myself, have scarcely
any, let us console ourselves! All creatures are equal
in happiness, and happiness is everything: fame is only
one of its ways—a very effective one—but its drawbacks come along with it. The Supreme Being holds
good and evil things in a vast balancing scale, and
whenever something good falls from one basket, something evil falls from the other to preserve the eternal
equilibrium. I knew about some of Voltaire's misfortunes—they were horrible, and so frequent that no one
would want his glory, at that cost! Those of J.-J. echoed throughout all Europe. Corneille—ah, who can
tell what he suffered, especially in the last years of his
life! [2] Poor, almost destitute, at times he lacked even
the necessities of life! *The Cid's* triumph was obscured
by *Attila*, by *Théodore*; and instead of redeeming
himself, he completed his ruin by *Agésilas*! The cold
and rigid Boileau did not spare him, and that unhappy
old man, the pride of our theater, tasted shame! Then,
in his own mind, he exaggerated the flaws in his plays;
he subjected them to analysis and commentary in an
attempt to justify them. He was no genius then! He
bent under the rising star of the elegant Racine, who
combined a pure and disciplined style with true
worth. . . .

But let me return to a discussion of our language,
then I shall come back to the gutters. I regard the
English practice of taking words from foreign tongues
as a barbarism. It is a barbarism and a stupidity unless
the word is analogous and thus drawn from one of the
two sources of the English language—German, which
is the primary, and French. But those who admire
them for introducing a pure word, be it Italian, be it
French, into their language, are admiring foolishness;
in introducing it, they should Anglicize it if it is not

incompatible, or ban it if it is. It enrages me whenever
I hear the Italian *bravo*, the *a parte*, even the music
terms. Ah, speak French, gentlemen, since you have
the honor to be Frenchmen! Regarding the gutters,
and their superlatives, the rainspouts, I have already
dealt with them, but the matter is so important that
it might well bear further discussion.

I went out at five o'clock. Night was falling; the
street lamps were not yet lighted; the rainspouts were
pouring water noisily onto the umbrellas. People were
coming out from the service at Saint-Séverin, and, of
course, at the very end of the narrow south exit of that
church are spouts that pour out floods of water; if rain
was not expected before they set out for vespers, which
lasts two hours and a half, then the women could not
leave the church without spoiling their delicate, costly
clothing. It would seem as though those who had so
arranged things intended to discourage people from
coming to church. But that is not the worst of it.
There is a narrow alley leading from the church into
rue de la Parcheminerie and rue Saint-Jacques—it is a
much-needed passage—well, in its very middle is a
pouring rainspout! The day I passed by there, a carriage was calling for its owners, and for five or six minutes it blocked the throng hurrying out. One could neither advance nor retreat, and I saw handsomely dressed
women and young girls in silks, flooded with cold rain
water that drenched them in a moment. Twenty of
them were soaked to the bone. I know three who nar-
rowly missed dying as a result, and a fourth who did
not escape! . . .

If some mischiefmaker had set that spout there as
a practical joke, to afford himself a wicked pleasure,
could he have done any better? And the church council[3] and the priests permit it to remain! (For it is still
there in 1788). I walked many streets, that evening;
in all of them I saw citizens of both sexes whose cloth-

ing was ruined and health endangered. Work had
begun on canals alongside the houses. Then what evil
spirit has undermined so wise a plan? I shall continue
to demand them, as well as subterranean conduits for
the gutters; and to demand that refuse not be thrown
into the river, but carried to the countryside; and that
straw not be burned; and that the streets be cleaner;
and that there be public sweepers; and that the truck
gardens surrounding the capital not be turned over to
senseless buildings; and that vast sections in the Faubourg Saint-Marcel, Mont Saint-Hilaire, and elsewhere,
not be left filthy, foul and deserted; and that criminals
be employed to sweep the streets, even those imprisoned for vagrancy, with a mark to distinguish them
from the others; and that the number of private carriages and public hackneys be diminished; and that
galloping on horseback be forbidden in the Paris streets;
and that cabriolets[4] be banned completely; and that
the sword be forbidden except for public ceremonies;
and that there be a tax set on unnecessary dogs kept
for pleasure, even on those claimed to be useful for
guarding shops; and that a law be imposed on the
cabarets that would forbid them to cause the downfall
of a class of productive men; and that the sale of
brandy be outlawed without exception; and that the
scandal of prostitutes be eliminated; and that theatrical
presentations be regulated in such manner that there
be days during the week when the billboard bears the
notice: "Respectable women may bring their daughters."

I was considering all of these matters as I went
about my business. On my return home I wrote my reflections in my *agenda*. I did not leave the house again
until ten-thirty; I went directly to see the Marquise,
and confided those ideas to her.

❦ 44 ❧

THE TWO PASSAGEWAYS

I have always been offended by the haughty proprietary air of house owners, and even of the head lease-
holders in Paris. A man lodges you; you pay him, and he
still thinks he can limit your enjoyment of the apartment as he pleases. He requires you to return home at
whatever hour he wishes; he prohibits you the use of a
certain passageway; he supervises your conduct. Someone might find this last admirable. I would not take the
time to answer him. I would oblige him to live under
such conditions for a week; if he does not come around,
for a month; finally, should he persevere, for a year;
and I hope that by then his pretty and philosophic
ideas will have left him.

The proprietors of Paris houses must be taught that
only the intrinsic value of a premise is theirs, and that
the enjoyment of it belongs to the one who pays. The
increase in value that the occupancy provides is an
advantage which the landlords enjoy, but which does
not belong to them. A Paris house owner is not a proprietor in the sense that a villager or an inhabitant of
a small town is. He owes the public whatever is of public usefulness. If this jurisprudence is not to be found in
the courts, so much the worse! It must be introduced.

Every day some malicious proprietor, some selfish
landlord, capriciously denies the public access to a con-
venient passage which would shorten their route and
spare them from crossing a river of filth. I point particularly to the one which goes from rue Saint-Jacques to

rue Galande, through an alley across from rue de la
Parcheminerie. In winter in the thawing snow, in summer when storms make the end of rue Saint-Jacques
impassable, I have seen an attorney or a bookseller
humanely open the gate of this passageway to women
frightened by a herd of cattle, or about to be covered
with mud by passing carriages. That's very well, but they
close it immediately, and a moment later I have seen
good women exposed to imminent danger, or at least to
the ruination of their shoes and clothing. All passageways ought to be open to the public; it is right, for it is
the public which gives the added value to your houses.
The passage I am speaking of here shortens the route
by more than half. It safeguards one from the worst
of the route; it must be opened, and it is to the interest of the owner who could rent it to merchants.

As for the coachmen—the reason for this article—
is it not true that they would never be duped if all passageways were opened and marked? They would be
familiar with them, whereas today these poor men do
not know what to rely on, because any fellow who has
lived near a two-way passage can use it when he wishes,
by keeping the key to it.

At night when I went out I came to rue Galande,
opposite the door to the Durand bookstore. A young
man got down from a cab which he had retained
since morning. The coachman, quite sure that the
way was closed on the rue Saint-Jacques side, grumbled
a bit but remained unsuspecting. I continued on my
way. At the entrance to rue de la Parcheminerie I saw
the same young man walking on his toes (he was wearing white silk stockings) and going into his house.
He did not come out again. A half-hour later I came
back through rue Galande to see a young girl whose
charms had struck me—they contrasted with her serious manner. I came again upon the carriage. "My
friend," I said, "you wait in vain; I have just seen your

man on rue Saint-Jacques." The coachman swore, and went into the house. No one there knew anything. The young man had once had lodgings on the double exit and he had kept or had made a passkey. It is apparent that the misuse of the closed passageway is very common. A hundred people can use it in such a way. To close it, moreover, is unfair to the public; for not only should this one be open, but it would be useful to order the passageways to be opened in all areas where the route is thereby considerably shortened. It is a consideration one must have for pedestrians since the scandalous multiplication of the number of gigs and carriages. The corner of rue Galande is one of the most dangerous; I have seen several persons perish there. It is a kind of sewer. Take the case of a woman heavily clad; she proceeds without hearing a carriage hidden by the turns, and she is covered with mud. I have seen this accident happen fifty times, and to myself at least ten.

Let me come back to my story. The coachman climbed to his seat, and I thought then that I ought to tell him the address of his swindler. He went there but still he was not able to get his pay. The man did not show himself.

❦ 45 ❦

THE LIVING CORPSE

It was only midnight when I found myself before a cemetery. I saw some medical students lurking around the gate, and I learned from a man of the neighborhood, who was on his way home, that a girl of eighteen had been buried that very evening. After I withdrew, the students entered. But I remained to observe them. After removing a plank from it, in order to view the body, they carried off the coffin. I saw them enter a narrow and dirty street where they had an amphitheater. This incident is very like the one I have already reported, but the details of it are quite different. The chill of the earth had revived the young woman; she sighed as soon as they had lifted off the plank. The students were then, of course, all the more eager to carry her off.

Reaching their secret room, they placed her on a bed and, to revive her, employed the gentlest of massagings. She came to. They gave her a cordial, and in very little time she regained complete consciousness. She was quite startled to find herself in such company, but they reassured her by the great consideration they showed her. Keeping from her the circumstances in which they had found her, for fear of causing her a seizure, they led her to believe that a serious illness had obliged her parents to confide her to them. She had a second attack, brought about by a too violent rallying of her physical and mental faculties. They soothed her in a manner which, though far from criminal or even lacking in the respect due virgins, they would not have dared in her home. She passed the crisis and seemed calmed. It was then that I felt more strongly than ever how admirable these youths really were.

In the morning, before daybreak—at that hour when one need fear neither guards nor lanterns—they carried her to her parents' home. They rapped loudly on the door. I went up to them then, and after complimenting them, offered to take the matter in hand, promising to see that they be justly rewarded. They were so truly virtuous that my proposition delighted them. Two stayed to carry the young woman to her bed, and the others went off.

The astonishment and even terror were extreme. The domestic who opened to us would have shut the door had I not anticipated his action. I kept him from it by pushing him off and throwing myself into the house. I ordered him to awaken his employers. However, they were not sleeping at home. It is a folly of our century to flee all that reminds one of a lost loved one. A chambermaid appeared. We put the girl in her bed and asked for broth and some spirits, but only to sweeten her lips for liquor would have been injurious to her. We made her sweat, for we noticed that she had contracted a violent cold and the ensuing fever could have killed her, and we prescribed a diet. During this time, the servant had gone to fetch his employers. They arrived at seven in the morning, three hours later, so difficult had it been to reach them. I went to apprise them of the proper attitude to assume, during which time the two students disappeared. The daughter was cared for by my orders alone. She recovered. And perhaps the cold she caught, which grew to terrible proportions, was what spared her by altering the course of her illness.

❧ 46 ❧

THE CRIMINAL TWICE KILLED

It is sometimes said, in jest, "Hanged the first time, broken the second." Such was the case of a man from Normandy. Everywhere one finds men hard and evil by nature. . . . A certain Lefèvre, son of a Rouen horse dealer, was so brutal that everyone feared him; even horses trembled before him. One evening he had a quarrel with a man who was returning a hired horse to his father; with one blow he killed the man. The fact became known, and as the horse dealer's son had often been arrested for his brutalities, he was quickly condemned to hang as a murderer. He was so generally despised that as he was about to be executed by torchlight the young men of the town shouted: "Lefèvre, if you survive, we'll see to it that you're broken on the wheel!" He was hanged.

M. Lecat, the prison doctor, had negotiated for his corpse, and as the hour was late, it was delivered to him straight off. The corpse was put in the library, where all the anatomical instruments were kept. A big fire had been lit there. It was suppertime: they sup in the provinces because they dine earlier, which is a great boon to health. During the meal there was discussion as to whether the vertebrae of the neck were always broken by the hangman. Another dispute, relative to the medical art, arose between the doctor and his colleague. M. Lecat, who had an extraordinary visual memory, cited not only the book, page and author supporting his view, but the shelf in the library on which the volume stood. He sent his servant for it. Reaching the library doorway the man saw, by the fire's glow, the hanged man who, instinctively attracted by the warmth of the fire, was dragging himself toward the hearth. In the countryside, and among common people of towns as well, superstitions are so strongly entrenched that it is rare for uneducated people to overcome them. The servant was terrified, and fainted from fright. When he failed to reappear they sent the colleague's servant, who didn't return either. He had been even more frightened, for he thought the ghost had killed his friend. The two doctors arose and went to the library themselves. They saw then what had caused their valets such terror.

They bled the hanged man, put him to bed, and tended him for three weeks with all the care one might expect of a skilled artist who wishes to enlarge the power of his art. The man recovered completely. When he had regained his strength, the surgeon said to him, "You see what a pass your brutality has brought you to! Why not leave the country, become a sailor, and try to restrain yourself in the future." He gave him ten écus to live on until he should find work. After leaving his rescuer, Lefèvre purchased a knife. He left town and took the road for Le Havre. A short distance from his native town, he came upon a cattle merchant he thought had a great deal of money. It must be that the atmosphere in our prisons inspires villainy, for men always leave there as villains. It comes from the system: the barbarous severity of the jailers, who, holding humanity in contempt, treat the prisoners as these latter had dealt with their victims; from the cruel indifference of the judges themselves, who show the accused nothing but a studied inhumanity. I am displeased with this latter explanation; I erase it and correct it in favor of the truth: the provincial judges, especially, seem to be hunters, fearful lest they lose their prey, and who glory in the most atrocious manner if they snare it. I have seen this: Lefèvre, who had become a villain in prison, with little respect for humanity's sacred laws which he has seen trampled underfoot, threw himself like a tiger on the merchant, but his defective knife closed, and instead of killing the man, it wounded the murderer's hand. He was arrested, led to prison, and interrogated the next day. When the judge saw him, he was struck by his resemblance to someone he knew. He said to the court clerk, "I have seen this man before."

"So have I."

"You! Do I know you?" the judge asked.

"Yes, monsieur." (Let us observe here that the judge, out of respect for humanity and for the dignity of his office, ought never to address the accused with such familiarity. If he be innocent, O judge, respect his misfortune! If guilty, respect the victim into whose throat you are about to thrust the knife of the law!)

"Where have I seen you?"

"Here."

"What is your name?"

"Lefèvre, Louis."

"Your profession?"

"Horse trader."

"Your address?"

"Such a street."

"Your father's name?"

"Bénigne Lefèvre."

"I'm sure I know you, all this sounds familiar. When have I seen you, and why?"

"To sentence me to be hanged, three weeks ago."

"Aha!—What? How come you're here?"

The assassin recounted all that had befallen him. M. Lecat was summoned. He recognized the unhappy wretch and defended himself with all the dignity befitting a doctor of the poor. "I did my duty," he said to the judge, "You must do yours." That was his entire testimony in all its sublimity. Nonetheless he added a few words by way of explanation.

"I had purchased the corpse to serve humanity by dissecting it; but in restoring it to life, I discovered another way to be useful to humanity in a hundred other cases; I did what my profession required of me: I seized the opportunity to treat a man who had suffocated by hanging, whether stupidity led him there or whether he was a victim of the crimes of others."

The assassin was sentenced to the wheel, and broken alive the next day. The doctor to whom the corpse belonged would have liked to experiment again on such a hardy man, without then setting him free, but he was not permitted to do so. The experiment could be made another time on a criminal guilty of a lesser crime: for example, instead of hanging the criminal, sentence him to be flogged and offer him, before the blows, the opportunity to place himself in the hands of a Hôtel-Dieu doctor after one, two, or three blows, depending on the gravity of the crime.

🕉 47 🕉

THE SWEEPERS

It was five o'clock when I went home. I came across several men who had undertaken the streetcleaning for private homes. They agreed on a system among themselves, and began at the top of a street that was low, narrow and filthy; they inconvenienced no one, and pushed the sweepings toward the main street. But I noticed that the obstinacy of a single party halfway down the little street, who would not employ the men, hampered them considerably! They were obliged to cross his property with the wet sweepings, and since they could not leave them there, to sweep his plot for nothing. I saw them proceed next to another street, near the river, and discard the refuse into the Seine. I disapproved of this. The inhabitant of Paris, who has no idea how precious fertilizer is, seeks only to dispose of it. The authorities could remedy this by requiring landowners to buy so many cart-loads of fertilizer from the refuse dumps, at one écu a cart-load and in proportion to their acreage, and the income would be used

partly to pay for public street-cleaning, partly to increase the number of sweepers. And precautions
should be taken that the city not stretch to enormous
proportions, by setting boundaries and by taxing any
house outside them. Above all, there should be a policy against building in fine, long-fertilized truck gardens, and removing still farther the agriculture that
supplies the city; the cleanliness of the streets should
be given more effective attention. They should be
kept dry instead of wetted; there should be a curb
on the increasing number of underground channels,
which constitute a threat to carriages and to health;
a thousand things should be done that are not. Men
have a false notion, a destructive notion: it is that life
is too short to spend any effort on being comfortable
in it. That idea does not affect all of men's acts, but it
has very serious consequences for public institutions!
It must be destroyed, rather than allowed to spread
through ascetic books.

48

NOCTURNAL DEFILEMENTS

There should be a very strict police ordinance forbidding the ordure that lines certain quays and pollutes
the small streets. Far from allowing even one house to
be without conveniences—and many such exist near the
boulevards and the quays, in the deserted quarters of
the Saint-Marcel and Saint-Antoine faubourgs, and on
the Île Saint-Louis, in front of and behind Saint-Paul—
public facilities ought, on the contrary, to be required
on the street level in certain houses, and the landlord be

responsible for their cleanliness, giving him permission to fine any man or woman he catches in the act of fouling. The toilet would be locked; the key would be at the desk, and would have to be returned. For example, all the houses across from street lamps would have such cabinets, and if one was in use, another would surely be free. An uncooperative landlord would be subject to a fine of twenty-four livres, a third of which would go to the informer, another to the Hôtel de Ville, and the last to the street constabulary tax.[1]

Preoccupied by these useful reflections as relevant to propriety as to hygiene, I arrived at the corner of rue Bailleul, where I was almost knocked down by a half-dressed man running off in alarm. A gentleman (for one calls gentleman any man who wears braid on his collar and carries a sword) was chasing him with drawn sword. I took the liberty of observing to the gentleman that the crime did not deserve a swords-blow. He agreed but added, as he led me to his carriage gateway, that it was most unpleasant for his wife and daughters on returning home to see. . . .

"I would have struck him," he said, "so annoyed am I with the indecency of our dirty citizens; most of them are just lazy, but others are malicious. If it were only those who couldn't wait, one would hardly notice."

"But the malicious ones can't be distinguished from the others."

"That is true, but I think a law should be passed which would require certain houses to have public facilities; for instance, conveniently located houses would be marked for easy identification with a red L.-P. in a black circle."

I found the idea an excellent one. I left the man, and after making a round through rue Saint-Honoré, the Place Vendôme, rue Neuve-des-Petits-Champs, the Place des Victoires, and rue du Petit-Reposoir, I found myself in that pardonable state. Before me was the small rue Verdelet, but, faithful to my principles, I entered a house, and on the fifth floor found the only available spot. As I was going back down an old woman opened her door, and seeing me in my cloak and hat, screamed, "Stop. Thief!" Immediately all the tenants appeared, lanterns in hand, and I was seized by the scruff of the neck.

"Take me to the commissioner!" I demanded. "Oh, yes, that's just where you're going" (it is clearly still a trait of the Parisian populace to be excessively crude with strangers). I was dealt several blows, mostly by a cobbler's apprentice, a real good-for-nothing. Despite the fact that I was going there at my own request, they dragged me before the commissioner. As soon as we arrived, (seeing that I was safe) I asked—before giving any explanation—that the guards be summoned. The clerk sent for them, and when they arrived I begged the commissioner not to permit any of my accusers to leave. This granted me, I pleaded my cause with great vehemence.

I told the commissioner that I had entered the house because, as a citizen, I had the right to do so, rather than foul the streets. I gave my reasons, I identified myself, and used the name of the Marquise de M***, my protectress. Next I brought a complaint against my accusers, who had struck me. I showed the marks of their blows. My accusers all felt so safely within their rights that they admitted to them. I insisted then that the cobbler's apprentice be arrested, handcuffed on the spot and led to prison for vagrancy and for having tried to strike me with his shoemaker's awl. This was granted. I then brought charges against the others, using their admission in order to have them summoned the next day. They went home, quite astonished by this dénouement and by the manner in which I had treated them before the commissioner. Above all, nothing could equal the confusion of the spiteful old woman who had given the alarm. But I owe this performance of exemplary justice to Mme. de M***, close relative of a justice of the Parlement, and not to my rights as a citizen.

49

BONE, WATER, AND ASHES

There are nights when all the disadvantages of a crowded quarter are apparent at the same time. As I was coming off rue du Fouarre, a large marrowbone fell at my feet. Its sharp point and the force with which it was hurled would have made a lethal weapon of it, had it struck me. I noted the window. I went up. I found a laborer, seated calmly at the table with his wife and children, eating his pot-au-feu. I confronted them with what might have happened as a result of their heedless act. The woman scolded her husband: "How many times have I told you not to throw anything out the window in this town; the streets are always full of people. I've told you these big bones are useful. There's still marrow in 'em, and tomorrow I'd have boiled it up with cabbage; after that, I save them for fuel: one of those bones is worth half a log."

I was pleased with the woman, and I asked her husband how he would like to receive a bone on his head as he innocently walked through the streets. The man was quite dull-witted, but the idea struck home. He promised solemnly never again to commit the same imprudence.

I had business to attend to near rue Saint-Victor.

As I came to that street I was blinded by a sheet of soapy water poured from a garret window. The droplets stung my eyes. I could barely see. I learned from the neighbors that it was a daily occurrence for things to be thrown from that window, sometimes more, sometimes less; often it was a large butcher's bone, injuring now a woman, now a child. I went up. I found five or six children and their father, a firewood-cutter. He was a widower, and he left his children alone while he worked. I was worried about the neighbors; children so poorly raised (for the girls, one of whom was fourteen, seemed unruly wenches) might well start a fire. I remonstrated with them; they answered with curses.

I went down and spoke with the landlord. He said he would give them notice, which was not what I asked: those poor folk had to live somewhere. The father and older children were brought downstairs and taken before the commissioner, whom I had already alerted. That official made the appropriate threats. He said he would appoint someone to keep an eye on them and at the first sign of trouble would have the guilty girl placed in the Hôpital and flogged; or, were it one of the boys, sent to the Bicêtre prison, clamped hand and foot, and lashed. Such threats, issued before a group of the neighbors, had their effect, and there have been no further complaints. When private training is neglected, public authority must take its place.

Next I climbed rue de la Montagne, and went toward the bookbinder's. As I passed rue des Amandiers I was suddenly blinded, suffocated by a fine powder. I realized from the odor that it was ashes. I moved upwind; I shook off my hat, my coat; I rubbed my eyes and waited. Another panful of ashes was tossed out and I saw from which window they came. Several people cried out, none more loudly than a young pastry cook who was bringing supper to a nearby house; most of the ashes had landed on the uncovered roast he carried, and he was inconsolable.

I entered the house. There I discovered four tailor's apprentices cleaning the chimney flue. I reprimanded them. One of them, whom I thought a Gascon, replied by tossing a fistful of ashes in my face. I left, but several bookbinders who had followed me, outraged at the insult, rushed into the room, seized the four lads and prepared to give them a thrashing. I opposed them with all my might, but succeeded in calming the assailants only by mentioning the commissioner. They led the culprits before this official; thirty persons disturbed by the ashes followed, as well as the pastry chef and those whose supper had been spoiled. The commissioner heard our plaint. He sent for the master tailor and asked the man if he would answer for damages and fines. He agreed, and the lads were sent away with a harsh scolding and threats of imprisonment, should they repeat the offense. The binders, however, were not appeased; they pretended to be, followed the culprits, and beat them, despite all my efforts to stop them.

I went to see the Marquise, and I thought to myself as I walked along that at night one must avoid the side streets. The more they need to be kept clean—because of the poor air circulation—the more their inhabitants seem bent on making them unhealthy by strewing their filth about. It is a folly of which animals are incapable; they never so contaminate their dens. And yet, they need be less concerned over this than we; their excrement doesn't contain the strong, acrid salts of the human body; for acridity seems proportionate, in all species, to the degree of intelligence.

On this subject I recall once meeting a man of very somber mien on rue Poupée; I was surprised to hear him singing at the top of his voice. For his part, he was a bit embarrassed. "You must have a strange opinion of me," he said, "but first you must know my motive. I have often been hit as I walk along these streets. I've discovered that one way to avoid the rubbish is to make one's presence known. A young bookseller I know uses the method of singing out loudly, and finds it serves him well."

"Then I will try it too," I answered, smiling. And I began to sing out in hopes of diminishing the embarrassment I had involuntarily caused him.

❧ 50 ❧

SMUGGLED BOOKS

I followed the boulevard as far as the Faubourg Saint-Honoré. I went down into the faubourg and headed in the direction of the tollgate. Then I went toward Champs-Elysées. There I saw several men, disguised as gardener's boys, who were furtively crossing some recently abandoned vegetable gardens (since destroyed). I followed them cautiously and saw that they were carrying bundles of prohibited books which had been brought from Versailles. They put them by small lots into the carriage coffers, and deposited them in a house outside the city gates. They were subsequently smuggled into Paris, between two and four o'clock in the morning. I saw them arrive at the house of a certain Lécuyer, a peddler, who lived in the New Market. I said nothing, for it was none of my business. As it turned out, the peddler was a spy for the police.

51

THE STICKY PLATTER

I went out early, weary of working, and walked by way of rue Saint-Séverin as far as rue Saint-André. As I entered the latter, a scamp of eleven or twelve, who was going into an old greengrocer's, shoved me rudely. I stopped short. He ordered a Brie; he had brought along a small platter to carry his cheese on, and threw it down on some change the old woman had just counted out for six francs. The little ruffian did not give her a moment's peace; finally she waited on him. Meanwhile, a little girl discovered a mistake in the change she had been given. The boy started to run off with his cheese, after having paid for it. I have heard before of this kind of legerdemain; so of course I seized the little thief by the arm and said to him, "Stay there a minute and don't you move!" At first he did not struggle; he was taking the coins from the underside of his board and slipping them adroitly into his pocket. When he had finished, he wanted to get away very badly; he cried out and struggled violently. But I held him fast, my eyes attentive to what was happening at the grocer's. She was arguing with the little girl.

"It was the right amount!"

"You can see for yourself that two twelve-sous coins are missing, one six-sous and two six-liards, and one two-sous coin."

"They were there."

"They aren't there now!"

After several more such exchanges, I dragged the little crook into the store and, showing the underside of his board, said, "Here's your thief! Look at this sticky board. He laid it over the money. Help me; we'll search him. You'll find the sticky coins in his pocket."

The little crook began to scream as if he were being murdered; the girl kicked me in the shins. I suspected her of being involved, so I blocked her way. I removed all the sticky coins from her pocket and the boy's, and gave the money to the woman.

At that moment, an ordinary man and woman came rushing up, attracted by the cries of the two children. They were about to throw themselves at me, which compelled me to have recourse to the guardsmen. A squadron was passing and I requested them to take the two children, with their father and mother, to the commissioner. I related the incident, as it had happened, and completely convinced them. The parents said that they were not a party to the theft, that it was just an arrangement between brother and sister. Nonetheless, they were sent away with a strong injunction to answer in the future for their children's behavior. I have since learned that the brother and sister had stolen about a louis in that manner over the past six months, and that having been caught in the act, they stopped their thieving. Convinced of the children's guilt, the parents threatened and even punished them, which one does not often see in Paris.

I went then to see Mme. de M***, who was very disturbed by my evening's adventures. The one about the little thief struck her as extraordinary, and she made me repeat the way he had placed his board with feigned carelessness on top of the counted change. The innocent and timid look on the little girl, in counting it a second time, seemed, she thought, a step toward all the vices of her sex.

52

THE LOCAL MAIL SERVICE[1]

As I sat reading by the light of a street lamp, I heard the sound of men running and shouting: "Stop! Stop!" It was at the crossing of rues du Parc-Royal and Neuve-Saint-Gilles. . . . "That's the one! There he is!" they said, surrounding me. "He has a blue cloak on." I was seized, somewhat mistreated despite my politeness, and taken to a house on rue Boucherat. There I gave the name of the Marquise de M***. The postman for the local mail service passed; I asked to write a few words; I read them over, and gave them to the postman.

"That won't reach her before tomorrow at nine o'clock."

"What! Your rounds are done? You are a step away from rue Payenne, and you can't take my note there?"

"No, monsieur, it's against the rules."

"A curse on people," I retorted in anger, "who do useful work in witless fashion!" And I snatched my note from the hands of the postman, who was now unwilling to give it back to me. I sent a special delivery to the Marquise, who came herself to release me. It was easily determined that I was not the thief. The servants agreed that I did not resemble him; but the master insisted, and it scarcely mattered to him who was punished, the true thief or myself, as long as his stolen property was avenged by the laws. That is the rich man for you; a shameful trial was held recently, in which a wealthy man demanded the death of a poor wretch whom he knew to be innocent, for this reason alone: "I do not have the real culprit, who threatened to kill me if I did not deposit a certain sum at the foot of a certain tree at night, but he will be frightened by the punishment of the one who was captured in his place. . . ." I could easily name this inhuman rich man, but I do not choose to do so.

I described my unpleasant adventure to Mme. de M***; then I read her two terrible passages from *Monsieur Nicolas*.

On my way home I met a man in a gray cloak at the corner of rue des Francs-Bourgeois. He looked at me, burst into laughter, then walked away slowly. Another man who was with him came directly up to stare at me and say, "Well, friend, you were in a fine fix a while ago!" Then he went off, laughing. I was sure these were the real thieves, and that they did not consider me worth robbing. Shabby clothing is sometimes useful. . . .

I shook with fright on rue Pavée, which is very deserted, and instead of taking rue Tiron I returned by rue des Ballets, and by rue du Roi-de-Sicile where men were lying in wait for someone. I shot off my pistol and they fled. I retraced my steps, and just then a man appeared. "Who goes there?" he said. "Are you one of those rascals?" "No, but they were here, just a moment ago. . . ." I walked with him. At his door on rue du Paradis, he thanked me, and I turned back along the same route. I saw no one this time.

❧ 53 ❧

I AM TAKEN FOR A MONK

I was walking slowly homeward through rue Saint-Martin, which was completely deserted at the time, when I noticed that I was being followed by a drunkard who had apparently just awakened, and who took me for a monk because of my cloak. He set about insulting me.

"This is a nice hour for a man of the cloth! Where is he coming from at such an hour? From a visit to his mistresses!" I continued to walk, without turning. "Wait! Wait!" the drunkard went on. "I'm going to beat you with my cane!"

This was becoming serious, and I looked to my safety. Across from Saint-Jacques-Flamel, a prostitute standing in her doorway took me for a priest as well. I realized then that the reason for the error was the high collar I wore. I had heard that prostitutes have monks and abbots arrested in their rooms. I was curious to confirm the rumor myself. The girl had gone back into her entryway; I followed her. The drunkard reached the door at that moment. He had evidently seen me go in. He spewed forth the crudest abuse and knocked with all his might. He called for the police, as if the public welfare were threatened. This is the way it was in ancient Rome, where the whole Republic was roused when a vestal let the sacred fire die, or broke her vows! . . .

I went to the woman's rooms. She turned me over to one of her colleagues, who was rather pretty, and disappeared. I waited a while; eventually I decided to leave. I found that I was locked in. I remained under lock and key until six o'clock in the morning. It was dawn when I saw the commissioner enter with his deputy. The girl I had followed, not having looked closely at me, had mistaken me for a man of the collar. As it happened, I was known to the commissioner; he asked me laughingly what I was doing there. I told him my story. He wanted to send the two girls to Saint-Martin. "Why?" I asked him. "Hasn't that one done her duty? And as for this one here, I assure you that she behaved like a respectable girl with me! A miss is as good as a mile; and a mistake is no crime when it is unintentional." They were released and I went home.

❀ 54 ❀

THE ERSTWHILE BEAUTIES

Yesterday I was taken for a monk; but daily it happens that I am taken for a good Irish priest, and many a young Auvergnat who has just arrived from his province has paid me reverence. Goodwives have sometimes come to me where I knelt at Saint-Séverin, to offer me the price of some august office which I could not fulfill. But tonight I shall discuss another matter.

. . . .

I wanted to take advantage of the lovely evening, which had brought me out early, to revisit a few former beauties and to learn how much they had changed in twenty years. I went to rue Montmartre, near rue des Vieux-Augustins, to the house of a very beautiful woman, whom everyone used to admire. I looked for

her in the lamplight but I did not see her. Meanwhile a
heavy woman moved about, back and forth. I stared
at her: not the slightest resemblance! . . . I decided
then that the beauty had been replaced by another. I
went in to be sure.

"Madame, allow me to ask you for news of
Mlle. S***?"

"I can give you some, monsieur, and you can do
no better than to ask her in person." She smiled and
was none the prettier for it; on the contrary, her ugliness was all the more pronounced. She recognized me,
however. She led me by the hand into her room, and
begged me to sit down on a sofa. I gazed at her.

"It is true, isn't it, I have changed a great deal?"

"Madame, I am astonished that with a stranger
such as myself . . ."

"Come now, you are Monsieur Nicolas!"

"That's true!"

"I am Mlle. S*** and there was a time when you
were an admirer of mine. That is not the role you'll
play now, but I have often wished to see my friend
again. Give him back to me, I did not deserve to lose
him!" At these words she seemed lovely to me again;
something in her glance made me recognize her, and I
threw myself at her hand and kissed it. I rose again
immediately, asking her permission to visit her often.
Her expression tender, she granted it, and I ran off to
another place.

. . . .

THE ERSTWHILE BEAUTIES, (*continued*)

The notion took me to go to rue Platrière, where I had
heard that a prostitute lived, once slender and dainty,
to whom I had spoken several times on rue du Four.
I assumed that I would find her where I was directed.
I did, in fact, see her on her doorstep. My cloak
frightened her; she shot the bolt. I stayed close to the
wall waiting for her to open again, which did indeed
occur after a quarter of an hour. I then introduced myself hastily, so that she had no time to close the door
again. She recognized me. "Ah! What a fright you gave
me!"

"What—is this really you? They told me so; I
could not believe it. Heavens! What has happened to
your trim waist, your lovely face? How ugly you've
grown!"

"Yes, close up, but from a distance people still find
me pretty."

"I'm told that you spend almost the whole night
on your doorstep?"

"What else can I do? I must; during the day no
one comes. At night I pick up the gamblers, the sons of
respectable families who can't go home, sometimes the
swindlers, the pickpockets in flight—for the police are
so strict now!"

"My poor Flore! What a life!"

"Ah! If I had it to do over!"

"But you are so stout that you fill the whole doorway!" She stepped out to show herself. She was hor-

rible! A huge ball! "Surely you can no longer enjoy a life of vice? What would you be suited for?"

"Do you want to know? For training young girls just starting out, according to the principles of a book someone lent me, which I then bought, and which I read and reread constantly. That is my talent. I would be highly satisfactory." I promised to let her know if ever that reform project were put into effect.

❦ 56 ❦

THE FLOWER GIRLS

One Saint John's Eve, after watching the vicar of Saint-Nicholas burn the ceremonial faggot, I set out by rue Saint-Victor and arrived at the Faubourg Saint-Marcel. Along the way I saw and heard nothing but flower girls, who adorned the street corners or strolled along shouting: "Bouquets for Jeannot-Jeannette!" Others, who wished to play the purists, were calling: "For Jean and Jeanne!"

Observing them, I reflected on the extent of luxury, which reaches its murderous hand even to the lowest class. And then I proceeded to define luxury: that which gives rise to occupations which bring the worker a profit for sterile labor. Thus, gambling—where one often wins immense sums—is a sterile occupation. Two gamblers or a hundred, who ceaselessly compete against each other, will end in ruin and die of hunger. Actually such labors of luxury as gilding, painting, embroidery and the manufacture of artificial flowers are not as worthless as gambling, for these products can be sold abroad—the first-mentioned especially. But I maintain in fact that such occupations, confined within the State, are deadly and destructive, that a country which employs a great number of hands in the building of vainglorious edifices must become impoverished—like a farmer or a vine-grower who spends his time erecting fences about his field or vineyard instead of tilling, sowing or planting. According to the lights of common sense, I claim that luxury and its manufactures should be tolerated by the government only insofar as they keep the population from procuring them abroad; that the prohibition on Indian calicoes, which went to the point of seizing them on women's backs, was a fine law and a just one, and that the punishment ought to have been still harsher than the fine. Luxury products are advantageous in a highly populated country only when there is a superabundance of food—and when I say advantageous, I only mean favorable to the augmentation of wealth and to the perpetuation of the inequality of riches, for luxury is always antithetical to sound morals and to the true happiness of the human race. It remains to be seen if in the state of affairs in Europe today a country with sound morals and an abundance of food, but little money, can be safe against outside enemies. But these are things I cannot know, since I have never been employed in public administration. Let us return to the flower girls.

I felt within myself that it was an evil for the women of the populace to be employed solely in uselessly peddling worthless things like flowers, which involve gardens and gardeners in pure loss. I felt sure that any individual who wished to purchase flowers would find them easily enough without the existence of flower girls. I felt, furthermore, that since there are fruit markets in every quarter, it would be wise and useful to gradually abolish all fruit peddlers, who are but idlers; that all peddlers of Paris make bad citizens whose children are but spies, thieves, and prostitutes; that we have everything at hand without such people. I thought further that a whole segment of the population is occupied in the vain, purposeless trafficking of light nourishments and petty wares; that to dispose of the poorest pieces of fruit whose greenness causes illness and degenerates the human species they sell them to children; that if such peddling were abolished little by little, and worthwhile occupations indicated to the populace, it would result in great benefit to the labor force engaged in useful manufactures; that in order to gain the greatest advantage from the populace, and turn it to good use, the export of grain abroad should be prohibited, and instead, the harvest should be devoted to easing the workers' subsistence; that instead of exporting grain, the low-cost products of silk and wool manufacturing should be exported; that the duty on wine should be lifted in Paris, and the cost of labor lowered in all trades, thus earning for ourselves—from the increased sales of our manufactures—the benefit perviously derived from the export of grain. I have no doubt that crops would be more abundant then and the people better nourished, above all if useless private parks were abolished and all large landowners rigorously taxed at a louis per acre for untilled land. Then there would be a surplus of grain, and after the whole realm had been supplied, the surplus could be disposed of at whatever price one wished, because everyone would have been provided for.

I reflected on the terrible drawbacks of the high cost of labor; I thought of this in terms of the noxious effects on the masses, who, like savage tribes, think only of the present. If they earn enough in three days for necessities, they work for three days only and spend the other four in debauchery. Then they can no longer afford their essentials, are miserable, borrow, neglect to pay up, ruin the baker, the cobbler, the wine merchant (although the latter poisons them so he can retire). Everything is in disorder. But, lower the price of labor, and the masses would automatically work for six days because they would need to work in order to meet their expenses; they would be less disorderly and less in debt earning nine livres a week than earning eighteen in three days. I know what I am saying, and I proclaim to the public and to the government that this is the exact truth, the result of observations made a thousand times over and which, given my position, I am perhaps alone in being able to make.

I strolled throughout the faubourg, and everywhere I saw men, women, girls, even children in rags, buying bouquets. Then I took a turn through the better sections. Flower girls were not so abundant there and they sold very little, because there were fewer *Jeans* and *Jeannes* (they have finer names there); and also because in those sections more people have done away with the custom of giving flowers.

❦ 57 ❦

THE BATHS

It started to get warm; the bathing barges were readied; the extreme heat drew throngs to them in the evening, for two reasons: because people are freer then, and because a kind of modesty still inhibited the women from visiting them during the day. I made a tour of the basin, and observed the different bathing establishments, all of them set up in a strange way, and in exactly the reverse of what their arrangement would be in Turkey, for the women's baths were always above those of the men. The first baths I saw were set up at the foot of the Grands-Degrés steps,[1] one at the bank of the Place Maubert quarter, the other across from it for the Île Notre-Dame or the Cité: these baths are for women only.

I continued my walk on the island, and I saw baths above and below the Pont Marie, with two great signboards nailed to the parapet. The upstream one read: *Public and Private Ladies' Bath.* It must be agreed that the language is shamefully abused on all the placards and signs of Paris, and that it should not be! But in this case the rank ignorance was scandalous, and if it was a poor joke it should be punished; I told the concierge as much. The sign for the men was quite simple. I continued my tour. I saw baths for both sexes at the Port au Blé.[2] I found others below the Pont Henri, across from the rue des Poulies; others on the Quai des Théatins; and lastly, I saw some at the foot of the Quai de l'Horloge, behind the Place Dauphine. It was very late. Some children and apprentices were bathing in the little branch that flows in front of the Augustins[3] and separates them from the Quai des Orfèvres. I noticed how these niggardly bathing facilities, no better than what poor savages might have, proclaimed the uncleanliness of the largest city in the world! Five or six cabin[4] baths for all of Paris! That's why practically no one bathes there, and those who do limit themselves to once or twice a summer— that is to say, a year.

As I was reflecting on the subject, and wishing that the practice of bathing were more widespread, I heard some commotion from the small branch of the river. It was the bathing children who had taken to their heels; there was an order forbidding them to wash in the river at the least dangerous point—indeed, where there could be no danger at all. I was told there was a bath for them at the tip of the Enfants-de-

Choeur garden, where they were supposed to go and
crowd themselves in, make mischief and be corrupted;
I was astonished and shocked, but I had no power
against that highly immoral barbarity! I spoke to the
sergeant of the guard; the reason he gave me was that
the children came there during the day, which was
most scandalous! "Scandalous!" I cried. "Scandalous
that children should wash themselves in an airy spot,
where the water is no more than two feet deep! I simply no longer understand the proprieties of our corrupt age! Next, wet nurses will be forbidden to slip a
chemise onto their male nurselings, and the midwives
will be unable to announce the infant's sex! Good
heavens! Let them—let those poor children wash and
groom themselves, not by night when it is often too
chilly but in the open and beautiful sunlight—even
if a few little bookshop girls do see them from their
windows, even though the little laundresses do make
them out from some fifty yards away, or some curious
young matron does lean over the parapet and inspects
them! What evil will that cause? And the benefit will
be: learning to swim, cleanliness, good health! It is
better than the private baths and facilities, where one
must pay. However moderate the sum, it is beyond the
means of children."

While I was talking to the sergeant the children
all escaped. One of his soldiers reproached him for
having listened to me. "Quiet!" the sergeant answered
him. "Don't you suppose I saw them as well as you?"
He continued on his way and found everyone gone.

I proceeded next to the upstream tip of the island
known as the Terrain,[5] passing through the barbaric,
gothic Cité, which is more a tangled labyrinth than a
city: imagine philadelphic[6] streets, where two persons
who meet cannot pass except by embracing one another; tortuous, filthy streets; stone houses four stories
high—it is stifling there, the air never moves; it is as

though one were walking at the bottom of a well. I had difficulty reaching the Terrain although my bearings were correct. There I saw a crowd of children who seemed to have gathered together less for bathing than for mischief; they were brawling and teasing one another. I left them, and I set out for the Île Saint-Louis over the Pont Rouge, that shameful vestige of the barbarous toll bridges of feudalism; I gave my liard, and I took a deep breath at last. It is true that the hateful Cité must seem like a dungeon, the turnstile a jailer. . . .

I went on, spending little time over at the men's baths across from the rue de la Femme-sans-Tête; there was not much noise being made there, but from the middle of the Pont Marie I heard the chatter from the women's baths. I went to a spot across from rue Poultier; I leaned against the parapet and I strained my ears, but it was impossible to make anything out, for the conversations were jumbled. I did hear a few peals of laughter, however. Public decency did not permit me to devise any means of drawing closer, though it would have been only to hear, since the darkness would have kept me from seeing. There were one or two lights, though. I awaited the bathers, whom I observed as they left. Some of them were quite charming. I was leaning over the parapet in such a fashion that I could hear the individual conversation of those who were climbing the stairway. Most of the young women were with their mothers, a maid, an aunt or a neighbor: I realized that from their talk. Eventually there appeared two young people, who came up alone.

"You were nearly caught! Really, I don't want you to take such a risk again!"

"My dear Sophie, what can you lose? With your charms, one can only come out ahead."

"It's not right! Besides, you startled me, and before I recognized you I almost gave you away. . . . You came here all alone, then?"

"Of course! And no one in the world would dream of doing it. It was the only way I could speak freely to you."

"But my aunt isn't coming!" the girl said. "I shall wait for her—you told me you lived quite near here; you'd better leave!"

"There will be time enough when she comes."

"Ah well, she didn't see me go out! There she is, calling me now. . . . Farewell."

The young man climbed the remaining stairs. When he was near me, I said, "I heard you, monsieur; I shall speak to the aunt."

"Now, what would this impertinent man want with me?"

"Now, now, none of those tricks! You don't answer like a girl. . . . Come now, monsieur sycophant.[7]" He thereupon begged me to say nothing. "No, I won't bring such cruel humiliation on the girl. But watch your step!" He went off. I awaited the women, and followed them to learn where they lived. The aunt went in. The girl hesitated on the doorstep for a moment, doubtless to see whether the young man had followed her. I seized the opportunity to tell her that I had discovered everything. The two lovers asked my promise of secrecy again and I gave it, but still with the same condition. I hurried to the Marquise. The young man in girl's clothing came along to speak to me —I was adamant. He turned back into his notary's house and I reached my destination.

Mme. de M*** thanked me for the trouble I had taken for her sake; she approved of both my views and my behavior (. . .).

BILLIARDS: PLAYERS

People play billiards during the day—there are so many useless people in Paris! Yet it is not, properly speaking, the idlers who predominate in the hall; it is panderers and servants. Their masters, even the ecclesiastics, do not condescend to look into their valets' activities, and with absolute confidence they leave their purses and their lives at the mercy of a loafer, a gambler— that is to say, of a man often led astray by idleness, and still more often carried away by an obsession that will heed nothing. Despite the fact that the game costs twice as much played by lamplight, the long winter evenings are the time for the interesting games. The reason for this is that all the domestic servants, back from the country or the provinces, have completed their daily service by five o'clock; the soldiers are on furlough in Paris; and the fallen women are earning more. For not only do they supply their pimps with money, but they invest in the games of a player who is dexterous, and canny about the arrangement of handi-caps or advantages: because the gentleman who is not playing for himself alone is bolder, he is more skillful, and his shots are better.

I had seen something of billiards a few years be-fore 1775. The hall I selected for my observations was at the end of rue Saint-André. The place was not so dissolute as the one on the Quai de la Ferraille, in the house where Ricci the tooth-puller used to live, and the players not so elegant as those in the room on rue

Mazarine or even the Verdelet hall—it was about average. I described my project to the Marquise, who approved of it heartily, and who strongly urged me to carry it out.

It was on the fifteenth of November, after the publication of my important work (*Le Paysan*) that my sessions began. I would leave the house at eight o'clock. The billiard room was so full at that hour that it was impossible to find a place, and it was stifling there, just like at the last session of the Académie Française. The crowd thinned out at nine o'clock, and the place was comfortable at ten—the session ended at eleven o'clock, to the great regret of the players and the bettors! As this billiard room will be the source for several *Nights*, the players should be introduced.

The provost, or manager, one L'Aloi, was a sly little man, brimming with acid, whose shrill voice was ideal for making itself heard above the constant and noisy chatter of the assemblage. As his acolytes he had two dry, nondescript characters, who played nothing but exhibition games; they bet only in secret, sharing in the wager with someone else. I learned since that they were sharks, banned from playing after a short stretch at the Bicêtre seminary.[1] But it was not enough to forbid them to play; they should have been ordered to work. Perhaps they had been, for they always appeared in the apron of their trade. One of these acolytes would oversee for the manager when he was absent, keep score, and so on. A fourth character was a blacksmith's apprentice, in a red jacket and leather apron. Next came two house-servants, ruthless players or bettors; then two procurers, canny handicappers, who affected an appearance of righteousness and who had so far evaded prison and the ban. Next, a whole throng of novices—habitual victims, among whom were two second-hand storekeepers from rue Dauphine, Esclabasse and Henri, who have since turned swindlers; a heavy lad, a master saddler, very stupid, very brutal, and very gullible, who was eating up the dowry of a lovely wife whom he had intimidated by his bluster. There was even a little tailors' apprentice, a native of Paris and a former altar boy who had become independent through an inheritance from an old aunt, which he came to squander at the billiard hall. He played very badly and demanded heavy handicaps. He kept up for some time under the circumstances I shall describe. It was he who had the table at the first session.

Every billiard hall has something called the *tripot*, a house committee, which must always be headed by the manager. It is usually the *tripot* that arranges the games between players—that is, decides that a certain man may play an even match with another, or that so-and-so must sell a certain number of points to so-and-so. These decisions are often partial, and it is up to the loser to change them, or to quit. But often the excitement of the game is such that since the winner is unwilling to quit the loser continues to play the dupe. It is also the *tripot* which decides the value of the shots, even though the manager seems to ask the opinion of the whole audience. All of this will become clear later.

To return to the tailor who was playing with a billiard shark when I arrived, and who lost as a result —he was greatly disturbed as his loss amounted to two and a half louis. At eight o'clock, L'Aloi said a word to the winning player, and the latter decided to stop. Among the spectators was a bishop's valet, a big, red-faced fellow who seemed very self-assured. He asked the little tailor if he had any money left. I noticed that the lackey was prompted—I learned since that it was by the members of the *tripot*. The little tailor exhibited two louis. At the sight of them a greedy shudder ran through the whole gathering; but the stout lackey was chosen because as the tailor already held the table, his opponent was spared the need to draw for it. The match began after a plurality decision that the servant, whose game was known, would yield eight points; in return, the tailor allowed him sole use of five pockets. Such an arrangement seems to give an enormous advantage to the one who receives the five pockets, but it means almost nothing. A good player can turn it to his own advantage, through the privilege he has of dropping the ball into his own pocket, and through his dexterity in bringing the red toward his pocket, thus causing an incompetent adversary either to lose his turn in trying to move it or to stand trapped, which keeps him from scoring points, and so on. It follows then that the match in which five pockets are allotted is almost the same as an ordinary match, where both players share the six pockets, and that the advantage given the tailor was exorbitant.

The stout servant, delighted at making a good match, played rather well at first, but with surreptitious guidance the tailor played cautiously, often dropping into his own pocket so as to afford only poor openings. He benefited by the *tripot*'s good advice, by the poor shots suggested to the fat servant, and by the latter's inexperience at using five pockets. The score reached fourteen-to-fourteen, however, and the fat lackey lost by an ill-considered shot. How he fumed! You would have to be a player and a fool to understand it. The lackey doubled. The *tripot* juggled the bets in order to draw in some of the bourgeois, who must be the only ones to lose if the *tripot* is to make a living. Finally the fat lackey paid the tailor the twenty écus. That made sixty livres that would soon come in to the *tripot*, which had the winnings on its wagers besides. These were cleverly handled: five *tripotiers* bet against three; the latter made a great show of enthusiasm and agreed to share the bet with the excited bourgeois who longed to join, while those who bet on the tailor shared with no one. This way the *tripot*'s gain was assured, and all its members shared it secretly.

This first session, to which I gave my full attention, struck me as entertaining, and I realized that there was a rich harvest for me to gather in these pernicious places, which are mistakenly considered useful to the police. I went off to give an account of my evening to Mme. de M***, who was pleased with my insight. (. . .)

<h2 style="text-align:center">🎇 59 🎇</h2>

BILLIARDS, *continued:* THE FRONT MAN

The explorer must dedicate himself to boredom, even to a kind of opprobrium, if he is to be useful. This is what I have done: you dainty little damsels, and you great ladies, whose lofty station keeps you too remote from the pastimes of your servants—you may read these *Nights* without compromising yourselves: the Marquise de M***, who is young, lovely and rich, did not disdain to hear me, to receive me, to speak to me in the miserable garments I wore, and which I have always retained. It is, thus, that often those whom I employ, whom I have been feeding for eleven years now, would blush when they greet me in the street if I had not exempted them from doing so.

I returned to the billiard room, dressed not in my usual night-time cloak but in another, shabbier one, which I still wear occasionally. I found the important matches already arranged. The worthy L'Aloi was active, bustling about, making quiet wagers; his acolytes

had their bets laid for them by a pastry maker from
Le Coq, across from the Comédie Française—a heavy
man, quite placid, quite decent, quite dense, who believed he was performing a very beautiful act of humanity by lending himself to the purposes of these
wretches, whom he did not understand. This good-
humored baker visited the hall to enjoy himself after
work and after he had left his instructions; it was so
delightful a spectacle for him that if he had had the
choice he would have preferred it to the masterpieces
his old neighbors performed. I knew the man slightly,
but he knew me only by sight. I engaged him in conversation. The match was played by the blacksmith—a
great bawling fellow and a poor player who always flew
into a rage, even when he was winning—but I heard
someone say that this manner was part of his game because it disturbed his partner; as for the good pastryman, he suspected nothing. The opponent, or rather
the dupe, was a provincial who was a champion at the
game in his part of the country. He had seen the blacksmith play with one of the billiard sharks. Actually it
is a well-known fact that a passable player is overwhelmed by a superior one. The reason is simple: in a
game of skill like billiards the good player prevents all
the good shots and allows only poor ones. For this reason the inferior player accomplishes nothing; and
while he might in reality be a half or a third as strong,
he is in effect ten times weaker. Thus the blacksmith,
who had just gone through a sham game with the
ablest of the billiard players—a man who was best fit
to play with none but great lords to provide them the
pleasure of losing while they learned some good tech-
niques—had seemed inept to the provincial.

The match was so arranged that the dupe gave
the blacksmith a handicap of two points, on an
ordinary game of twenty-point billiards. The sly blacksmith made a few poor shots at the start, and plunged

into despair. At this his opponent felt unbounded confidence, which procured him a few lucky plays. Then came recklessness; that is the usual pattern. But before it became manifest, the wagers were made. All the backers seemed interested in placing their money on the provincial. That was enough to arouse the same desire in all the fools. Then I saw in wonder that it was those of the sharks who had said nothing who timidly offered bets for the blacksmith. They were accepted. The provincial won the game.

I followed the proceedings. The sharks, who were quite unfamiliar to the betting public although the latter had been visiting the parlor for some time, made a show of hesitation over demanding a return match, and handed over their money. But the winners jeered at them for losing heart so easily. The bets were doubled. I saw clearly that the blacksmith was sure of his game. He played coolly, complaining all the while. He only won, though, by 19-19. The bourgeoisie paid up, and the sharks took it, without proposing a revenge. But early in the third game, the blacksmith dropped behind by 10-2, and he was being given three. At that point, the bourgeois bettors ventured a new offer; the sharks would give no more than fifteen, which was an even match; no takers. The sharks offered seventeen for the blacksmith. No one. He moved up two points, and the bets were made for the game; but I noticed they were as low as they could be. The blacksmith lost. The sharks made some show of irritation and they abused him. He flew into a rage and wanted to fight; he was held back, but he growled for a long time, like a resentful dog. The sharks proposed an overall wager, that is, for four games. The blacksmith's bad humor gave the bourgeois high hopes; they were confirmed in their feelings when they heard him reject his opponent's suggestion to double the return game. They took the overall bet. The blacksmith won, but only by what seemed mere chance. The four-game set was proposed once again by the provincial, and was refused. The bettors, on the contrary, held out until all the money these rash bourgeois had eventually moved into the sharks' pockets. Not that the blacksmith won every game—he lost from time to time—but in those games the bets were small ones. This system seemed to me marvelous for its skullduggery, and I realized that a politician could learn some profitable lessons from the connivings of these thieves.

When the bettors had exhausted their resources, nearly all of them left, and another scene began: now the sharks pretended to bet among themselves, for and against, with preposterous frenzy. But then the two acolytes, who had gathered in their own harvest, came and told the pastrycook to keep calm. I even heard one of those acolytes tell the blacksmith: "It's all yours now!" And actually, from that moment on, the blacksmith gave his opponent whatever advantage he liked, and played a fine game. The provincial thereupon reproached him for having concealed his skill with Monsieur (indicating the able player).

"Not at all!" everyone told him. "But, with Monsieur, he was overwhelmed by superiority; you, on the contrary, especially now that you're playing scared, you provide him with all his good shots. Postpone it till tomorrow, take hold of yourself, and you will be a match for him."

"But I won't give him any more points!"

"No, of course not."

The blacksmith seemed unhappy at submitting to that decision. However, he accepted it. He then played two fifteen-sous games, to keep the table in use till eleven o'clock, for L'Aloi was determined that his employer's interests should not suffer by these arrangements. The blacksmith lost, against a shrewd, though mediocre player. This man, who was one of the sharks,

made no secret of his wiles—he called them gimmicks
—and he succeeded in upsetting his opponent by
forcing him into a series of poor shots. This gave the
provincial new confidence. That was the intended purpose.

. . . .

❦ 60 ❦

THE HIGH HEELS

On my way back I came to rue Saint-Louis: the frost
had made the pavement dry and clean. I saw a lovely
woman step out of a large house. "I'll walk," she
told the man whose arm she held. And the carriage followed behind them.

"How do you manage to walk," the man asked
her, "with such high heels?"

"I lean on someone's arm, or when I walk alone
I do it as befits a woman, without haste. I should feel
I was shod like a man if I wore low heels. Once, at the
Palais-Royal, I saw a pretty woman looking like nothing
but an old crone from wearing heels that were practically flat, and ever since then I have detested flat
heels. Besides, they make our legs look ugly."

I was bold enough to address them: "Madame is
quite right! Observe, monsieur, what grace there is in
her noble step, and what majesty two or three more
inches afford Madame." I believe they did me the honor
of taking me for a thief! Whatever the reason, the man
dropped the lady's arm, went on his guard, and
returned to the carriage; the lady walked on alone,

and never have I seen such loveliness, nobility and ease. I continued: "Everything about women should have a gender—their apparel, their coiffures, their footwear—especially the footwear, which should be all the more carefully groomed since in itself it is the least attractive part of the costume. It is very important for moral order, very important for women, that their clothing show contrast with our own! They would lose their appeal by any similarity. But let us suppose that they did not lose by it, and that instead they brought their feminine charm to men's attire! This would deal a serious blow to moral order. . . . This is a matter in which the police should take a hand. Let them permit all kinds of dress—fine!—but give the order that any lady who dresses in clothing that resembles men's be treated as a trollop by the patrol and the police commissioners.

"Yesterday I saw a woman wearing heels that were broad and flat; I would have beaten her if I were capable of beating a woman. She was spattered like a spaniel, for broad heels fling up more mud. Our Parisian ancestresses adopted high and pointed heels in the past from a desire for cleanliness. They were wiser than their granddaughters who, following dictates from some unknown source, have lowered their heels at a time when the pavement is more than ever broken up by coaches, at a time when the ineffective sewers laid under all the streets by stupidity and greed turn those streets into swamps. It is at this moment, I say, that an insane fashion decrees that the heels of women's shoes be lowered and broadened! Young sylphs, hear your enlightened admirer—shun all that profanes your attire by bringing it closer to the dress of men; all that makes you clumsier, by deforming your leg and foot! . . ."

Here the lady broke in: "Aren't you the Marquise de M***'s Night Owl?" [1]

"Yes, madame."

"Monsieur!" she called to the man. "He won't harm us."

The man returned. The lovely lady offered me her hand, which I kissed. They went in.

𝕰 61 𝕰

BILLIARDS, *continued:* THE RETURN MATCH

The pastry maker and I were both curious to see the contest between the blacksmith and the provincial. The good-hearted baker was pleasantly excited, while I, on the other hand, was convinced of skullduggery. I had come only to see how far the sharks would carry their audacity, and, indeed, to watch it was most intriguing! I arrived before eight o'clock, and I found the pastryman already standing on the bench, for the throng was so great that no one could sit down. L'Aloi seemed terribly preoccupied, terribly anxious! Finally the provincial appeared. He had evidently been delayed by business. I noticed that L'Aloi took him aside the moment he entered. I was curious to know what he might be telling him; I slipped through the crowd, and approached them.

"Monsieur," the manager told him, "I am a man of honor. Yesterday you made your match yourself; I could not advise you, as I am obliged to, because I did not know your game. You even made some surprising shots at the beginning, but later on you lost control. Today I know your game; do not play the blacksmith, or else make him give you three points—that is, as many as you gave him yesterday." The provincial thanked him. The blacksmith was at the table, playing through a casual game with someone else, on which no one dared a bet because they were sure that nothing was at stake. The blacksmith had no sooner caught sight of his opponent than his expression turned haughty and indifferent. The provincial did the same. Nevertheless the two men confronted each other.

"Monsieur," said the blacksmith, "I have decided that I can't play an even match with you; no one would bet on me."

"I can believe that!" replied the provincial. "It would work on your conscience; and you're going to give me a four-point handicap." At this the blacksmith threw down his cue and asked for his hat.

"You owe the return game," put in the manager, "for in this house a man owes whatever he has promised."

With a great deal of shouting the blacksmith demanded a two-point handicap. "I want three from you," said the provincial. Finally, after long controversy the blacksmith consented to play an even match. Then he offered one point. But L'Aloi said the game was not on, and ordered the blacksmith to give the three points. He had to obey; for the blacksmith was on the red book of the police commissioner across the way.

The game began. All the sharks offered odds for the provincial; the bourgeois longed to take them up on it, but they were afraid. I drew close to the pastryman and asked him whose side the acolytes were taking. "The blacksmith's." I was quite certain then that the provincial was to be stripped bare. The match proceeded meanwhile in favor of the blacksmith, despite the points he had yielded. The betting began to grow animated; the bourgeois were for the blacksmith, who won the first game. The two acolytes collected their winnings for a while; they told the pastryman to bet against him. This turnabout startled me. The playing continued; the sharks bet heavily on the provincial, who won every game but never doubled, so that he recovered only half of his previous night's loss. Meanwhile the sharks were winning impossible sums, as one of them put it; he was called "Impossible" for that reason. He was an erstwhile domestic servant, who had quit his position to make gambling his trade. (He was arrested that same evening, and sent to Bicêtre for six months.) I was puzzled by what I saw. But when the acolytes took the pastryman off with them to the cabaret, I decided to join the group, paying my share. My simple-minded manner, the friendliness with which the baker had begun to honor me—at one time I used to buy three-penny tarts in his shop—made them regard me as a harmless man. There I learned that the manager's actions had been prescribed by his employer, the owner of the gaming room, who, upon hearing his account, feared that the provincial might bring charges. He was to find out who the man was, and whether he might be abandoned without risk to the voracity of the billiard-hall sharks, who need dupes from time to time in order to eat. I also learned that from their winnings the sharks reimbursed the blacksmith for his evening's losses, even though it was only a reduction of his winnings from the night before, and though the blacksmith had lost deliberately.

After gathering all these insights I went off to confide them to the Marquise, who was spurred by more than idle curiosity; she planned to inform a highly placed kinsman of hers and urge him to remedy the situation.

On my return I found "Impossible" in the hands of the police; he had just pilfered something in a gambling hall in the Faubourg Saint-Jacques, and he had been caught. He was put in the Châtelet[1] to go before the first police court that Friday, the same day as the fallen women.

62

THE CARPENTER

I have mentioned a carpenter's apprentice, an almost honest gambler, who habitually went to the Verdelet billiard hall, near rue Plâtrière. That establishment is somewhat more respectable, and Montigui, the manager, is not a wily little rogue like M. L'Aloi. At first I was pleased enough with the way things were run in that place. It had two functions: that is, there was a card room on the second floor, above the billiard hall. However, I did not go up there right away, for I wanted to follow the billiards without interruption.

By chance I found myself next to the carpenter's apprentice. He was betting at the moment. He seemed to be acting on his own, with no part in a conspiracy, and playing a straightforward game. We chatted. "Those two are honest players—two bourgeois from rue Montorgeuil. I trust them," he said. "But those devils who have lodgings on rue du Bouloir are full of tricks, and you can never trust 'em." He became silent and absorbed in the game.

"That was a serious foul!" he muttered to himself. "An underhanded shot—and not a word said about it! . . . He's stupid enough not to challenge it! . . ." The match ended, and the carpenter's apprentice had won his wager. Someone proposed a match. He set his conditions with great care and started to play. Never have I seen such composure, such impassivity. Nothing bothered him. Each shot was made with care and forethought. His game had a unity in which the first move matched the last—like a game of chess or checkers. He always left a ball for a specific purpose; he generally placed the ball where he wished, and admirably repaired his mistakes. It was the pure science of the game. He beat an excellent player. Several connoisseurs openly admired him; as for me, I was transfixed. I would have preferred, however, that he kept to his trade. His opponent—a very sullen man—was the proprietor of a lodging house.

I inquired of a chatterbox standing near me as to who the self-possessed player was. He told me, and added: "He has won an income of twelve hundred livres from the game by the composure you see in him, for it is self-assurance that has made him a good player. He makes no brilliant shots, but possesses the essentials of the game, which always enables him to win three out of five; he counts on it. Never does the man come to the game with more than twelve francs. He quits if he loses them. But that is infinitely rare. It's not with the cue that he most often wins though, nor with the mace, although he plays with mace and cue both; it's rather with his wagers. He has an admirable intuition for sensing whether or not a player will win a certain match. He studies the players' tendencies according to the losing or winning of the preceding match; from the first shot he can tell if vexation disconcerts the player, or if blind confidence will make him lose, or if he pulls himself together. He likewise notes the dispositions of the opponent; and with this in mind, he modestly offers his wager. Those who do not know him always accept, and even those who know him, not having his intuition, want to try to beat him, so he always has someone to take him on. Besides, he is honest; no one ever squabbles or has to wrangle with him. Watch while he plays. No bets! No one dares to bet against him. Only his opponent is that reckless, and he only stakes six francs, and six francs per player is twelve. If he wins, he puts his winnings of twelve francs safely aside, and plays again or bets the rest, but he must leave with his day's earnings, which is twelve francs against twelve francs. If he wins more, so much the better! But he still returns the next day with only twelve francs. Everyone knows this, but the man is so nice! He sometimes gives such good return matches to the losers that he always finds an opponent. They are usually merchants, who want to relax and play with a polite man; these wealthy men limit themselves each to losing six or twelve francs, and the carpenter, by his rectitude, draws all that profit for himself. Two years ago he married the young daughter of a poor master carpenter, but a very pretty girl, and he is working now to build her an income of twelve hundred livres, like he has. To do this, each morning in his shop he planes implements for billiards; evenings, the game occupies him; each day he pockets his wife's portion without touching it; and then he plays or wagers on his own account. I know him well, and I follow all his little systems; not that he tells them to me, but he talks about them sometimes to a woman, who repeats them to me, just as I tell them to you. Oh, he's a good man all right!"

"Yes," I said, "but I would rather he made this income of twelve hundred livres with his carpenter's plane." But I was speaking to deaf ears. I saw no *tripot*. It existed nonetheless, but it was hidden from the manager. I had to study it before catching on to it.

63

THE APPRENTICE WIGMAKERS

I had followed billiards at the Verdelet without being much enlightened on the subject of the *tripot*. I intended to return to it, but in the interim New Year's Day arrived, and I had an opportunity to make a fresh observation in the billiard hall in rue de l'Arbre-Sec opposite the Place des Fiacres.

I was surprised to see as players nothing but wigmakers' apprentices, who had received their New Year's bonus. Men of this profession earn very little, so when they find themselves with thirty-six livres, two louis, sixty francs in New Year's money, they think they are possessors of inexhaustible funds. I do not know if they came to play with the intention of doubling their money, or if they simply set out to amuse themselves and to enjoy the pleasures of life, or if aimlessness led them there—for all those who have had to take a lot of abuse from their masters or from their ill-tempered wives no longer restrain themselves once they get the New Year's money, and they go out in groups. There is an excellent rule in this trade, which ought to be established in all others: it is that the officials of the guild have the right to ask the arrest of boys who are idle and unemployed. It is an excellent means of preventing the lack of discipline caused by too much leisure. I believe the same rule applies for apprentices of bakers, blacksmiths and tailors.

As soon as the wigmakers had arrived, all the *tripot* rubbed their hands together, and prepared themselves as much for the game as for the betting. But the wig-makers, who are very much in touch with the world, are crafty fellows. They followed a course which quite disconcerted the intriguers: they played among them-selves, wagered among themselves and broke one an-other, without any profit for the manipulators, who looked on with mouths gaping. However, two or three of the craftier wigmakers, having taken their colleagues' money, grew cocky over their victory and, believing themselves heroes, dared to challenge the speculators. It was then that hope sprang up again with all its charms in the hearts of the sharks, who proceeded with ad-mirable dexterity as much in their betting as in their game. They did not have any scruples about how they treated the players, the bottom of whose purses they could see and from whom they need fear no complaint to the commissioner. They beat them then and there without mercy. The wigmakers argued and were ready to fight. But they gave in. They knew only too well that if the guard arrived unexpectedly, they would be sent to prison, simply for being out of work. So they departed, without the wherewithal to buy their supper. Those who had lost at the outset to their colleagues jeered at those who had just been so thoroughly shaken down. I did likewise as I heard the step of the mounted patrol.

🕸 64 🕸

THE MALE MODEL

As I crossed the Pont Henri on my return, I encoun-tered a big handsome youth who was walking briskly. I stared at him. "Young man," I said, "you are out very late! Have you been gambling? Beware of being taken."

"Good heavens, no!" he answered. "I've just come from a session as a model. Finding myself in the middle of Paris, with no resources, with a wife and two children, I had the good fortune to meet a master painter at an inn. We talked, and I asked him if I might grind colors for him. He looked me over, and seeing how I am built he suggested that I work as a model to a group of young students. Each of them hires me in turn, and I don't leave until all of them have studied the part they want to draw. I earn twelve sous an hour this way, between a hundred sous and six francs a day."

❦ 65 ❧

THE CAFÉ

. . . .

As I entered this new observation post (the café on the Place de l'École) I noted that the clientele comprised four different kinds of people: the checker players, the chess players, the passers-by, and the loafers. The checker players ranked highest; and the chess players, rejects from the Café de la Régence,[1] were given short shrift. The passers-by were of three kinds: the strangers who entered out of need; those who came in to change their boots, or to watch the checker games,* and who ordered nothing; swindlers watching for a random opportunity for cheating. Finally the loaf-

* The owner of this café had written a book on the game: he had even published a new edition in 1787. (Restif's note)

ers, who neither played nor read the public newspapers of A *Thousand and One Kinds*,[2] had no other purpose than to gather about the stove and gossip among themselves, waiting for bedtime. This large group of idlers also fell into three categories: the breakfasters or coffee-drinkers, who took nothing in the evening except perhaps a little glass of Hendaye, but who had come for a snack in the morning, or their watered cup of coffee after dinner; the gossips, who came only in the evening and never ordered anything; and the beggars. These last were poor devils, more than limited in resources, who would attach themselves to some talker with means, would pay him court, praise him, admire him. This comfortable conversationalist would order something and offer his parasite a cup or a *bavaroise*; the poor devil would usually say that coffee with water did not agree with him; he would have milk put into it and ask for a roll. What with five or six cups, and as many rolls, on one day, a *bavaroise* on another, half-bottles of cider or beer on a third, the poor devil would manage to feed himself.

. . . .

(AN ACCOUNT BY THE NOCTURNAL SPECTATOR TO THE
MARQUISE DE M***)

"The first Café de Paris dates from 1705. It was run by a foreigner, who was at first believed to have invented the liquid he served. Coffee was drunk without sugar, and it brought a grimace to the faces of the first people to taste it. But the cleanliness of the cups and the tables and the caliber of the company were such that respectable people came to the Café de Paris. Most of them did not take coffee and would have preferred wine. But the sense of well-being, the clarity of mind it induced, soon became widely touted, and everyone ordered it. There was a certain fear, however, that overexcitement would result from putting sugar into it; the taste of certain people was even depraved enough to enjoy the bitterness of the drink. It was only realized much later that a generous helping of sugar did not diminish the quality of the coffee. Instead, it added a nutritional element which tempered the coffee's action and made of it a most wholesome stimulant. Nonetheless, the prejudice that sugar overstimulates persists even now among people and the provincial bourgeoisie.

"The cafés have long been the meeting place for respectable people—it must be agreed that this meeting place is more proper than the cabaret, where one was obliged to shut oneself into a room, or than the barbershop, where one was spattered with powder and treated to the hardly entrancing spectacle of soapy beards—but they sparkled only in their early days. They have fallen a long way in the past twenty years. Yet, they will never become so foul as the cabarets, or the barbershops where even the apprentice locksmiths no longer dare to go. I believe that as of today I am the only man who does not have a barber come to his house; I have several reasons. It would be inconvenient for me to receive a man at his time rather than mine. And then, I find it useful to know barbers in every quarter of Paris. In the third place, since 1760 I wear my sideburns pulled back into a cue in imitation of my dear and respected friend, Monsieur Loiseau, or Losolis. One day, madame, I shall describe to you how I benefit from the barbers.

"To return to the subject of the cafés, here is the conclusion I have reached: the Parisians and the provincials bring to them the harsh thoughtlessness of the capital; it is virtually only the foreigners, or . . . people of great good sense, who behave politely there. You might see some young fool simply come over and stand in the light when you are reading a paper with small type, or the *Mercure*,[3] so badly printed that it is *inlisable* (allow me the expression; but *lisable* is one word more in our language, and a very necessary one, for then *lisible**** will continue to pertain to the written character, and *lisable* will describe the style and the content). There are others who rudely hold on to the newspaper for which some busy man is waiting; who spell it out; or who chat without releasing it. Others ask you for a paper which you are about to read, and do not fulfill the obligation of returning it to you; others read aloud—something which should be prohibited except for a very short and very noteworthy item; others shout, banter crudely, and deafen the peaceable coffee-drinker who has come in for a moment's rest. It is this lack of civility which gradually drives all decent people away from the cafés. Already men of letters no longer dare to appear there; others scorn to come because of what they believe to be their importance, and they are right. The cafés are frequented by a crowd of arrogant young men who never suspect that before the age of thirty, three quarters—and three quarters of the last quarter— of men lack maturity of mind, lack soundness of judgment—in a word, see things inaccurately simply because they are not sufficiently seasoned by long enough experience: and these arrogant youngsters would be the scourge of the man of letters, whom they would provoke and compromise. And yet I, madame, I shall continue to go to the cafés, because I know that my kind of work requires it, just as I go to the barbers, and as I sometimes look into the cabaret, or the billiard hall. But I shall not deal with the cafés in succession."

. . . .

* Read "legible" for *lisible*, and "intelligible" for *lisable*. (Translator's note)

"Each day you astonish me anew," the Marquise told me, seeing that I had ceased to speak, "and you open an enormous career before me, just when I thought you were reduced to repeating things you had already seen! You are truly essential to me, Monsieur Nicolas. . . . I suddenly remember that you promised me the account of your early adventures, and you still owe it to me!"

"I shall not tell you about them, madame; you shall read them. In a short time I shall compose a work entitled *Monsieur Nicolas,* in which everything will be described. You have just seen Mme. Parangon[4] outlined, in *Le P.-P. Pervertis*—ah, how much lovelier she is in reality!"

"That book has caused quite an uproar! . . . But I am pleased by it because my Owl[5] wrote it."

🎋 66 🎋

SHYNESS. THE THAW

Could one imagine, after all one has seen happen to the Nocturnal Spectator, that he was born the shyest of men? It was because he had not associated with people, that until 1772 he did not dare to enter a café. If he is seen today at the Marquise's, it is because their meeting came about in an exalted fashion which sustained him until it became habit. However, he never entered a discussion without a little touch of reticence unless he had very important things to say, and in that case his zeal emboldened him. He is still not free of that painful timidity which has its source in his pride. Often when he goes to a big house, it befalls him to lift the knocker and not dare to let it drop. He turns away despite the fact that he is expected. But what is even more astonishing is that this same reclusive nature caused him to become an observer. He found it so heroic to observe people and to be seen by them, to dare to fathom them, that vanity made him attempt it. A bold young Parisian, blasé about everything, would find it so natural that he would not be tempted. The Nocturnal Spectator found it wondrous and he took it up. Thus, the most positive results come out of the unexpected—everything depends on the resources in one's soul.

It was thawing, so the streets were still a picture of chaos. The disorder was further augmented by the Auvergnats on the street corners who, to make a bit more money by laying their boards across the narrow streets where they ran into the large ones, deliberately built dams which they abandoned in the evening without draining them. The stagnant stillness of half-melted snows made the dam appear solid, and one sunk in over the ankle. I was quite enraged at the sight of a hardship so easily avoidable.

First of all, the street cleaning should not be left to private citizens who do not and could not agree on its execution, whereas public sweepers, proficient and well supervised, would clean the streets in an orderly, correct and punctual fashion. The Auvergnats should be forbidden to set up their planks; the street cleaners would place them free of charge in indispensable places only. The street cleaning and the planking would be paid for by the public, by the addition of two liards to the per capita tax of thirty-six francs, and so on, up to twenty-four sous for the highest per capita tax.

As I was crossing rue Saint-Honoré, by way of rues des Poulies and d'Orléans, I saw a poor girl who was using an Auvergnat's plank. When she did not have the means to pay him, he brutally pushed her into the muck and the pool of melted snow, whose depth he had increased by building a dam in order to make his plank necessary. The girl's poorly shod feet came out of her shoes, the hems of her skirts were soaked, and the water that dripped from them as she walked nearly froze her legs. Now, I am not cruel—I am kind and benign, but very irascible. At the risk of being beaten myself, I gave the Auvergnat a thrashing; his comrades came running, and except for the arrival of the guard, I would have been in great difficulty. I explained what had happened. The corporal reprimanded the Auvergnats and ordered them to drain off the pool; I ran to the young woman, escorted her home, and bought her a faggot of firewood, for I found that her mother had no fire going. I made her dry herself and then I ran to recommend them to the efficacious kindness of the incomparable Marquise, who was quite willing to be of service to them.

The young girl was pretty and therefore in more danger than one less attractive. When I returned she told me that she had often been accosted at night, but so roughly that she had never been tempted. She lived on rue Thévenot. She was the daughter of a journeyman coppersmith, who had died of verdigris; she supported her ailing mother and three brothers and a sister by embroidering cloth shoes for a shoe vendor.

❧ 67 ❧

AT THE HAIR- AND WIG-DRESSER'S

I said not so long ago, I believe, that in the past, before the barber-hairdressers became separate and distinct from the surgeons, the shaving shops used to be centers of news and wit. One spent Saturday night there, or Sunday morning, and while waiting one's turn, discussed news, politics, and literature—such as it was at the time. All that is quite changed! Was it wise to separate the barbers from the surgeons? Is shaving such a lowly profession? No more so than bleeding. From time to time men have rather baroque ideas about dignity. Shaving became vile only after it was reviled. Even wigdressing is not unworthy of a surgeon, nor a physician. In fact, a physician first invented the wig—to prevent old magistrates from catching cold. It is true that the wig then became a fad and a corruption. But let us leave that.

No one goes any more to the barber-wigmaker-bathkeepers for steam baths, though we could all profit by them. Instead, we go to inhale unhealthy air, piled up one on top of another in a café, a museum, a school, at Nicolet's,[1] at Audinot's, and at the Varieties—which are far superior to the Nicolets and to the Audinots, to the Beaujolais and the Associés. We go to stifle at the Ariettes, or the Tragedies. It is only at the Opéra that one still does not suffocate, but that will come. Well then, gentlemen, go to be bathed, sweated, scrubbed down, massaged; may your barbers, hairdresser-bathers, as surgeons once more, preserve your health, and humble the physicians and the surgeon-protractors, their haughty and barbarous oppressors. *O tempora! O mores!*

I am the only man in Paris who still goes to be shaved, or to shave myself, at the hair- and wig-dresser's. Alas, I find no newsmongers there. I am always alone with an ignorant army doctor and his pupil who learns, on my chin, how to shave solicitors' clerks. As you know, every morning regularly, the barber's apprentice goes into the garrets of these gentlemen, but before entering, his twenty loudly applied

knocks at the door have jangled the nerves of the neighborhood and chased sleep far from the lids of poor
invalids, who were just beginning to snooze (excuse
the expression!). I might perhaps have drifted with
the current fashion and, like the others, summoned a
barber to comb my few hairs; but for twenty years, like
a miser, I have collected all the hair I have in a purse.
And besides I go to the barber to learn what I could
learn elsewhere only with great difficulty.

❧ 68 ❧

THE *O FILII* OF THE CARMELITE FRIARS

On Easter Day I went out before seven o'clock. Since
1776, I have never missed the O *Filii*[1] of the Carmelite
Friars.[2] This is the reason: Ill and wracked with pain,
I received a visit on Easter evening in that year from
Edme Rapenot,[3] the bookseller. He suggested we go
to evening service. I went down, leaning on his arm. At
the door of the Presles School I met Mlle. Agathe, a
lovely neighbor, who like us was on her way to the service. "Ah, you poor sick man," she said to me, "you in-
spire me! . . . Give me your other arm!" It was thus
I climbed the steps of the church, leaning on an exalted
convulsionary[4] on the one side, and on the other upon
one of nature's most admirable, fresh and natural in-
ventions! I marveled at my situation. A moment later
the O *Filii* began. The voice that sang it was harmoni-
ous and sweet. I was moved, and softened; my very in-
sides were shaken. Tears of delight flowed from my

SAVINGS CERTIFICATE

FREE POWERBASE DISK
* * 3.5 Tips, Macros and Utilities

☐ YES! I want to save almost 33%. Send me one-year (12 issues) of PC WORLD for only $23.75. I'll save $6.00 off the regular subscription rate, and almost 33% off the annual newsstand price. PLUS I get PC WORLD's PowerBase * * macros/utilities disk —FREE—with my subscription.

Name _____

Company _____

Address _____

City _____ State _____ Zip _____   4DF85

*PowerBase * * diskette is offered solely by PC World Magazine.
It should not be confused with 'power-base' which is
database software offered by Compuware Corporation.

PC W**O**RLD

BUSINESS REPLY MAIL

FIRST CLASS   PERMIT NO. 1262   BOULDER, CO

POSTAGE WILL BE PAID BY ADDRESSEE

PC World
Subscription Department
P.O. Box 51833
Boulder, Colorado 80321-1833

eyes, and the impression was so profound that it has
never vanished.

. . . .

❦ 69 ❦

THE SIX-SOUS INN

As I walked through rue des Mauvais-Garçons, in the
Faubourg Saint-Germain, I saw a great many workmen
—tailors, carpenters, saddle makers, locksmiths—emerg-
ing from an inn which seemed nicely kept. In order to
know this sort of place, it is not enough to look at it;
one must eat there. I had dined at ten o'clock, according to my custom at the time—this had a double advantage for me, since I saved the time of a meal and
did not weary my stomach by leaving it too long without food. I felt sufficient appetite for supper, so I went
in, and I saw a heavy woman, who had once been quite
handsome, seated at the moneybox. Two rather pretty
girls—one of them especially, who I heard was called
Julie, was as well shaped and graceful as she was
demure—were serving the plates as they were filled by
the carver, Julie's brother. They were the fat woman's
niece and nephew; Thérèse was their cousin. The two
girls were marvels of activity! They did everything with
ease and the most appetizing neatness. I watched their
behavior: it was reserved without being impolite. Julie
and Thérèse repelled the frequent liberties in a manner at once authoritative and good-humored, which is
to say that they paid them no more attention than
was necessary to put an end to them. Both girls wore

supple peasant skirts; they slipped like fish among the licentious hands of the diners and did it quietly—not an exclamation, not a "Stop that!" was heard. Only the orders from new arrivals reached the ear, after the bill of fare: roast veal and lamb, beef à la mode, ragout, lentils with lard, salad. Whenever a decent man spoke to them they answered with a modest blush enhanced by a pleasant smile. There were, besides, a scullery maid and a young delivery boy.

The two nimble waitresses reminded me of a pretty girl I had seen at supper once, in 1757, at Lecoq's restaurant on rue des Boucheries. My rough fellow-diners tried her patience, but she never ceased her cheerful, courteous behavior; she put off the most impudent attacks with a decency that pled for mercy. I said a respectful word to her, and the tears came to her eyes. I was young then, and rather a handsome boy, it was said; all my comrades were ugly like their remarks and their actions. This was her expression, and it is a fine one! I add nothing to this incident; happiness is everywhere if vice is banished.

Julie and her companion approached me, although I had not called. "Monsieur," said Julie, "what would you like me to bring you? It's your turn!" She recited the bill of fare. I chose the roast and the lentils with lard, for one could have two dishes for six sous; add a sou's worth of bread and the half-flask at three sous. The roast was excellent and the other dish delighted my rustic palate; thus for ten sous I had all that my appetite and senses could wish.

I said to Julie, "It's a pleasure to be served by a pretty girl like you—friendly, courteous, delectable!"

"Monsieur," the fat aunt said to me in a low voice, "I don't say a word when I hear filth coming from a filthy mouth—there's no danger there for my niece and her cousin—but I will not stand for compliments!" I felt respect for that woman. I saw a

great many young workmen sighing after the two serving girls, and they were polite. I also glimpsed a few
smiles of preference, but so discreet that they seemed
to be nothing but politeness. It was an imperceptible
leaning which was never clarified by an exchange of
words; the aunt never lost sight of Julie and Thérèse
for an instant (according to a master carpenter who
had supper there occasionally with a view to pursuing
Thérèse after a refusal by Julie). He added: "When
someone oversteps the bounds, it is the aunt and no
one else who retorts, and that, curtly, with a "Shame!"
or some such expression, and she says nothing further.
Julie's brother is strictly forbidden to speak up in defense of his sister or his cousin! Peace and order is the
rule here, through a simple system—nothing is said
or done in anger, even after the worst provocation;
and for this reason I prefer these three women to all
the rest of their sex."

I was highly gratified. I marveled at the presence
of decency and order in a kind of sewer, for the good
fare, at a low price, drew the billiard players, the swindlers, the informers, and all that rabble—the vermin
of society concerned with spending very little for lack
of regular income. I noticed too that customers ate silently and rapidly. A gregarious middle-class character
decided one evening to hold a conversation. He made
a few genial remarks; all jaws stopped; François the
carver stood with his knife in the air and his mouth
agape; the two pretty serving girls were caught short in
their tracks, one foot raised, with flushed cheeks and a
half-smile; the fat aunt herself was all grave attention.
But ten hungry apprentice tailors burst in at once,
and they shattered the spell by their shouting. The fat
aunt shook herself, astounded at having succumbed to
the magic words. She mumbled under her breath, and
then she uttered these solemn remarks: "Monsieur,
what you say is nice, and witty—but it doesn't belong

here! The jaws stop, the bites don't go down, and the newcomers find no empty seats. With a mind like yours, you should go take your meals with a minister of state, and not in a six-sous inn!" The goodwife Torel was right. She fed a hundred and twenty persons in an hour; her tables would hold thirty to forty; that meant a quarter of an hour for each of them. . . . It was remarkable how this speech spurred still greater activity! (. . .)

❦ 70 ❦

THE CLOUDY EVENING

Sometimes in autumn, and even from the month of August on, there are days—gray, sunless, rainless— that flood the soul with some strange, sweet melancholy. On one such cloudy evening in 1751 I had gone into the Vaudelannard valley and felt that inconceivable enchantment I described in *Le Paysan et La Paysanne Pervertis.* I went out at five. I crossed to the Île Saint-Louis (. . .) and turned down the Quai d'Orléans. Never had I known such a pure, delightful sensation! The weather was gentle. The cathedral bells were tolling; the air, set trembling by their vibrations, teased my ear and seemed to shake my soul. I missed the rustic setting of the ninth of June, 1751, on the eve of Corpus Christi, the song of the solitary finch, and the headiness that comes at sixteen years. In my memory I saw again all that had happened to me, all that was still happening! I remembered my early years (. . .).

I walked briskly and circled the island. At the spot

where I had saved a hapless girl [1] from committing a crime, I dropped to my knees and offered homage to the Supreme Being (. . .). I rose. A doorkeeper had seen me. He took me for a madman and approached me: "Just what are you doing there, you? This is no church here!" I am not haughty, but I was revolted at being disturbed by a fool in the course of my prayer to the Divinity, to celestial love. My voice was somber as I pointed to the first star beginning to shine (it was Vega in Lyra, and I said to him, "Do you not see the starry vault of God's great temple? You limited man! In the future, never disturb him whose thoughts are flying upward to the Supreme Being, and go guard your door." The doorkeeper retreated, but backwards, went inside and held the door half open, his head showing until he could see me no more. Since then he has always done the same thing when he has seen me on the island.

❧ 71 ❧

THE BATTLE OF THE MASQUERADERS

Not a single year has gone by without my seeing some outrage committed by the masqueraders. On my way home I came upon two bands of them at the Grève, flinging insults and brawling. One of the figures from the band that called itself the *Greeks* suggested making slaves of the losers, and prisoners of their women. The idea was received with delight. The two groups drew up into battle formation, and clashed. Contrary to their expectations, the *Greeks* were conquered, thrashed, stripped of their costumes—and a sorry

bunch they were without them! The *Trojans* took the
Greek women, unmasked them, and were herding
them away over their protests, when the sound of the
mounted guards was heard. That was enough to set
the *Trojans* to flight, after shredding their lady cap-
tives' clothing, dealing a few blows to some of them,
and smearing the others with mud. They then vanished up rue du Mouton. The crippled group was picked
up by the guard, which, finding only victims, and having no wish to wake the police commissioner, allowed
them to disperse.

❦ 72 ❦

THE CAFÉS, *continued*: THE POLITICIANS

I had promised the Marquise to observe the cafés for a
few more evenings. On one night in particular I found
the politicians in quite an uproar. The discussion
turned on the American Revolution, which was beginning at this time. . . . "In situations like this," a
thoughtful man remarked, "the problem is not the
power against which the rebellion is aimed, but the
cowards, the rascals who fear failure, and who bring
it about. They are the ones who become traitors, cruel
enemies; who reveal the rebels' secrets, and cause
it a hundred times more trouble than the armies of
the great power. I'd give no quarter to those vile creatures, who are guilty of high treason once the general
will is manifest!"

"That's all very well," said another, "but the loyalists can prevent revolution too, and thus do a great

service for the mother country, toward which the insurgents are guilty of ingratitude."

The first speaker hunched his shoulders and said no more. A third man took up the argument: "You talk like a man with no experience, if you'll allow me to say so! Since the rebels are greater in number, British America would be ruined, devastated forever if the loyalists succeeded. The English loyal to the Crown on the one hand and their American supporters on the other would persecute whatever remained of the old party; they would plunder it and subject it to cruel and constant humiliations. The banner of freedom has been lifted; it must stay." (This last speaker was right; the Dutch Revolution, which occurred since I wrote this, has proved it only too well! Oh, what a disaster for the Americans if they had yielded like cowards!) "The Anglo-Americans will never set themselves up as a republic," said a fourth, "England today is too wise, too powerful, too . . ."

"And you are too—" a fat man in a furred cloak broke in furiously. "I tell you, it will become a democratic republic; the very earth there is republican, like the earth of all countries that are new, and not yet sufficiently populated."

. . . .

🕸 73 🕸

THE CARD ROOMS

Summer had returned, and I no longer went to the café at night, nor to the billiard halls. I had just left rue du Fouarre for lodgings that had been rented for me in an inconspicuous house in rue de Bièvre. This dwelling suited me better. The landlord was a large blond Flemish woman, still attractive, who had an only daughter of fourteen. This young lady promised great beauty. She was put in a convent.

I needed three keys to get into the house; one for the outside door, one for an iron grille at the foot of the stairs, and one for my room. I was very comfortable in this little fortress. I have said nothing of my morning pains. They ceased at that time, and I was well pleased to have left my other lodgings, which had been profaned by a scoundrel. I lived in rue de Bièvre for five years, and it was during this time that two adventures happened to me.

Since I happened to be free at eight the first evening, I went out and strolled at random. At the corner of rue de la Bûcherie and rue des Grands-Degrés, I saw two men leave a house which was painted black. They were quarrelling, and went to fight in the passageway to the Abreuvoir. I tried to tear them apart, but they were in a fury and the stronger hurled the other into the river. I called for help, nonetheless. The man was recovered, and his antagonist departed. I learned later that they had come out of a gaming house above the billiard hall on the corner. I went up.

I found an assemblage of people who make a living on the river, workers of every trade, and a few small merchants. Some played piquet, but the majority écarté. The bettors surrounded the tables, and were deeply absorbed. I placed myself behind an écarté player and watched his game. The man raised his eyes to me, and from that moment on, he was unable to sit still in his chair. He lost. Then he called for the owner; for all those corruptors, those deceivers of mankind who peddle vice, indolence and trickery, are proprietors of these gaming houses.

"Monsieur!" he said to him. "Get this man away from here"—pointing to me—"he makes me uneasy!"

The proprietor politely said to me, "Monsieur—players, you know, have their sensitive spots. Forgive me!"

I placed myself behind the opponent, who gave me an obliging look. The ill-tempered man continued to lose as long as I was there, but he did not have the right to have me removed, for I could no longer see his cards. I left nevertheless to observe other players, and I noticed that the loser was winning again. I told the proprietor, "That player is not honest; you'd better watch him!" Not knowing me, and fearing me for this reason, the proprietor watched him surreptitiously for several hands; he then spoke to the man in private, made him return the ill-gotten winnings, and sent him away—which attracted little notice.

The bettors occupied my attention for the rest of the evening. I saw that they connived with the players, and that there was a *tripot* as at billiards; that they arrange to play the empty positions, solely to see that their cronies win their bets; I saw too that they were cheating, hiding their cards, and so on.

✺ 74 ✺

THE CAFÉ, *continued*: SPIES

Let those without discernment say what they will—the truth is that spies are necessary to the government. It is up to wise people to realize this and to behave accordingly in public places; this knowledge is in itself useful to the authorities in that it discourages rashness and ferment.

I had gone into a café in the old Palais-Royal which I shall not identify. I heard affairs of state being discussed with great freedom! I even noticed that certain persons whose faces, despite their composure, evidenced no particular education expressed themselves more freely than others and made extreme statements. I felt some suspicion. I approached two of these men; I talked ethics to them—nothing, they did not even hear me; science—no better; they did not deign to listen. Finally I risked a casual reference to politics. They became all ears. I knew who they were then, and I watched them. They stirred up a young man from the provinces, who seemed quite hot-headed and who continually cited the people who had influenced his opinions. I drew close to the young man. I broached ethics to him. Immediately he took fire, and gave me a whole dissertation on the subject. I was sure then that he was nothing more than rash. I saw that we were being observed; I continued to speak in a loud voice. But a little political brawl flared up at the other end of the room, and when everyone had run over to hear it, I took the opportunity to tell the reckless youth to slip away and to meet me later at the Pont au Change. He left unnoticed; I went over to listen to the dispute. It was about the insurgents. Two things were being claimed, one of which simply had to be true. With a little deliberation one is almost certain to make the right choice when there are only two possibilities. One wager was for, the other against future independence. A great many people took up the two bcts. I saw that it was a kind of game.

Afterwards I noticed that the two anti-ethics and anti-science men were looking around for the young man. One of them asked me if I knew what had become of him. I conducted myself exactly as this man had done when I had spoken ethics to him. He seemed taken aback and commented on it. "Why should you complain?" I said to him. "A while ago, when I spoke of my trade to you, you yawned, turned your head away and changed your seat. I return the favor when you talk to me of yours; I'm only being fair, and you were being discourteous."

He grew angry at my words. "My dear sir," I said to him, "watch your temper! The publicity would do you more harm than me." As I said these words in a very low voice, he thought better of quarreling with them, but he went to confer with some other men. I found myself under heavy scrutiny. I took little notice. I went to join the political idiots, and whenever I saw them on the point of going astray, I rebuked them sharply, which seriously discomfited them.

The evening drew to a close. We left the café. At the door, the men I had provoked surrounded me and one of them said, "We don't know who you are, but you speak very well!"

"Yes, gentlemen! Each of us this evening has plied his trade: you, that of seeking out indiscretion and the spirit of improper criticism in order to report them; I, that of reprimanding those indiscreet persons who would do much better to support the judicious aims of the government than to kindle mistrust and discontent in the heart of the citizens. But perhaps they are only speculators with their own private notions, for as to notions of revolt, no one ever has them in France—we are too clear-headed for that."

. . . .

THE BEGGAR WOMAN WITH THE CHILD

Our role as nocturnal spectators pleased Du Hameauneuf and suited his unusual character. . . . We set off
by rue Saint-André. At the top of rue de la Comédie-
Française, in the shadow of a doorway, we came upon
a beggar woman who held a swaddled infant in her
arms. My friend was a man of feeling; he was touched.
As for myself, I had seen that woman over a long period of time, and I almost knew her. She used to stand
on rue de l'Arbre-Sec, and her child had grown no
bigger! I confided this observation to the original.
. . . He was enraged. "This woman," he cried, "is a
miserable thing, using little creatures this way when
she borrows them, or perhaps has them put in her
care!"

He approached the woman and gave her alms, but
he asked to see the child. She refused. He seized it
deftly. Startled by its lightness, he uncovered it—it
was a four-pound loaf of bread! . . . We laughed, and
left the woman, saying only, "My dear woman, you'll
be reduced to eating your child as people did during
the siege of Paris!" She could not keep back a smile;
but she mended her ways, for I have never met her
since.

"So many shams, for the sake of living without
working! And work is so simple, so honest, so fulfilling!"

"Yes, but one must enjoy it!" I replied.

Ah, things will be different in 1888! Everyone will

have to declare his means of livelihood, and those who can show nothing acceptable will be made to engage in some useful activity. . . ."

. . . .

✸ 76 ✸

THE DAINTY SLIPPERS

On rue des Lombards,[1] which is always very filthy, two women were escorted by a man, the husband of the younger of them. Their skirts were well tucked up, and the young woman especially had perfect legs, the prettiest of shoes, and consequently pretty feet. The daintiness of her slippers was enhanced by their shape, and by raised, slender heels. Yet she walked with admirable ease, and, most importantly, without getting dirty; a lantern-bearer lighted their way. A very well-dressed man, followed at thirty paces by an elegant carriage, stepped along behind them on tiptoe and greedily eyed the young woman's feet. We watched him. That was indeed the thing that had brought him down from his carriage to track through the mire. Du Hameauneuf, who was a bit unconventional, approached him, and touching the man on the shoulder, he said, "Monsieur, it would be better to lend your carriage to those lovely women than to let them cover themselves with dirt!"

"I'll do no such thing!" the gentleman replied. "I am like the Grand Dauphin[2] and Tévenard, who could never come across a pretty female foot without going into ecstasy. I particularly love those high, well-formed heels—I love them to distraction."

The two women and the man overheard us. They reached their door, on rue Saint-Martin. It was opened, and at that point the husband spoke to us. He told us that his wife had adopted this style through love of cleanliness, and that she could walk across all of Paris without a splash of filth on her stockings or her white skirt. He asked us to enter, and somewhat against her wishes, she showed us how clean she was. On the other hand her sister, whose heel was broad and low, was frightfully spattered. "The reason is very simple," he continued, "my wife's foot touches down on only one point; she picks up very little mud, and flings none about. This is the origin of women's high-heeled shoes in Paris. Made like my wife's, they are suited to the environment. She had this preference as a girl, and I confess that before I knew her that was the foremost of her charms; I was in love with her before I had seen her face. Now it's a simple means she has for sustaining my physical appetite."

We admired this philosophical merchant, who was very rich and who had made the fortune of his wife, the daughter of a poor tavernkeeper. The gentleman with the carriage said to the merchant, "Monsieur, I beg you to do me a favor. I should like to have that perfect slipper. It is only fair that I reimburse the lady to whom it belongs. . . ."

"This calls for some thought!" said the merchant. "Are you in love with my wife?"

"No! I find her lovely, but I never fall in love with a woman who would become guilty by listening to me. I should like to have this shoe, which has been made perfect by the foot rather than deformed by it."

The merchant assented to the request despite his wife's reluctance. The gentleman gave a handsome ring for the pretty slippers and fled as if he had stolen them. It was then that the pretty wife told us blushingly that the gentleman had been following her to church for two months, and that he had tried every means to seduce her. The husband was somewhat irritated at having given away the pretty shoes, but he consoled himself with the thought that the pretty foot remained with him.

At the Marquise's house, we told her this story— of so little interest in itself but so important to the daintiness of Paris women, to the loveliness of their legs, their feet, and their footwear—whatever was once said by the author of a contrived and scarcely philosophical letter, published for some incomprehensible reason in the *Journal de Paris*! "To my mind," said Mme. de M***, "any woman who wears flat heels, a man's hat, a man's redingote, and her hair dressed like a man's, should be shunned in the streets by sensible people! We must be feminine."

"I agree!" cried Du Hameauneuf. "A womanly woman is such a lovely creature that I regard it as a crime against nature to disfigure her by making her resemble our sex in her apparel! The police should brand every mannish woman as a whore." As we all held the same opinion, we did not dispute him.

Later I learned that the man with the carriage had done his utmost to win the heart of the merchant's pretty wife; but that having had no success, he had sought a good woman whom the pretty slippers fit, and that he had married this new heroine à la Perrault[3], who might be called Cinderella the Second.

THE FATHER OVERRUN

Men of wealth, do you know what your behavior proclaims the day you climb into a carriage? . . . No, you don't know. It proclaims: "From this day forward, when I go out it shall be to cause more congestion in the streets than ten men. From this day forward, when I go out it will be to fling filth in the faces of all the townspeople I may encounter, and to set them fleeing in fright; to run over some poor old codger with my carriage; or a pregnant woman; a child; a young beauty all bewildered and fearful. From this day forward, I shall be the scourge of town and country. In town I shall be the steer escaped from the slaughter, and I shall deprive the countryside of my lackey's hands, my horses' toil, and the fertilizer they produce. Gaze at me, citizens! Ah, how terrible, how fearsome I shall be! . . ."

But, man of wealth, what if those citizens should once acquire a single ounce of good sense, should join together to say to you, "Mad dog, by what right do you drench us in mud? By what right, as you approach, am I forced to flee your path to avoid death?" What if they simply stopped your carriage to ask why they must give you the right of way? In what way is your business more important than theirs? What answer would you give? None, man of wealth—for there is none to give. The carriage should be the appanage of the sovereign, his chariot; the coach should be the lot of those who travel on urgent and useful business. Only the abolition of every disastrous luxury will put an end to vice. Vice and luxury are father and son; luxury is the father. Embrace loftly morals, O you poor humans, if you want to find happiness!

I was walking along rue Dauphine; I had reached the Buci circle, that murderous crossroads where more citizens die each year than the blade of justice offers up to the public welfare. A man was knocked down. People shouted: "Stop!" And the coachman, a heartless brute—the guilty coachman cracked his detestable whip to get away. . . . The wheel rolled over the wretch's chest! (The wheel should be the punishment for the coachman and his master—it is the old law: break, villain, and you shall be broken! And you shall be displayed upon the instrument of your crime!) A gush of blood. . . . The carriage vanished. . . . My former agility is gone; I could not catch up with it. . . . When I got back I tried to enter the Café Montmayeux, where they had put the injured man. The idle and inquisitive crowd blocked my way. A tall young girl, with the sweetest face, and dressed with the respectable neatness that bespeaks a decent family, came near; she tried to see, to learn what had happened. They told her about the accident. "Good heavens! But are they taking care of the poor man? . . . All they do is stand there, staring at him!" Just then the door opened. Someone pushed his way through the crowd. The girl saw the victim. "It's my father!" she cried. She tottered. I tried to hold her up. "Let me go," she told me, "I'll be twice as strong." The crowd let her through. She called for a surgeon, for stretcher bearers. I was the only one who listened to her. I brought a surgeon. I ran to find bearers. They took the poor man home. Oh, God—what a sight! His daughter was pale; her lips were white as death, but she did what she could. The mother, who had been ill, fainted and could not be revived. I took care of her. The man died at midnight.

. . . .

❧ 78 ❧

THE DRUNKARD'S REBUKE

"Imagine," the drunkard said from his doorway, "my wife and my maid have put me out of their house— for it's not my house, as I'm not master there. But I want to go back in."

He opened the door to the entryway with his master key. "But come with me, I beg you, and hear the sermon I plan to give that wife of mine." I did not care to go up, but Sara's mother[1] was curious. We followed the drunkard. He opened the first door, and made such a racket that the wife and the chambermaid were forced to open the second to him. I am not sure what might have happened, but the wife, a very beautiful woman, controlled herself when she saw us. She said only, "What a state you're in!"

"My dear, I do it to forget the pain your flirtations cause me! Especially . . . especially the latest one! . . . I tell you this, before Madame, whom I know . . . and before Monsieur . . . whom I don't know . . . but Madame, she knows him, she must, since she's with him, and . . . any friend of a friend is a friend of ours. . . . To get back to you . . . I'll tell you first of all that as long as you had that judge—a solid, discreet man—I was patient. He was a good magistrate, and he loved you, and a person has to make certain allowances for people who are useful. You've got to repay them for the trouble they take, especially . . . when they have influence! . . . Then you took that official . . . he spoiled you by turning you into a spendthrift. But still, he was a decent type. . . . Next you had that—(here the woman put her hand over his mouth). . . . Oh! Now, that one really hurt me! But at least he kept to himself, and never bandied your name about. But now! Now! Madame, now what have you got? A wastrel—a confidence man who's fleecing you and ruining me, a swindler. . . ."

At this last word we heard, not without some alarm, someone leap out of bed. We heard him moving about; finally we saw a man come out, a naked sword in his hand, shouting, "Swindler! Confidence man! Swindler!"

I stepped in front of the rest of them, my two pistols ready, and I announced to the bully that unless he sheathed his sword . . . He had not known we were there, I think, for he was astounded! Had he been sleeping when we arrived? He must have been. The lady was terribly ashamed!

The drunkard began to preach at his wife's lover for the impropriety of his behavior. "Should you have let yourself be seen?" he asked him. "You are bringing disgrace on a woman; you are a heartless, soulless, ungrateful man! A cur! Out of my house! And don't ever set foot in it again! . . . . Come now, my dear, forget this dreadful man, this cad! You can see he doesn't deserve your kindness."

I could not get over my astonishment. I looked at Mme. Debée, who told me, "That's the sort of man he is." As for the wife, she put the gallant out, pushing him by the shoulders; Sara's mother helped and added a kick and a few blows, which my pistols prevented him from returning. The husband and wife were reconciled. But what contempt I felt for that woman!

And yet I have heard since that this extraordinary episode reformed her. I must admit that I would not have expected it!

❦ 79 ❦

THE OPÉRA FIRE

It is July.

. . . .

I walked down rue Saintonge, and I felt highly susceptible, for I was unhappy. I turned into rue Saint-Sébastien. . . . I reached the garden walk, and imagine my surprise at seeing a bright and terrible blaze rising in the middle of town! It had been raining; the path was flecked with pools of water, and the fire, which looked to be more than a league away, gave off enough light for me to avoid them! I have never seen a more exact replica of Vesuvius or Etna. "How many unhappy people must be moaning at this very instant!" . . . This thought overwhelmed all others. I learned only on my return that it was the Opéra fire. . . .

. . . .

I went back into the city. I ran to the Opéra. But on the way, a heart-rending thought occurred to me! "If I find victims there in need of help, I shall have to look at them exactly as hard-hearted people do, with no way to help! . . ." I uttered a cry of pain as I remembered the Marquise. . . . And yet I had not reached the pit of despair! She still existed, that heavenly woman, and I was to see her again. . . . The

Opéra alone was burning, thanks to plentiful and competent aid. But it was totally destroyed, and the nerve center of the capital was stripped of one of its most important faculties! . . . One female and two male dancers perished, suffocated by the smoke in the stairways. The fire was a horrifying sight from close quarters. What power nature has, in this terrible element! How fearsome a blazing volcano must be! . . .

I had seen three terrible fires previously: the Saint-Germain Fair's in 1762, the one that consumed the first Opéra in 1763, and the one at the Saint-Ovide Fair, in 1776. The first was horrible. But it is certain that if there had been some cooperative effort, if there had been a fire brigade right on the square itself, as there is today, the fire would never have occurred. My first impression of that fire was of a volcano, for it resembled one. If it had not been in a low area, it would have illuminated all of Paris.

The first Opéra fire was more contained because the building was less extensive. As to the fire at the Saint-Ovide Fair, it was alarming only because of the high combustibility of the booths; to be really terrible, it would have had to catch onto the Nicolet and Audinot wooden stalls which formed two clusters in the best possible arrangement for burning.

What I have said about firemen is not meant to signify that I think their institution an admirable one. Alas, it only proves the imperfection of human institutions. Paris maintains about fifty fire brigades. It is clear that at the end of a certain number of years the firemen will have cost almost as much as the damage that might have been caused by fire. I will be told that men have made a living. Pitiful argument! Men sustained by luxury, or by precautionary expenditures which resemble it, are not usefully supported. They should do other worthwhile things beneficial to the State. The organization of this institution should be altered somewhat to employ the hardiest disabled soldiers as firemen, and busy them profitably with drills which will keep them alert.

The same evening I heard two men walking in front of me discuss fire and electricity. One of them spoke an apt truth. "All matter would ignite, because it is permeated with fire, if it didn't at the same time contain water. The electric machine produces sparks only because humidity is eliminated from the element contacted. It isn't *charge* we should say, it is *eliminate*. Now, my friend, the amount of water on earth diminishes because of the continuous concretion of shells which no longer release what they absorb. Once all water is so absorbed, there will be bodies which, no longer receiving any, will lack it totally. They will catch fire of themselves, will drive all the water from those bodies which still contain it in the form of steam; those bodies will burn and will cause the conflagration of the entire globe; all water will turn to steam."

I lost sight of them. I had, however, an observation to make to them: that, like water, air combines and becomes less abundant. And without air, no conflagration is possible. . . . Let us return to the fire.

But where lay the blame for this horrible accident? It will seem incredible! On a game! Two of the theater flunkeys were romping together, and this was the cause of that terrible accident! Our age is afflicted with two great evils—thoughtless banter among the upper classes, and tomfoolery among the lower. I have often been pained at the sight of workmen playing, brawling, knocking one another down, for hours on end, in the very sanctuary of labor! There is nothing more dangerous than profaning the sanctum of the workshop! It must be sacred! People should indulge in no diversion there. But from where does this disastrous attitude come? From the doctrine that laughter is the sole joy of the human race, whereas it is the least of them; from the inane doctrine that frivolous comedy is preferable to serious drama; from the ill-considered maxim that one must laugh in order to relax; from the frivolous upbringing which enemies of human nature give to children. And this to such a degree that by some sacrilegious contrivance there are tutors who advertise themselves in the public papers for instruction in reading, writing, and the basic principles of ethics—through play! . . . Wretched man! The drastic consequences of your despicable notion will be seen in the younger generation! Only the sober man is a man; the man you mold through play will be pretty as a little kitten; one day he will come to be like an aging cat.

80

THE PIOUS SHREW

After I looked at the frightful fire I walked away. Near the Palais-Royal, I saw all the servants of a large house hurrying back to it. I knew one of them, who asked me to come in. "Would you like to hear," he asked, "the tongue-lashing Madame is going to give us? At the first news of the fire we rushed to it. Madame inquired, and on learning that it was the Opéra, she sent word that we were not to offer our aid to any but the neighboring houses. When she heard later on that the fire was contained, she had us called back. No one came; she flew into a rage. 'I shall fire them all! What? They are giving succor to the devil's house! The temple of lewdness! They are godless people, I will not have them near me. . . .' We're going in there now. Come with us."

I entered with the servant, and stayed to one

side. All of them were there, from the steward down to the last scullery boy, and all of them were laughing up their sleeves. I saw a thin, bright-eyed little woman emerge from her study, shrieking from the threshold: "What! Despite my orders, bringing aid to the demon! Let them burn, burn, burn, all those henchmen of Satan! Let them burn like him! I wish not a single one of those actors or spectators had escaped!"

"Madame," said the steward, "none of your people helped. There was no need. Everything was taken care of."

The first sentence had soothed her a bit. But the next two sent her into a rage again. "Ah, I'm certain of that, there was no need! Those accursed places get all the help they want. I wager nothing was burned, and they'll play again tomorrow!"

"Everything went up in flames, madame, and the very stones are baked white."

"Ah! Praised be the Lord! . . . You're not deceiving me?"

"No, certainly not, madame!"

"Come then, everyone on his knees—and let us thank God for this ineffable blessing!"

I went down on my knees like the others. But I did not thank God for having destroyed the Opéra.

🎕 81 🎕

ANATOMY OF THE HUMAN HEART

. . . .

If I would describe the anatomy of the human heart, should I not take my own? I have faults; well, they are Nature's as much as mine! I have always tried to conquer them, but when they triumphed I did not despair; I have lain in wait for them to even the score. I have virtues too; yes, I have as many as the next man! But I have gone through all the follies, all the quirks of the human mind. All the inept notions of our noblemen, who build parks, or English gardens; who level villages to round out enclosures which they circle with walls, the better to ensure their property— I had them in my youth. And I have been more than moderately surprised to encounter all the follies of my own head in those of other men. With the difference that they execute them, and I was unable to put mine into practice, for lack of money. I had the soul of a nobleman indeed—I, the very poor son of a tenant farmer! For during the first exuberance of youth, between fourteen and fifteen years of age, I saw myself with property, with mistresses; I built luxurious castles in Spain. All of it remained unrealized, because I was poor. And how many times did I not prostrate myself in spirit before the Supreme Being, to thank him for having caused me to be born poor! For surely I would have done both much evil and much good if I had been rich, but more evil first.

All the good that I have seen done or contemplated or expounded, all the reforms in public administration, have passed through my head since I was young; and I have sometimes wondered: "Would they have heard me? . . ." But between the good and the evil that I have mulled about in my head, like two snowballs, there is this happy difference—that I have sometimes found someone who has supported me for the good. The good has been done, and I have had only the dismay of being unable to carry it as far as I would have liked.

What conclusion is to be drawn from this? That all men have approximately the same ideas; that they are all either wicked or good depending on a very slight impetus, and the circumstances; that training makes the man; but that training must be done indirectly if it is to be effective. A competitor profits more than the son of a household from the advice the latter is given. Men should seem to have been reared by Nature. My worthy father had fourteen children; his every remark breathed uprightness and honesty, but only on three occasions did he give me advice directly, and then in a gentle manner that I recall with bliss. It was this that made me love rectitude. My two elder brothers, the ecclesiastics, always told me what to do; they revolted me. At fifty-three years of age I still hate it, that unsolicited advice; not for its content, which was good, but for its form.

I have always sworn to sacrifice myself, to expose myself totally, even to shame myself, for the good of my fellows. By my faults, my mistakes, and their causes I would like them to realize what is the proper training to be given to children. J.-J. R. recognized that fine truth, the foundation of his *Émile*:[1] that man must seem to have been reared by Nature. And, though younger, I recognized it before him, very strongly. I trembled with joy when I met it in his *Livre de l'Éducation*. But then I was so displeased with the details that it was two years before I finished it. Not all the details displeased me; I often recognized the great man again. But I felt that the book would have a bad general effect in Paris; an effect which would not be compensated for by certain worthwhile reforms.

The women of Paris, most of them, should not nurse their children, and *Émile* has been disastrous to this city for that reason alone. Noblewomen should not nurse their children; I shall demonstrate this in physical and moral terms, and it requires mere common sense to follow my argument. If the aristocracy wish to obliterate their race quickly, *Émile* offers them the

surest method. Who should nurse her children? In the
state of nature, as well as in the state of a republic
where all are equal, all mothers should, or with very
few exceptions, for among women, as among animals,
there are a few females who cannot nurse. In a state
of advanced civilization, however, as exists at present
in France, England, Germany, Italy, Spain, and some
other countries, the exceptions are very rare in favor
of wealthy mothers or mothers in the mercantile class
who can nurse. This is what J.-J. would have realized
if he had examined the question. Really, should
women like our duchesses, most of our marquises and
our countesses, women like the wives of our presidents
and financiers—should they nurse, with their feverish
milk, their extravagant passions, their pungent food—
with their dissipated, overstimulating way of life? No,
anything but that! Let them entrust their children to
some good peasant woman, fresh and healthy, whose
nourishing milk and peace of mind will counteract
the flaw of their conception! But let her be well paid,
that wet nurse! May a sacred law make her forever re-
vered by her ward! May two families be thus bound together, one from the aristocracy, and one of simple
farmers! For it is peasant women who should be
chosen. . . .

. . . .

✥ 82 ✥

THE CLOTHES MAKE THE MAN

At last I regained my strength, and I came to life again,
through the divine Marquise! (. . .)

I was walking along haughtily, like an important man! . . . I noticed it, and I smiled at my conceit. I was reminded that in 1758—young, in love, with beautiful eyes, tempting lips (I repeat the compliments I was given, and I do not repeat them all—some small quarter must be left to modesty)—I happened to have a outfit of satin and white silk stockings, and thus arrayed I set out to visit a young beauty. Well, then? En route I caught myself feeling proud, disdainful; I worried lest a man of the people touch me. I even believe I said, or thought: "Good Lord! What is a man like me doing without a carriage?" It was entirely natural, and my smugness seemed instinctive.

Just then a carriage went by; I stepped aside; but a slight twist of the coachman's hand brought four broad hooves into the gutter. I was covered from head to foot with slimy water, as black as ink! Farewell to the fine white stockings, the handsome satin outfit! Everything was filthy, down to my lovely embroidered cuffs, before I ever appeared before my mistress! The footmen jeered at me. I wiped my face, and made myself look like a mulatto; even my curls were spoiled. . . . At first I was angry; but soon realizing that instead of being arrogant and proud I had become modest and even humble, I thanked the mischievous coachman for his lesson, and his horses, too, who had so effectively assisted him! . . .

I continued along the back streets, I entered my sweetheart's house quite matter-of-factly; and where I might have acted the dandy, vain and pretentious, I was tender instead. She laughed hysterically, and wiped me clean, but my handsome outfit was stained. It never looked elegant again; afterwards I wore it only modestly, with my stockings dyed black. It is incredible what indulgence I learned in that school for popinjays I meet in the streets! I am honestly not offended by them! But since then I myself have always been careful not to dress elaborately because I have learned the consequences. The proverb that "it's not the cowl that makes the monk" is a poor one—it certainly does! It makes the monk—morally as well as physically, literally as well as figuratively. Let a man assume the robe of a solicitor, a barrister, a clerk, a magistrate—he takes on the *esprit de corps* immediately. A cassock makes a man the zealous champion of the clergy's privileges, when he had railed against them the day before as abuses contrary to religion. A cowl monkifies the man who puts it on, whether he does so playfully or for a masquerade.

. . . .

🎝 83 🎝

THE STITCHED MAN

. . . .

As we walked, dreadful but muffled cries struck our ears! We listened. At last we discovered that they came from a house on rue des Barres, where we were at the time. I looked for the secret catch to the entryway; I found it, and we climbed up to the fifth floor. Reaching the door, I knocked. A woman in a shift, her sleeves pushed up above her elbows, came to open it. I asked who was being murdered in her house. Without a word, she took me by the arm and led me in. Sara followed me, trembling.

The woman showed me some sort of thing sewn up in one of the bedsheets; then a stick like a porter's, thick and short. Next she led us back into the first room and told us: "My husband is an incorrigible

drunkard. Our affairs are in a dangerous state; I have
six children. In desperation, I'm trying a method
someone suggested to me. When he comes home very
drunk I sew him into his sheet, and then I give it to
him—I really give it to him! . . . This is the second
time. The first time he never knew where it was coming from, he was so drunk, and for the past two
months he has behaved. If he stays that way, it will
have been worth it!" I remarked to the woman that
the method was a dangerous one. "Find me another
then!" I promised her that I would give it some consideration, and we left after seeing the husband un-
sewn. He must have thought it was I who had beat
him, for he quailed at the sight of me. I took Sara to
her house, and hurried home to rest.

🎗 84 🎗

MARIE-MADELEINE

It was the winter of 1782. It was cold; the ground was
covered with an icy snow; I was crossing the deserted
Place de Grève. Where the fateful scaffold usually
stood I came upon a bent old man on his knees, almost prostrate. I thought he must be ill; I went to help
him. "No, leave me alone!" he said. "The closer the
time comes, the more I tremble! For forty-five years
now I have come here every night to ask pardon of
Marie, who was hanged because of me."

"Hanged?"

"Hanged unjustly! . . . I recognize you! Fifteen
years ago I saw you and you spoke to me! . . . Now I
know who you are. . . . Restore Marie's honor to her

one day, without tainting my family's, for they are not guilty! . . ." He leaned against me as he said, "If justice were done, my bones would be broken here on this very spot . . . and you would drag me through the slime, instead of supporting me. . . . I am eighty-five years old; I was only forty when a young girl from the provinces, named Marie-Madeleine, was sent to me by one of her aunts to serve in my house. Marie-Madeleine came of a decent family, even a respectable one; she had been carefully raised; she was pretty, energetic, clever; she did the cooking, kept the books, she was tidy—in a word, charming. I was struck by her good qualities as much as by her beauty. I had a son; I felt this girl would be a treasure for him, and I decided that he should marry her. I talked to Marie-Madeleine who replied demurely.

"That son was somewhat quarrelsome; he had done military service. Some months after I had made my views known to him, and while he was courting Marie-Madeleine, a nobleman came to our shop to make some purchases. He noticed the pretty girl working in the shop alongside my wife, and his valet, who was helping her lay out the fabrics, appeared very much taken with her. Was it a trick to pass her over to his master, or was he smitten on his own account? I don't know; what still amazes me is that when he and Marie-Madeleine were going through a kind of narrow little corridor, the footman laid his hand on her breast. My son saw him, unfortunately! He struck the footman, whose master commanded him to fight. My elder son was killed. . . . As my one remaining son was too young to marry the girl, I had the misfortune of being unable to control my criminal desire—for I believe that it was out of my own love that I had betrothed her to my son.

"I took her aside one day and made her a proposition, which she rejected. I put it more strongly a second time—adding such advantages, short of an honorable situation, that I was surprised that a poor girl would not accept them. But it is difficult to imagine what a good and solid upbringing is given the daughters of an honest farmer who has achieved some degree of comfort! In a third attack, I outlined on the one hand all the advantages that I had offered, which could assure Marie-Madeleine's security; and on the other, the dreadful threat of her downfall. I swore to her that I was determined on it, and that her family would be disgraced. She shuddered—and an astonishing thing! She told me, 'You may ruin me—but do not bring shame on my family! Have me hanged in the Grève; I will conceal my name and nothing will make me tell it.'

"Alas! It was these unfortunate words, which I found too defiant, that impelled me to carry out my hideous notion! I believed that I could change her mind; and remembering the liberty the footman had taken, I thought that Marie-Madeleine was not so virtuous as she appeared. I could not live without her —that is, without possessing her. My mind was in a turmoil; I urged her, and she answered lightly; I tried violence, and she did not submit; in a fury, I made a formal complaint against her—hoping she would defend herself. But imagine my despair—she pled guilty! She wrapped herself in tatters in the prison; she appeared before her judges as a wanton, unprincipled woman. . . . She was condemned. . . . After her death, at her request her confessor himself brought me this note, which had been written and secreted by her:

I loved your son more than myself. After his death I would have served his father with joy; but when his propositions, their nature, and the nature of his threats forced me to hate him and never to expect peace again, I resolved to sacrifice my life for the honor of his dead son, whom I shall rejoin with this virtue; and to preserve the honor of the son who remains to him. May the Lord forgive you, beloved and cruel enemy! I am no longer on earth, but your son and I pray God for your sake. Do not lose your poor soul! Do penance! . . . Your own flesh begs it of you! . . .

M.

P.S. And do not confess to the police! I forbid it! I have won that right!

She had signed it with only an M. As I read that letter, my guilty heart was transformed! Marie forbade me to give myself up; I have not done so yet. . . . I have wept every day of my life! My nights are horrible! What will I say to God? What will I say to Marie? What will I say to my son? Alas! I pray to that poor luckless girl—it is she who will gain me my pardon, if I can be pardoned!"

I shuddered as I listened to the old man. I said nothing in answer; but it enraged me that the merest accusation of theft in the home, by an employer, should bring a death sentence on a poor girl or boy! That law is an unpopular one, aside from the fact that it is too harsh—which destroys its effectiveness.

🎇 85 🎇

MY DATES ON THE ÎLE SAINT-LOUIS[1]

In times of affliction one's soul is open and susceptible; circumstances become very important, and one feels a desire to commit them to memory. Why is that? Do people enjoy suffering? No, surely not. . . . During the time I was deprived of the sight of the Marquise, and of Du Hameauneuf's company, I was most unhappy! Instead of seeking to distract myself, I held onto the pain; I feared to let the moment slip away; I cut it into the rock! Far from continuing my usual expeditions, I was dejected and listless; my outings were limited to the Île Saint-Louis, which I circled sadly.

. . . .

Whenever I had stopped along the parapet to ponder some sorrowful thought, my hand would trace the date and the thought that had just stirred me. I would walk on then, wrapped in the darkness of the night whose silence and loneliness were touched with a horror I found pleasing. On this evening, I left my lodgings early for the Île. On the stairs I was handed a letter; I did not want to go back up to read it. On the Quai d'Orléans my eyes turned to the first date I had written, on the same day in 1779: 5 9bris malum.[2] I cannot describe the emotion I felt as I thought back to the year before—as I remembered my situation at the same instant, at that same place, and the pain that had made me write the word malum in regard to Mme. de M***. A rush of memories came to me; I stood motionless, preoccupied with linking the present moment to the preceding year's, to make them one. I was moved, my tears flowed; and the sentiment was exquisite! I kissed the stone. . . . It seems to me that the passing of time makes us less ourself than our closest friend: we regard that other self of a year ago with interest and tolerance, as if, through the date that represents him, we were there in the presence of our closest Friend. . . .

. . . .

By the light of the street lamp, on my way back I found *Desperium!*[3] *Diva Mul. nob. adempta 25 7bris.* Farther on: *Silvia mort. 29 Aug.* And farther: *Nouvelles de la Marq. Mal. 29 7bre.* That date is inscribed across from rue de Bretonvilliers. Thus I went on, rediscovering on stone everything my spirit had felt during that period of sorrow. Finally, across from the second garden, I found *"Marches, recup. hod. 22 9bris sacra.* I uttered a cry of joy at the sight of that inscription, which was like a real rebirth to me. . . . Ah! If I had only seen inscribed on the stone the night of our first encounter—I in the street, she on her balcony—what bliss it would be to reread that date! I determined that henceforth I would inscribe everything on the island, for it provided me real nourishment for my emotions.

❧ 86 ❧

THE PRETTY SISTER AND
THE LITTLE BEAR OF A BROTHER

. . . .

At the top of rue de Bourbon, I came across a small boy of sixteen and a girl, his sister, of about eighteen, standing with a bundle near a milestone. The girl was saying, "Good heavens, hurry, George! Look how late it is!"

"I don't want to! I'm tired."

"But suppose we're attacked!"

"Let them attack you! What do I care?"

"You're really . . . oh . . . if I wanted to get you a scolding. . . . But no."

"I don't give a darn if they scold me!"

I went a little closer. I saw the most delightful girl—gentle manner, pretty eyes, good coloring, nice figure. The little boy, on the other hand, looked like a bear: fat red cheeks, deep-set green little eyes, a coarse look. And yet he had some of his sister's features.

"Where do you live, mademoiselle? I shall carry your bundle."

"Very near here, monsieur, rue Beauregard."

"Oh, sure, go ahead!" said the little urchin, moving off. "Let him take the bundle! You'll see how he runs away with it!"

His words frightened the girl, but I reassured her. She was carrying her parcel in her apron, and I asked her to give me her arm.

"We've been walking for two hours now," she told me. "We're coming from Porte Saint-Martin, where we went to pick up these two bundles of calico and muslin. He's stopped at every milestone to plague me. But I won't say a word when we get home; they would punish him, and he . . . he'd pay me back for it. . . . Besides, I don't like to be the cause of a beating; I would rather take it myself."

I commended the girl on her goodness, and we were proceeding on our way when the urchin, who was behind us, began to shout: "Thief! Catch the thief!" A passing patrol unit heard him. "It's that man there, that one, he's running away with my bundle and forcing my sister to go with him!" The patrol ran up and stopped us. I explained. The girl confirmed what I said. But the little bear insisted on his charge, and he was brazen enough to declare that his sister fell in with my story because she did not dare to contradict me. I was astounded at the excess of insolence and ugliness on the one hand, and the charm of face and sweetness on the other!

We reached their door. The parents opened it

and began to scold. Their son hurried up to repeat his accusations to them. The little devil even dared to take advantage of his sister's gentleness, insisting to her face that it was because she did not want to hurt me! She defended me with great spirit. But I was enraged. I pounced upon the little demon; I demanded that the patrol arrest him and take us to a police commissioner. The parents ended by apologizing. I thereupon coolly related all I had seen. They were convinced. I demanded that the little monster be punished in my presence; the father and the mother consented. He was bound up; the father did not spare him and the gentle sister turned away to weep.

"If you love your brother, you must understand that this punishment is necessary!" I told her.

"Oh, good heavens, I do! He went further today then he has ever gone!" Her words completely persuaded the police of my innocence, and they withdrew.

❧ 87 ❧

TUILERIES: PLEASURE PARTIES

There are certain persons who live beside public parks and have access to them through their own gardens. In one house near the Place Vendôme I had heard talk of a plan for a moonlight party in the Tuileries on a certain night. I went there toward ten o'clock, and proceeded to conceal myself within the enormous pile of chairs stacked at the end of the main walk. At midnight I heard the company arrive. They ran about; they had a good time. However, as the gathering was large and made up of persons of all ages, gradually each found himself a partner. I took great care not to show myself—my cloak would have attracted attention. But as I had published the story of the girl who hid in the mound of chairs,[1] the idea occurred to someone. An officer of thirty-two brought a young lady of eighteen over to it; a gallant priest, a widow of twenty-two; last, a very impressionable young girl arrived with her admirer. The three couples had made no agreement among themselves as to the choice of this spot; from their hiding place the first heard the second and fell silent; the second heard the third, and said not a word, so that this last pair heard no one—but I had heard them all. The first two couples were only curious; the third set to its purpose.

I followed the skillful play of corruption, as carried out by a thoroughly vicious young man intent on seducing a young woman betrothed to another. He used all his wiles: his love; his misery at being a younger son; the character of the future husband, a contemptible man. He assailed the principles of morality and religion, but like a schoolboy; I realized that he was reciting to her what he had read, probably that morning, in *Thérèse Philosophe*; finally, he brought forth a powerful argument for a girl of fifteen—that she would save him from despair by yielding. He spoke with spirit. The girl resisted him; he was determined to take advantage of the opportunity. She cried out! Someone came running; he hid himself and the girl escaped, slipping out among the trees. She went to join the company.

That episode delighted the second of the two couples, and they felt no further restraint. But the company, uneasy now, thought a thief or some insolent fellow was hidden in the mound of chairs. Orders to surround us were given without our hearing them— neither the two and a half couples nor myself. The

servants charged with torches; the chairs were surrounded; their masters, and even the women, demolished the pile. They came first upon the priest clinging to the gentle widow, and they laughed; then the
amorous officer, and the husband did not laugh! Then
the young gentleman, alone—which caused consternation among all the mothers! Finally they reached me,
and I had the honor of causing some alarm! They recovered rather quickly, however, remarking, "Now,
there's an extraordinary pair!"

The jest did not deter certain persons from giving us some dark looks, the young man and me. I gave
a simple account of the truth, insofar as I was concerned. Just then someone exclaimed, "Ah, he is the
Marquise de M***'s Nocturnal Spectator!"

At his words the attitude toward me changed. I
was asked the real story of the three adventures. I recounted the young man's, but without identifying the
girl; I even implied that she was a chambermaid who
had slipped away. There was a great deal of joking!
I am not quite certain I accommodated the brash
youth; he scowled at me. The officer and the young
wife, as well as the widow, were clearly relieved at my
discreetness. Indeed, I spared all four of them as well.
I am not sure the husband was thoroughly convinced,
but I assured him in private that his wife had resisted.
That is what she ought to have done. . . . I ended by
urging him to take precautions against any such mischief. The assault on the chairs interrupted the festivities. I attempted to take my leave, and I succeeded
better than I might have expected if I had not been
recognized.

It was three o'clock; I did not visit the Marquise,
and I put off my account.

A NIGHT IN THE LUXEMBOURG GARDENS

I reached the Luxembourg before the gates were closed, and took up a remote position. Company was to arrive by one of the gates leading to the park. This was not to be a ball, like the night before, but a still more delightful entertainment: an Arcadian Night. The whole party was dressed as shepherds and shepherdesses. They played at tending flocks by moonlight; they ran about, wandered off, sat on the lawn in clusters or two by two. . . . But I anticipate. They did not arrive until after supper, that is, toward one o'clock. I saw the company enter through a gate across from the pool; they left it open, as that private garden was itself very pleasant. They scattered over the meadows, through the woodland—the Luxembourg combines the two landscapes. I folded my cloak, laid it aside, and followed in coat and breeches.

Never have I seen anything so picturesque, so exquisite. This was no libertine game; all was decent, and symbolized the innocence of the golden age. I saw a young Italian woman, with her cavalier;[1] her husband offered his hand to a lovely lady. I watched the cavalier especially. . . . Ah! He was a lover, but of the most ardent kind. I vexed him a little; he was on his guard. It was a simple matter to keep my distance from him in that vast park, but my presence kept him from straying from the golden-age innocence.

An adventure of my own befell me. Two young ladies mistook me (shall I say it?) for . . . a Marshal

of France, to whom I apparently bore some resemblance. "You're dressed as a shepherd, monsieur
le maréchal?" the elder remarked. "With nothing to
show who you are—that's very good!" I smiled. The
young lady took me by one hand; her sister, who was
thirteen years old, took my other; we strolled and ran
around. I was delighted. I cannot tell you what Elysian
enchantment lay over that whole garden! The light of
the moon, the shadows, the sense of freedom, the
beauty of the women, especially of my two companions, gave that party the atmosphere of a dream; it
was as pleasurable as happy fantasies.

I met the cavalier; and as the two young ladies delighted in addressing me as "monsieur le maréchal,"
without naming me, the marquis was convinced that I
was some nobleman, enamored of his lady. He came
close to my ear: "Melibeus," he murmured, "you
should be happy with your lot—at this moment you
are not Melibeus,[2] you are Anacreon,[3] led by the
Graces."

"Yes, but I shall not lead them to a precipice, as
the price of their faith. Ah! *Corydon! Corydon, quae
te dementia cepit!*[4] The dagger lies beneath the
flowers! *Anguis latet in herba!*"

"Melibeus is clearly a friend of Vergil!" said the
marquis. "He uses his expressions."

"*Alexis! Corydon* loves you—but respect his *Galatea!*[5] You keep her faithful for him, and I have a prize
in store for you that will please you!"

My two young Graces listened to us as they admired the beautiful Italian lady, who told me, "Monsieur le maréchal, you enchant me! I want to deserve
your esteem, and I shall deserve it."

"Yesterday, yesterday!"

"It was you!"

"It was I!"

"Ah! My fate is in your hands! . . ."

"I have returned it to the hands of prudence. See the Marquise de M***! She knows everything."

"The Marquise de M***!"

"Yes. . . . You must see her, tomorrow, and open your heart to her."

"I shall, monsieur le maréchal." I was confident, then, that there was nothing more to be feared. I walked on. How I congratulated myself on my happy fortune in meeting the two young ladies! I expressed my tender affection to them. I paid them several compliments, and they said I had never been so witty. . . .

We were at the very end of the garden, in the most secluded part. A few groups of shepherds had gathered there. One of them picked up his flute.

. . . .

All the shepherdesses were overjoyed! Another played his musette, and a round dance began. I took part in all of this, clasping the hands of my two Graces. At one point, as I was praising their light step, a man came and tapped them on the shoulder. "Leave us alone!" they told him without a glance around. I looked up at that man—I resembled him. . . . I realized it was the Marshal. For his part, he thought that the two girls were pouting at him and he withdrew, laughing. Meanwhile, in order not to discredit myself, and jeopardize the effect I hoped for through the pretty Italian lady's error, I slipped away, unnoticed. I left by the enclosed garden, and crossed through the mansion; the porter opened the door for me, and I was outside at four o'clock in the morning.

I hastened to the Marquise's house. I gained admittance, and in Élise's[6] room I wrote an account of my night, so that Mme. de M*** should know what to say if the young woman with the cavalier should call.

✢ 89 ✢

THE OPÉRA

The Opéra has been banished to the Porte-Saint-Martin.[1] What a barbarous idea to have moved it to that isolated spot, in a remote district, only half-policed, at the very edge of the capital! There is a quarter which is the nerve center of the captial—rue Saint-Honoré; it is there that the apex of amusements and fine arts should be. I will not be accused, I hope, of being lenient toward the corruption I have attacked relentlessly for twenty years. And should anyone doubt this, he would be convinced by the furor with which I am disparaged. The corrupt of the capital have not dared address themselves to those newspapers edited by enlightened persons; they make their sentiments known through those vile, obscure beings, the stupid editors of a few provincial sheets.

I was saying that the quarter named for the Palais-Royal is a kind of nerve center of the capital, that it is there that all entertainment should be located, as well as the center of taste, the quintessence of good manners and urbanity; that, dispersed as they are in all the quarters, the spectacles only extend frivolity and the taste for dissipation; that I perceive this to be true; that I have proven it to myself before writing it down; that this matter, which I have been publicizing since 1770, is urgent and all other considerations must yield to it. But I say even more—and I must dare to say it: that I am perhaps the only man, and surely the only writer, who sees things in their true perspective. Once all our witty authors, our elegant artists are hurled into fashionable society, they see nothing else. I alone, the day after dinner with a duke and peer, supper with a pretty marquise, a witty and talented countess, return to ordinary clothes and heavy shoes, in the midst of workers of the most common sort; not playing the dandy or the fine gentleman with exaggeratedly elegant manners, but working with them, like them, reading the depths of their soul and consequently seeing cause and effect. And how many times have I been the sad witness to blunders of every sort! Public administrators, humanity beseeches you—remove the prostitutes and entertainments from the midst of the working quarters; concentrate them in the sections of wealth, of frippery, and you will have the benefits, real or false, of your wealth, without corrupting an entire immense city, which is, in effect, a nation! Here are some useful truths, and not the twaddle with which your journals are overloaded!

I went to the Opéra. They were playing Gluck's *Armide*. Legros and Mlle. Rosalie Levasseur[2] were in it. I was moved, even frightened by the terrible chorus: *Un seul, un seul guerrier!*

Nothing that Lully and Rameau have written can equal that chorus. But Mlle. Rosalie spoiled the best scene; she played it so poorly that I thought I would have to give her some advice in a little satire entitled *Armide*. Legros sang the opening of the fifth act deliciously: "*Armide! . . . vous allez m'inquiéter.*"

After the Opéra, I wrote my satire in the café on the corner of rue Saint-Merri.

THE DISHWATER FROM THE WINDOW

I was walking along rue Geoffroi-l'Asnier. As I turned into it, I recalled that twenty-five years earlier I had come to this street with the pretty Madelon Destroches to seek an attorney there. She had found me in my sister Margot's house, and because she did not dare go alone to visit a professional man, she had asked me to accompany her. I was immensely proud to be with such a lovely woman, and I remembered the proprietary air I tried to assume—in the midst of that pleasant reminiscence, a potful of dishwater, carrots, parsnips and such came down over my head. . . . I was truly frightened. I protested very loudly. I declared that in Paris nothing should be thrown out of the windows without warning, for there was always traffic in the streets. I heard weeping; it was a girl's voice. I tried to enter, and succeeded.

A mother was slapping a girl of fifteen, the one who had flung the water out the window. I interceded for her and promised not to lodge a complaint, which mollified the mother. They cleaned me up and the pretty scatterbrain showed such kindness, such remorse, such sweetness, that I was grateful for the accident. I inquired about them. They were people of some means. The father and mother, both born in the provinces, had met and married in Paris; their daughter was born there, as were three other children. I resolved to introduce her to Mme. de M*** in order that she might contribute to Julite Zombert's well-being. That girl, who did indeed become happy, has since done me the greatest service!

✤ 91 ✤

THE GIRL WHO PREFERS A PORTER

. . . .

At the corner of rue des Noyers and rue Saint-Jacques, on the steps of the Saint-Yves chapel, we saw a very pretty girl conversing with a young and sturdy porter named Louis. As she had the manner of a lady, and it was rather late, we assumed she had come to find him for some errand. But just at that moment, a young tradesman emerged from a mercer's shop across the way and attacked the porter with his measuring stick. The latter was bewildered at first. However, he recovered quickly, seized his short crook and battled so vigorously with it that he put the shopkeeper out of commission. All of this occurred without a cry, without a word. We were truly surprised! While Hercules and Acheloüs fought over her, the girl had come to stand near us. Du Hameauneuf asked her the reason for the quarrel. "Ah, monsieur! Separate them! . . ." But at that moment, the mercer quit the battlefield.

"Are you his kinswoman?" we asked.

"No, gentlemen! This shopkeeper asked for my hand in marriage; I refused him as courteously as I could, because I prefer Louis, and as I am on my own, I would rather marry him. I have property in my village. In Paris, I make an honest living; I bleach silk bobbin-lace and stockings, and do lace-mending. Louis earns a good amount, for his trade! Some days it comes to as much as nine and twelve francs, for he is strong and works hard. We agreed two years ago that I would hold his savings for him and that we would marry when we had a thousand écus. Today we have them, with all the expenses subtracted, and even counting two or three gifts he gave me. I was telling him the news as he passed, for he never comes into my room because of wagging tongues."

We did not feel that the girl was wrong; we urged prudence, and offered ourselves as two of her witnesses. She accepted.

. . . .

🕸 92 🕸

EXECUTION BY TORCHLIGHT

The crier had announced a death sentence during the day. "It would be a horrible thing, this proclamation of death sentences, except for the necessity of an example! But considering that necessity it is not horrible enough. When there is an execution the whole city should be set shuddering; bells should toll the culprit's appearance, and that dreadful moment when he meets his fate. They talk of the unceremonious way executions are carried out in England—that is a greater horror still. And we find that the number of convicts executed there, not to speak of the two-thirds more whom the king reprieves, is three-quarters greater than the count of executions in France! But it is no less true that our vile scandalmongers, with their savage joy and the comments they allow themselves, are in conflict with humanity, with reason, with religion, with the value of the execution of death sentences. . . . Look at those wretches, listen to them (this is clearly Du Hameauneuf speaking), and you will be outraged by their dissipation, their maliciousness, their barbarous jubilation!"

We were proceeding toward the Place de Grève. It was late, and we thought the execution over. But the gaping mob proclaimed the contrary.

"Let us go on," Du Hameauneuf continued, "since the opportunity offers itself; let us observe the great hideousness of crime and the great severity of civil law on the one hand, and the great beauty of religion on the other! When a culprit rides by in the fatal tumbrel, I see only the consoling minister as he strives to restore to Nature the monster who has violated her."

As he spoke, I caught sight of some movement on the steps of the Hôtel de Ville. It was the first of the three convicts going to meet his end! . . . When the penalty is too great for the crime it is an atrocity and the effect is lost; it inspires not dread, but outrage.

The man was broken on the wheel, as were his two companions. I could not endure the sight of that execution; I moved away; but Du Hameauneuf watched it all stoically. I turned to look at something else. While the victims suffered, I studied the spectators. They chattered and laughed as if they were watching a farce. But what revolted me most was a very pretty girl I saw with her sweetheart. She uttered peals of laughter, she jested about the victims' expressions and screams. I could not believe it! I looked at her five or six times. Finally, without thinking of the consequences, I said to her, "Mademoiselle, you must have the heart of a monster, and to judge by what I see of you today, I believe you capable of any crime. If I had the misfortune to be your sweetheart, I would shun you forever."

As she was no fishwife, she stood mute! I expected some unpleasant retort from her lover—he said not a word. . . . Then, a few steps away, I saw another young girl, drenched in tears. She came to me, leaned upon my arm, hiding her face, and she said, "This is a good man, who feels pity for those in anguish!"

Who was that compassionate girl? . . . A poor thing who had abandoned herself to the procurers on the Quai de la Ferraille! I looked at her; she was tall and attractive. I led her to the Marquise's shelter without waiting for Du Hameauneuf.

Then I went to her house; she was in, and I reported what I had done. Then my friend appeared. He was overwhelmed with respect and feeling for the priest, the confessor of the guilty men.

93

THE COMMONER'S WEDDING

. . . .

M. du Haneauneuf took me, with his wife and her aunt, to the Faubourg Saint-Antoine, to the wedding supper of a bargeman of comfortable means who was marrying a pretty girl from the faubourg. The four of us reached La Rapée at six o'clock. The wedding party had danced, drunk a few glasses of wine, but they had taken nothing solid since the scanty lunch at the house of the bride's father. They had all shared the cost of a royal feast of fish and fowl! There was fried and stewed fish, turkey pullets, roast beef. When we appeared the wedding couple was awaiting us. They received us flanked by the girl's father and the best man. We were the groom's friends. We asked permission to make our own contribution. They protested, and the whole company exclaimed that we did them honor. But we each put a louis into the hat nevertheless, and so did our two ladies.

Then Du Hameauneuf proposed some light refreshment while supper was being prepared. It followed us in great baskets, each carried by two apprentices of the pastry maker Beaucousin, who was renowned in the faubourg. From our carriage Du Hameauneuf drew twenty-four bottles of burgundy; he took up a position at the end of a long table, and the guests came forward in turn to be served a glass when they had downed a pastry. We danced until supper. There were pretty girls from the faubourg and a few bridesmaids from the Île Saint-Louis, the bargeman's home. They came over to sit beside us, and we made them welcome. We were struck by one of the girls from the Île Saint-Louis, a tall, stunning girl with a distinguished look about her and beautiful eyes. We thought she was an aristocrat. We asked what her name was; she told us that, and her trade. She was a dressmaker; she had been courted by the bargeman, who had several large boats of his own; but . . . her heart belonged to someone else. . . . And she sighed, which made her most appealing! In the course of the evening we learned that the man she loved had wed her in secret, that he worshiped her, and that despite his lofty birth he found joy in his life with her as a simple commoner. It was a charming dark-haired girl, the daughter of a tavernkeeper, who confided this story to us.* Another

* In 1788, this nobleman, who is today in high society, with a great name and a great fortune, mourns his beloved dressmaker from the Île Saint-Louis, whom he had in fact married, and who died in childbirth. He asserts that in all his life he was happy only with her. Thus he was capable of happiness . . . and so many noblemen lack that priceless capacity! (Restif's note)

young woman, the daughter of a wine merchant, had such grace and beauty that we could not stop gazing at her! She was a dear friend of the tall beauty's, and their intimacy had more than one basis; she was being courted by a friend of the secret husband.

We talked with these young women and the bride until supper. Finally we sat down at table and gaiety reigned. There was singing when the meal was over, that is to say, before dessert. The commoners bawled or shrilled. But there was silence when the bridesmaids prepared to perform their songs. The tall beauty was extraordinary; she was applauded, even by the rustics and their womenfolk. Her friend captivated us! The pretty aunt did no less well. Then, when all the bridesmaids had sung, we noticed that the silence continued, and we did not know the reason. We learned what it was before long from a delegation of four women, second-hand dealers, who came to ask us to persuade the pregnant lady to sing a little song, as short as she liked. The pretty aunt looked at them, saddened, and shed a few tears, without answering!

"What is it, my good lady?" asked one of the four women.

"Did I say something I oughtn't to?"

"No, no, ladies! . . . But . . . my niece cannot hear you! She is deaf and dumb!"

"Deaf and dumb! . . . Oh, such a turrible shame . . . She's so purty!"

The whole party was listening. The four women wept; the other women were moved; the girls grew tearful at seeing them weep. The men did the same, without quite knowing why; Du Hameauneuf sobbed, and I was quite moved. At last I said to him, "What makes you so sad?"

"In truth, I don't know . . . But . . . still, I think that right now . . . I think I wish . . . that my wife weren't mute!"

"She would owe you less," I countered.

"That's true! It's true! . . . Ah, my good friends! It is because she is mute that she is my wife! I was deeply touched by her misfortune, and I have tried to make up for it, as much as was within my power!"

"Then, up on your feet!" exclaimed a master boot-maker, "let's drink to Monsieur's health, for he is a good man!" "Let's drink a toast to the health of milord and his lady!" "He made a good choice!" "Still, a man likes to have a woman say a few words!" *Chorus.* "To the health of all speechless ladies!" From that moment on, till the end of the supper, there was such an uproar one couldn't hear oneself think. . . . We left the table at eleven o'clock.

There was dancing again. But the wedding couple and the attendants vanished after a minuet and a con-tredanse. We left with them and escorted them back to the Île Saint-Louis. They were about to go to bed, before our eyes, without ceremony on the bride's part, when the house was besieged by more than fifty men. They forced the doors and came in; they demanded the garter. The bride stepped forward, laughing, and offered a very pretty leg, from which they removed a handsome red ribbon; it was immediately cut up into fifty or sixty pieces, and pulled through the button-holes of every male in the wedding party. They returned to La Rapée then to finish swallowing down the remains of the supper and to empty the tun of wine that had been rolled to the head of the table to slake their thirst.

. . . .

94

AN EVENING IN THE NEW PALAIS-ROYAL

One evening at five Du Hameauneuf, who had taken
another house, called to take me to see it. We had his
wife and her aunt with us. Our way led through the
new Palais-Royal, which we crossed rather quickly. But
what we saw there made us want to come back. It was
the first or second week that one could stroll beneath
the colonnades; they were unfinished, and were covered over while small shops or booths were installed.
When we returned, after seeing the new residence, the
Palais-Royal evening activity was at its most brilliant.
The two small galleries especially were thronged with
people to such a degree that one could not move. As
we were inspecting everything, virtually borne forward
by the crowd, we caught sight of a girl so pretty, so
completely beautiful, that a statue sculpted by the
graces out of every charm, and animated by love, would
have had less appeal and less perfection. Du Hameauneuf murmured to me, "I know that beauty. It is
a story I must tell you. For you don't know everything
—and I have sometimes discovered things that you
could not have seen, since I was a libertine before I
became a wedded philosopher—a great libertine!"

"I'm sure of it!" I replied, laughing, "and a bold
one at that!"

We left the matter there. But I observed the pretty
girl; and the more I studied her face, the more perfect
I found her. I could think of no one but Sylvie to com-

pare with her. Sylvie had had that beauty, that smile, those lovely eyes. But the girl before me was taller.

I asked Du Hameauneuf, "Do you know where she lives?"

"I shall find out." And he went to speak to her. I saw that she knew him. While my friend was talking to the lovely Swindam I mused that she resembled Zéfire, the girl who is described in the *Paysan,* and whose true story is told in *Monsieur Nicolas.*

"I know what we must know," Du Hameauneuf told me when he returned. "Take our ladies to the Marquise's house, tell her our plan, and come back. You will find me here; otherwise wait for me."

I did as my resuscitated friend [1] suggested. He seemed to vanish in the crowd, which was beginning to tire a pregnant woman, and which especially exasperated the pretty aunt. (For she was still pretty, and astonishingly so, at thirty-six! She looked no more than twenty-five, because of her vivacity, her freshness, her trim waist.) . . . We left, and walked along rue des Petits-Champs, the Place des Victoires, rue des Vieux-Augustins, the Passage du Saumon, rue Tire-boudin, rue du Petit-Lion, rue aux Ours; and from there into the Marais, by rue Grenier-Saint-Lazare.

I told Mme. de M*** privately that Du Hameauneuf was awaiting me and that we had a plan. I described the beauty I had just seen. . . . The Marquise sent me away, so that I would return the sooner. I made my way back in an instant; it was as though I had recovered my old agility.

I did not find Du Hameauneuf, but I watched the scene as I waited for him. I saw a good deal of turmoil. Native Parisians are orderly enough. But the recent arrivals from the provinces—that is to say, within six months—have only a partial knowledge of the city; they abuse its vastness, its complexity, of which they have an exaggerated notion. It is almost always they who create the indecent disturbances; the most unruly of them, who come from the southeast, did their apprenticeship in the Yonne and the Seine passenger-barges. True, the troublesome native elements join them. But it is always a half-Parisian who starts. When a person has resided for some time in Paris, he feels less immune. He knows he is not invisible here, and that he might well be noticed. There is a man who takes the astonishing liberty of lightly tapping every woman he encounters, holding his hands behind his back. Paris is enormous; he walks all its streets, and there is not a child past crawling who does not know him, and hoot after him. All the women, all the girls avoid him, and he is known by a name that denotes his actions. (By what singular paths one sometimes achieves celebrity!) I am sure that when that man began to acquire his habit he never believed he would be noticed. I suppose even now he does not imagine how notorious he is! This is a fact which should be made known to the ex-provincials—that not everything is secret in Paris—in order to keep them within the bounds of discretion. . . .

I was saying that the rascals were causing disturbances under the small galleries. They surrounded certain women, perhaps wantons; in so doing they caused knots of congestion serious enough to burst into some shops. It became necessary to call for help. The sneak thieves, who appear everywhere, took advantage of the crush, and added to it. Some persons were injured, nearly smothered. . . . This disorder occurred only once, thanks to the wise police system which the princely proprietor succeeded in establishing. Otherwise, the Palais-Royal would have become the dread of all decent people. I have indicated the chief movers of this sort of mob: they are ex-provincials and (especially) young, very young officers, just out of school, who bring all their disruptive energy into the midst of freedom.

. . . .

❦ 95 ❦

FIGARO[1]

I was going out at five o'clock; Du Hameauneuf accosted me, breathless.

"Do you know what play they're giving? Have you seen the bill?"

"No."

"*Figaro!* It's *Figaro!*" . . .

"Ah, I am curious to see the crowd! The author did me a great service once; since then, I feel strong gratitude and love for him."

"I don't like him."

"That's your loss! To hate a man of merit is one's own loss. But perhaps you'll like his play—shall we go?"

"Let's go! . . . Let's go! . . . That's easy enough to say! Everyone is wild with excitement, all of Paris is at the theater entrance! I have two tickets. But I'm sure we won't find places."

We hurried off. (. . .) Never had I seen such confusion! I felt as though we were back in Molière's time, at the first performance of *Tartuffe*. (. . .)

The play began. I tried to listen and follow it. I shall not give a cold analysis of it. All its men are unimportant, Figaro excepted; Almaviva has only one scene. But Contat, Olivier and the younger Sainval are delightful in it. The story unfolds not with art, but with *nature*; only Figaro makes some superfluous remarks, but those too are natural. I was enraptured by the little page. The Countess seemed to me to be a susceptible but worthy woman, who feels, almost without realizing it, a tender inclination which she represses as soon as it is fully grown. How appealing the young page is, with Olivier's fine blond hair and bewitching face! . . . (Ah, modest Olivier, you are no more! Lovely girl, you refused to give up your art, when relentless death approached! Yes, why give it up? You were the nobler for it! In virtuous plays you made virtue beloved, and you rebuked the licentious pieces by the sweetness of your angelic face and the modesty of your performance. It would have been a crime if you had given up your art!) At the page's love song I was so moved that tears were streaming down my face. It was one of the most exquisite moments I have ever known in the theater! . . . But Contat—what freshness, what ease! All the graces of her sex, all its delicacy bent to the service of each word, each gesture. . . . And all that was said did not keep a single spectator from the play. People went to see the most delightful things there are—Olivier, Contat, the noble and fascinating Sainval, a hundred times more fascinating in this play than in any of the tragedies she enlivens by her beguiling, enchanting talent. . . . The scene where the page is locked in the closet, and leaps from the window, with Susanna slipping into his place, is the strongest anywhere in our theater! It is such a real situation that it surpasses those of tragedy in terror. The viewer is caught up, seduced; despite himself he sides against the deceived husband—I would say against morality itself, if the Countess were guilty. But she is not. It is a start toward indiscretion, a very pardonable start, but of a nature that only makes her the more pleasing and more intriguing.

This play was so absurdly criticized, yet how well

its fluctuations describe that of the human heart! Consider that lover-husband, so tender in *The Barber of Seville*—he has become like any other husband! And that loving mistress, for a while a happy wife—neglected now! Her love lessens; it is close to flickering out; it no longer protects her from a secret infatuation with a young page, an inclination motivated by the most honorable interest, a kind of compassion and maternal feeling! What a vigorous and skillful lesson! You accursed critics, more inimical to morality than to the author—you would have wished the play to be immoral! You have slandered it, you have had the slander broadcast by your shortsighted little pamphleteers, who have usurped power, by what means I do not know. What was your motive? The truth is that you would be in despair, you vile corruptors, vile bachelors, if women were to learn a lesson from the morality of the Countess's whole role! You cried immorality, because you would have delighted in persuading the public that the government authorizes immoral plays and that, consequently, adultery and its acolytes are no great evil! . . .

But what enraptured me, what made me cherish the author, was the dénouement, where I saw the Countess cured of her secret passion by another passion that reveals its power to her—by jealousy! I was totally satisfied, and from that moment I foresaw the play's extraordinary success, as well as the corruptors' frenzy and the rage of personal enemies. . . . Does there exist a fortunate man who has no enemies? And what if he is a man of letters besides, and if he has extraordinary successes? To my mind, what is astonishing is not that the author and the play of *Figaro* should be calumniated, but that the man should not be murdered, or else accused of murder, of poisoning, haled before the courts, condemned, executed as he watches his play burned at the foot of the scaffold. His success

is great enough, his views lofty enough, beautiful
enough, to merit all of that. (. . .)

✤ 96 ✤

THE SLASHED SLIPPERS

To what we have just said we may add a singular
phenomenon, similar to slashed gowns! On one of the
Pont Henri sidewalks, on my way to the *Français*, I
had noticed what seemed to be a schoolboy who
dropped to the ground whenever a lady approached—
I did not understand for what purpose. Then I heard a
young lady cry out, but I assumed it was some coarse
trick, and I did not stop to ask.

That evening, as we set out for Mme. de M***'s, I
saw the young lady again in a milliner's shop, at the
beginning of the Quai Pelletier. I told Du Hameauneuf,
and we entered. I asked the reason for the cry she had
uttered on the Pont Neuf.

"A scamp slashed my brand-new shoes with a
pocketknife! . . . As this is the second time in a year,
I realized what he was doing when I felt him touch
me; I cried out, and he ran off."

"It is a new kind of mischief," a pretty bystander
said, "they cut them with a pocketknife, and I was
nearly crippled by it six months ago! People should be
warned of this outlandish mania."

97

THEATER. JUSTICE

. . . .

"Today, Your Honor,[1] I am going to tell you certain
harsh truths! You have theater. But what an array!
For the upper class you have handsome, meaningless
tragedies—fine incests; excellent murders, like that of
an old woman by a priest for his grandson's sake;[2]
splendid parricides in the name of religion; exemplary
duels with the father of one's mistress; the butchering
of a mistress by her jealous lover; blood served up in a
cup; a heart presented in a bowl; and other, equally
nice things! . . . You have sweet comedies—in which
a nephew kicks his old uncle; in which someone makes
up a fraudulent will; where the demure reticence of
maidens and wives is held up to ridicule; where everything that you would desire for your own home is publicly disavowed, and where the paragons set before you
and even extolled are loose women and sly lackeys, dis-
respectful sons who deceive and scorn their fathers, and
so on. This is how your upper class is nourished, enter-
tained, *exampled* (allow me the expression)! Worst of
all, you amuse them with scurrilous operettas, which
you term good taste; with love songs which, contradict-
ing nature and the action as they do, rob you of the
meager degree of naturalness remaining to you! You
have instructive dramas as well. But, as might be expected, they are disdained, held in contempt; your upper class abandons them to your middle class; and to
ensure that this latter will not fully profit from them,

the former locks up its boxes, which it books by the year, taking great care to keep them empty; or, if they do go, that class takes vengeance on the play, on morality, and on the author, by raising a shameful racket! So much for your upper class. It is simple to see, Your Honor, what these people get out of your theater. Clearly it damages them as well as your middle class, which attends the large theaters.

"Will it find salvation, that middle class, by visiting the smaller theaters? Ah, you have seen to that, Your Honor! At the Variétés:[3] follies, *Jeannots, Gilles Ravisseurs, Ramoneurs princes*; at the Petits Beaujolais,[4] children whose innocence is profaned as it was once at the Ambigu-Comique;[5] inanities or filthy jests, at Audinot's;[6] at Nicolet's, platitudes, cheap tricks and squalid disorder! This is the fare you offer to your lower class—to those who, as the foundation of your society, should in your own interest find only decency in the theater. This little item of entertainment demonstrates how illogical you are, Your Honor! . . . But, since you have already been taken to task about it, I shall go on to other points.

"Your laws set forth, Your Honor, that adultery is a crime, and that divorce shall never be allowed you. Adultery is a crime, and you do not permit the victim to leave the guilty woman! Have you considered, Your Honor? Is your goal then to let the adulterer poison the person he or she has deceived? What! You mean that a good man shall go on living with a trollop he loathes? Well then, you have lost every vestige of morality! It is best for the children. . . . What is best for the children is that a criminal mother, a mother who is a bad example, not sully the earliest impressions of childhood, and that, if she has done so, she should be punished for it by denial of the rights of motherhood! Do relieve the decent man of that unworthy wife! Do relieve that virtuous woman of that debauched and dis-

solute libertine! If possible, let him or her find another mother, another father for the children, for they
should remain with the honest husband, the honest
mother. You are very blind, very cruel, very unreason-
able, Your Honor, to forge absolute and indissoluble
chains for depraved people, and to prevent them from
turning over in their pallets that are hard and infested
with devouring insects! Allow me that repellent image;
here is a more cheerful one.

"I find you in the Palais-Royal, joyful, lighthearted,
frivolous, tripping toward seduction. Judging from your
manner, I would think you are free; I must confess that
I would assume you have the right to choose a new
companion for yourself every day, and that you have
come to market. How gallant you are! What risk you
take! How easily you succumb to it! This is a garden
of delight, where you forget your laws, your obligations,
your religion, your family—as son, as husband, as
father! Here you think of nothing but the present. The
disturbing future vanishes; you are a happy throng.
. . . But the gnawing worm is in your soul!

"What is this I see? The courtrooms of the Palais
de Justice, where an eager mob of fools rushes to lay
its puerile quarrels before grave magistrates who cannot help laughing at them! There stands Crime in
chains to await its sentence, and receives it in a fashion
to make Innocence shudder! Next to the camps and
the battlefields, it is here, Your Honor, that you are
maddest! Like a gang of schoolboys telling tales on one
another, squabbling over poppycock, trash, nonsense!
Dishonesty, malice, spite reign on every face and in
every heart. Men in robes—real public enemies—lend
their cunning to this depravity and laugh at the madness of the antagonists. . . . Ah, who will rid you of
your attorneys, your lawyers, and even some of your
judges?" (. . .)

98

THE BALLOONS

A sublime invention has recently brought honor to the age of Louis XVI, this age forever memorable for the wisdom of its reforms: it is the invention of the aerostatic balloon. What great usefulness it could have, despite its detractors, if instead of abandoning it to charlatans the original inventors, MM. Mongolfier,[1] or its perfecting experts, MM. Charles[2] and Robert, had condescended to seek ways to utilize it—for investigating what occurs above the clouds, or for controlling hail and ravaging storms; or for climbing high enough, though still bound to the earth, to observe the stars in absolutely clear air! What an observatory for Hertschel,[3] Cassini,[4] or Lalande![5] But these regrets are academic! Charlatanism is making inroads on this fine invention and usurping its honor by puerile and purposeless ascensions! Indeed, Lunardia was met with contempt in London. As for the French aeronaut, after bringing derision upon himself by announcing his flying ship (which, incidentally, is not his own invention; M. Humblot,[6] M. Diderot's cousin, diverted himself with that notion on sleepless nights, and discussed it with everyone); after being prompted by the flying man in *La Découverte Australe,* M. Blanchard[7] leaped upon the fine invention of the Mongolfier brothers; he appropriated the ingenious method of MM. Charles and Robert, and without any genius of his own, supported by his audacity alone, he is left the unchallenged usurper of aeronautics! And you, unlucky Pilâtre,[8] you have perished, with your intelligence! How true it is that Fortune is blinder still than Love!

As we turned homeward we noticed a balloon moving among the clouds over Paris. It was not M. Blanchard; that fame-seeking man goes up only by day. The aeronauts seemed to try to observe the moon by a clear sky and a calm night; that's what we saw, or at least what we believed we saw. The balloon rose higher then, having lightened its weight by a few stones which fell into the Seine between the Pont Henri and the Pont au Change.

🕉 99 🕉

THE LITTLE PEASANT GIRL DECEIVED

At the close of the day, Du Hameauneuf and I were passing from rue Bailleul into rue Saint-Honoré, when we noticed a young peasant girl of about sixteen, her skin tanned by the open air. She was walking alongside a young woman in white, quite coquettishly dressed—and very provocative. We took the latter for a seamstress. The two girls looked at us and went in directly, waiting for us near the foot of the stairs. We no longer doubted what they were, and approached them. Without uttering a word, the girl in white went up, pushing the peasant girl before her. Once inside the apartment, we found the white-clad girl alone, and asked what she was doing with her young friend. "You will see," she answered, "let's have an écu from each of you." We gave her the sum she asked for. At this, she opened a slot into which was fixed a concave glass

through which we could see the little peasant girl . . .
totally naked, and about the size of the caryatids on
the Louvre entablature. I will admit it: during the
nearly twenty years I had been exploring Paris, I had
never before seen that kind of prostitution; it was a
novel thing for me. We looked at the young procuress
and asked her how she had devised this manner of making money. She replied that she was a spectacle-maker's
daughter, that at first she had exhibited herself, but not
having been prudent, she had to find someone who
was. We didn't say a word, but asked to speak to the
peasant girl. The girl in white had her get dressed and
led her to us. We questioned her, and discovered, with
a gentleman's joy, that she was innocent, misled, and
completely ignorant of what was going on. Despite her
protests, we took her away without bothering to explain. It had to be done, and Du Hameauneuf carried
her off like a feather, after intimidating her friend in
white.

🎇 100 🎇

THE WAGONLOAD OF PROSTITUTES

. . . .

"I have been to watch the trials of the prostitutes arrested and sent to Saint-Martin. When I arrived, I saw
great confusion; some were weeping, others were laughing and fooling around. All the informers sat on
benches along the two sides; the girls flung insults at
them. Behind the women were the men. None of the
latter was behaving brazenly; brazenness is the trademark of the corrupt woman, because women do not

have the common sense that the superior sex has.
When the magistrate appeared a deep silence fell; all
those wretched women were decorous and respectful.
But my friend, what a spectacle! Our practices are too
degrading to humanity! I shuddered! . . . A single
word, pronounced upon the mere testimony of a
commissioner both judge and plaintiff, determined the
fate of a hapless girl, for whom the Hôpital is an irreparable disaster! Ah, why the Hôpital? What can
be the meaning of such an inhuman procedure?
Remedy—remedy and do not punish! Are they tigers
who made our laws, then?"

"My friend," I broke in, "I too feel as you do."

.   .   .   .

We passed before the horrible building on rue
Pavée, and we scrutinized it. What a mass of stone!
What a terrifying door! We did not disapprove of providing prisons with such hideous entrances; they may
act as a deterrent factor. . . . But those subterranean
cells, which we had seen excavated beforehand—what
good are they? Then Du Hameauneuf said, "It was by
no idle chance that I yielded to the curiosity of the
Marquise and her little society. I wanted to go out for
the night. Let's cross to the Île Saint-Louis; we'll wait
for the wagon of girls condemned to detention yesterday. . . ."

I do not seek out horrors, but as I had never
yet witnessed this sorry spectacle, I agreed. We circled the island, taking note of my dates which were
beginning to be legible; then we took up a position at
the end of the Pont de la Tournelle. The poor women
were not long in coming. The crude onlookers, the
bargemen especially, shouted insults at them, to
which the brazen girls replied; while others, half fainting, died of shame and misery. One especially, pretty
and young, seemed nearly dead. We asked about her.
. . . She had been played a cruel trick! . . . That is

not punishing crime; that is not reforming; it is degrading the human species, to condemn it to infamy before the crime!

🎆 101 🎆

THE *JOURNAL DE PARIS*

In the evenings at the Marquise's we usually read the newspapers. These are the ones to which she subscribed: The *Mercure*, the *Journal de Paris*, the *Petites affiches*, the *Affiches de province*, the *Journal de physique*, the *Année littéraire*, the *Lunes du Cousin Jacques*, the *Ami des enfants*, the *Feuille de Normandie*, and the *Affiches de Guyenne*. Tonight I will only discuss the *Journal de Paris*. Du Hameauneuf told us of its origin in these words:

"In 1775 or 1776, a M. du Rosoi, author of *Henry IV*, a lyric drama which had forty performances at the old Théâtre des Italiens, published a *Gazetin de Paris* which had no success at all. There you have the father of the *Journal de Paris*. It's like seeing a good peasant whose son has become Minister of State. The progeny was born in 1777, several months after the death of its father. As for its mother, she is still around and in good health; she is my neighbor and seems to be doing well; she is the head of a littérateur who frequently visited the printer of the poor *Gazetin*. The grandfather of the paper is English, though I don't know his name, for it is claimed that several London papers gave M. du Rosoi the idea for his *Gazetin*. The origin, then, is foreign, and the birth is not noble— which doesn't prevent hizzonor-monsieur le *Journal de*

Paris from being a great nobleman." We laughed a bit at the Marquise's over this storytelling manner which was peculiar to Du Hameauneuf.

"The *Journal de Paris*," he resumed apropos of an article which he had just read, "is very useful and could be even more so if it had an industrious contributor who would turn up worthwhile news, but as it is now, it contents itself with whatever comes its way. Certainly the task is easier this way and brings in no less, for even as it is, it arouses a daily curiosity; but it should be possible for diligence never to run idle. The government might draw an inconceivable advantage from this paper by arranging it better than it does. I would like to see a column on the second or third page regularly devoted to short reports on debates within the government; I would like the book announcements to be purely expository, with these words: 'In three months we will give the public's reaction to this work.' This should be done without fail, for it is easily enough accomplished. I would like the article on entertainment to occupy only the last page, and its useless filler cut back on the occasion of a new play; care should be taken not to print the endless number of insignificant letters which stuffs the paper when there are so many important things to be said! The *Journal de Paris* should report all the public events of the previous day: such-and-such a case tried—civil as well as criminal—without an analysis; such-and-such a meeting, at the lecture hall or the clubs, or even the Freemasons; every accident, without exception—it is easy enough to learn of them, and the *Journal* brings in enough to go to that expense.

"What use is the half-page devoted to title? '*Journal de Paris*' in small type and the meteorological observations reduced to the smallest possible space—all that need take but an inch. I would like to see this important paper keep a tight rein on lawyers, solicitors, notaries, bailiffs, professors, merchants—even more exalted personages—by reporting their misdeeds without mentioning their names, up to the third offense when it would be required to do so."

❦ 102 ❦

PASSENGER-BARGE INCIDENT

We left when Du Hameauneuf had finished. Reaching a point across from the Porte Saint-Bernard, the new station for the arrival and departure of water-coaches,[1] we were puzzled to see a crowd. They were awaiting the arrival of a passenger-barge, and those who had relatives or friends aboard the vessel were greatly distraught! Unfortunately there was good reason! It was learned, through a man who came by stagecoach, that an Algerian who had boarded the barge at Auxerre had been insulted by two brash soldiers, and by some other fools. He had at first ignored them, but after a mocking word against Mohammed had been uttered in the course of the evening, this fanatical wretch, who resembled all the rest of them, had resolved to take vengeance and to die a martyr. He waited his chance, extinguished the only lamp in the common room, and armed with the *Gouvernailleur's*[2] axe he struck about in the darkness, in the belief that as he did not see his victims, he could be considered to have aimed at no particular person, and would thus be innocent of the crime of murder. He spared no one but the wet nurse, proof that he was not insane, as is claimed by the very eloquent concessionaire of the coach in his clumsy letter (published, number *** of the *Journal de Paris*). The constabulary, called to the rescue, stopped him only by firing some pistol shots, one of which shattered his jaw. He died of this shot, at Sens in Champagne.

We were aware of how inadequately the passenger-barges are policed! We had seen terrible things on them ourselves, among others the incident of that poor girl who was tarred by unruly youths from Joigny, not over her whole body but, hideous act! on that part which distinguishes her from us. . . .

Thus we were not astonished by that catastrophe, in an age when the insolence of youth has grown to an intolerable level, and goes so far that soon it will be impossible to go to the theater, perhaps even to walk in the streets, without being subjected to some outrage! . . . What have we come to? But I foretold this dire effect when I saw J.-Jacques' *Émile* being misused.

However, I did not think it would come so soon.

❧ 103 ❧

TUMULTS— OUTBURSTS

"What a century ours is! What an age we are born in!" exclaimed Du Hameauneuf as he entered my house. "The children are leading men; hooligans, clerks, apprentice jewelers and clockmakers are usurping the nation's name and covering it with their filth, with their spite! . . . Oh, J.-J. R., I warned you of this! The Parlement,[1] wiser than all our *philosophes*,[2] than all our devotees, condemned your *Émile*. The reason for their action was not appreciated; there was an outcry, and I believe that they were finally made to blush over it! And yet they were right! It is *Émile* that has brought us this arrogant generation, stubborn, insolent, impudent, willful, which speaks loudly, silences the elderly, and demonstrates with equal audacity first its native foolishness reinforced by upbringing and then its unripe understanding, bitter and sharp as mid-August wine.

"It isn't, oh, J.-Jacques, that your principles are bad; only that they are susceptible of abuse, and that is what the wise heads of the Parlement feared. I have seen since 1763 how the women readers of *Émile* have raised their unruly progeny! Most mothers had been giving their children to wet nurses. That was contrary to nature; but it is even more so that certain mothers should themselves nurse, and J.-J. did not say so; this omission has killed thousands of infants! . . . People determined to overthrow all the traditional practices, because some of them were wrong! Babies had been swaddled, wrapped in hard forms that cracked their ribs; girls, especially, were kept pomaded and coiffed; they were held to immobility and silence. That was wrong. J.-J. stated it strongly, because you must move your audience if you want to be heard. What was the result among the Parisians, and among those in the provinces who styled themselves *philosophes?* They left their infants stark naked; they washed them in the river, in the midst of winter (I have seen it all); they put them in a loose sack, instead of supporting the waist gently with flexible corsets like the ones on rue des Bourdonnais. Their hair flies free now in hideous, disgusting fashion. They are no longer restrained, instead they climb all over you with their filthy feet. When you visit their parents they make noise enough to deafen you, and at the very moment when their father or mother is on the point of answering some important question of yours they choose instead to satisfy some childish query from their dear son or their darling daughter. It is fifteen or twenty years now since this style of upbringing, supposedly patterned after J.-J. (for *Émile* was only the incidental cause and not the beginning), came to Paris; and we can see its effects already! . . . Come, come with me, my friend, let me show them to you!"

"What in the world has happened?" I asked him.

"You saw nothing this morning; you stayed in your room. But come with me."

I followed him, and we walked to the Palais.

From the Pont Saint-Michel I heard some noise. "What is it?" I asked Du Hameauneuf. But he did not answer. As I watched I caught sight of a young man fleeing along the Quai des Orfèvres, with the whole horde of locksmiths', jewelers' and clockmakers' boys in pursuit. They overtook him on the quay. "Ah, gentlemen, what do you want with me? I am a plain citizen, I came to watch like you did. . . ." He was given no time to say more. A police clerk who bore him a grudge had chalked the terrible sign on his clothing. He was assaulted; he was thrown to the ground. Du Hameauneuf and I mingled with the mob and we were fortunate enough to save the poor man, insulting him all the while. We gave him the word under our breath, and, struggling, he came along with us.

We went through the halls of the Palais de Justice. There was another incident. A chalk-marked woman was undergoing a cruel whipping by the clerks. Again, we succeeded in freeing her. The poor woman was exhausted. But as soon as she understood that she could leave she regained all her strength. There is nothing like terror to set a pace. . . . Finally the late hour sent everyone away. We visited the Marquise, and we delighted again in the sight of her. . . . Alas! we did not know that this joy was soon to be denied us!

We told her what we had just seen. She moaned at

the tale, and her sincere sorrow intensified our own. We spoke of nothing else.

Du Hameauneuf returned to the Palais. All was calm. Youngsters and thieves alone had caused the rioting; the men had taken no part in it. I would not speak of these troubled days, except that I want to vindicate the nation.

I told the Marquise, "It's those fifteen- to twenty-year-old adolescents raised according to J.-J. who do all the harm. Oh, people of France, return to your old stern ways, and change only the abuses!"

. . . .

✤ 104 ✤

THE POLITICAL CLUBHOUSE

. . . .

My steps turned toward the Palais-Royal. Everything there was distasteful. I was opposite the Caveau,[1] when Du Hameauneuf emerged from it.

"My friend," he said to me, "step into this den for a moment, this sanctum of speculation. You shall see men you have never come to know because you have always avoided them."

"Others besides myself have described them," I replied. "Why do something after others have done it, and do it less well?"

"Come in anyway. Should Rembrandt refuse to paint simply because Raphael and Rubens had painted? Come, come!"

So I went in. I saw one side of the room filled with men talking in low voices, scheming, and looking absorbed. In another part, I noticed some men observing them, but acting as if they did not see or hear anything.

"Here are the spies," Du Hameauneuf told me, "there, the speculators."

"But those men don't speak up!" I told my friend. "I won't hear anything!"

He approached one of them. "Explain the mystery of speculation a bit for the Nocturnal Spectator!"

"Gladly; I have given it up myself. It's a game as mad as it is ruinous. Shrewd dealing can turn a profit, but there is no solid foundation. The system here is different from England's, where the brokers take advantage of true or false public reports to send the stocks higher. That is what their speculation amounts to; but those stocks have a fixed, real value besides, and the buyer is not subjected to the ruthless snares which are all the French speculators deal in. The latter engage in despicable manipulations to corner all the shares of a venture, after having run them down. They buy them at a low price, and meanwhile they make sales to be payable in these same stocks that have already been cornered, but are not yet scarce. When payment is due, the shares are no longer to be found. The speculator demands them nonetheless and forces settlement to his advantage.

"The capitalist authors of these schemes are a gang of bandits in mutual agreement for mutual assistance, and they bring swift ruin on the banker and the tradesman who dare to take them on. With that in mind, you may consider the legitimacy of the enormous profits made by certain persons! Scandalous profits, which are more outright robbery than a game. Armed robbery is less dangerous; you can at least defend yourself. Add to this the fact that this wretched activity is totally unproductive; it does nothing but shift the wealth. . . . Look at all these men so shamefully occupied! They are busy with something insignificant which they themselves have given all its value. They are like those players at lansquenet,[2] or faro or brelan, who stake their whole way of life on a card. . . . The government will no longer tolerate them. . . ." I had learned enough. (. . .)

❧ 105 ❧

THE IRREPARABLE LOSS[1]

The Marquise had been indisposed for a few days, but we had felt no anxiety. As I went out I saw Du Hameauneuf approach and noticed how sad he looked. He grasped my hand and sighed. "My friend," I said to him, "has something dreadful happened in your home, and must we be alike in everything?"

"We are indeed unfortunate!" he replied. . . . "I must warn you or you would be too shocked. . . . She is dying!"

"Who? Who is dying?"

"That beloved woman. . . ."

"Your wife?"

"The Marquise."

"The Marquise! . . ." And I collapsed. What a hideous blow—I thought I would lose my mind! . . . My friend would be no more, my protectress—the one it was essential that I not survive! . . . I was prostrate! . . . Du Hameauneuf spoke to me, and did what he could for me. I could not hear him, I could not see him! . . . I was not prepared for this cruel moment! I had sometimes thought about it, and trembled! But I was not expecting it when it actually happened! . . . Suddenly, I came back to myself; I rose. "Hurry, let us hurry, my friend!" I said to Du Hameauneuf. We left.

At Mme. de M***'s door, I knocked and the chambermaid and Zéfirette, both in tears, opened for us, followed by the Demerup girls. . . .

"She is asking for you! Come in! . . ."

I was brought to her bedside. She was pale; in place of her fine coloring was a deathly lividness! "My friend," murmured the woman I worshiped, "stand here by me! . . . It gives me some consolation to see you again. . . . My life will soon be over! . . . Ah! I shall miss you . . . and all those beloved creatures you have given me! They were my children!" She could say no more; her face contracted; it ceased to be beautiful. . . . Émilie de G*** could not cease to be beautiful except by ceasing to live. . . . Zéfirette, who had been supporting her as she spoke to me, uttered a shrill cry. Élise, Félicité and all the others were in despair; Du Hameauneuf raised his tearful eyes to heaven. . . . And I, for the second time in my life,[2] I saw myself robbed of my soul's soul! . . . Oh, women! Without you I am nothing! . . . From the instant the Marquise had expired, I became nothing again! I had neither repute nor strength nor value now! Ah, what a moment to have lost her! At the moment when her great influence was vital to me, against the vilest of men! [3]

Sorrow choked me. . . . The young marquis and marquise would have to be informed, and from the moment they arrived we would become nothing! . . . From that moment we would never again see the Marquise—we who were willing to give up our own days to call her back to life! The house would be closed to us forever! . . . The little society gave way to despair, especially Zéfirette. . . . I postponed sending word to the children. We stayed with the Marquise, trying to revive her. . . . Alas, it was all in vain! The mortal stroke had been dealt! . . . But because it was a stroke, we waited, sparing no effort. One moment, a single moment set a ray of hope shining, only to banish it forever. It was six o'clock in the morning when we saw a movement. We started up, all of us, and cried out, except for Zéfirette, who had just fainted and let go of the Marquise, whom she had been holding. The rumor running through the house that Mme. de M*** was still breathing emboldened me to put off the disclosure, and it was seven o'clock in the evening before I sent a messenger to the marquis. I hoped in this way almost to double the interval between the death and the burial. . . . The marquis and the young marquise arrived at eight. Mme. de M***'s daughter was in tears. She fell to her knees at her mother's bedside and asked pardon for her wrongs. In our presence she asked an account of all the remedies we had already attempted without avail. The whole body was rubbed with soft, warm linen cloths; fresh air was breathed into her, and so forth.

The will was then sent for. The young marquise had it read aloud. There were provisions for all the women of the little society, especially for Zéfirette, Rosalie, Félicité, Sophie, and the layette-maker.[4] For Du Hameauneuf and me there were such touching thanks that I was overwhelmed. They read:

Art. XX. I thank M. du Hameauneuf for his good kindness toward me and mine, and especially for his attachment to Monsieur Nicolas; I leave him my diamond ring so that he may let his wife wear it, and so that they may both remember me.

Art. XXI. And as for Monsieur Nicolas, to whom I owe the days of life he restored to me and all the happiness I have enjoyed for the past twenty years, I know neither words nor deeds which could express *my gratitude and my heartfelt friendship. I know that he is not happy, and that if I precede him I shall leave him in deep sorrow and, worse still, deprived of his truest friend. To discharge my debt and to avoid certain difficulties, which I shall not mention, I bequeath to him the small estate of **, purchased with my savings since my widowhood, if he will accept it. I make this bequest against his will; he refused the estate during my lifetime.*

"And I shall not accept it from any hand other than hers!" I exclaimed. . . . "Monsieur," I said to the notary who was reading, "write that I would accept if Monsieur le marquis and Madame la marquise had no children, but since they have four, I cannot in good conscience do so. . . . As to the other bequests," I added, "they must stand; all these unfortunate women would be without shelter, without resource, and I request that Monsieur le marquis and Madame la marquise give their assent here and now."

They did so with good grace, especially the lady, and the notary wrote at the bottom: *Accepted.*

"Let us say farewell to our mother, to our image of divinity!" I exclaimed. Everyone dropped to his knees. It was ten o'clock in the evening then. No one had eaten or rested for twenty-four hours; Zéfirette, Rosalie, the layette-maker and Félicité were faint. I made the whole company take some chocolate prepared by the chambermaid. That fine girl asked the whole little society to remain at the house till the day after next. But I noticed that the marquis made a gesture of disapproval. Therefore I pronounced the farewells. "Heavenly woman! You are no longer with us! You have gone to the bosom of the Lord, your father and ours, whose gift you were! Adieu, divine Émilie! Your children and your friends bid you farewell! We shall never see you more! But we shall carry your image in our hearts to the grave!"

. . . .

I went out with Du Hameauneuf, who had said nothing since the Marquise died. On the threshold my knees folded, and my heart faltered. My friend supported me. . . . I still had a friend! . . . I turned around; I ran to the Marquise, and I kissed her icy hand . . . for the last time! . . .

We went to arrange lodgings for the society. With the concurrence of his wife and her aunt, Du Hameauneuf returned to offer them a welcome in his own home immediately. But they refused. For these poor women were reluctant to leave the apartment as long as the Marquise's body was there.

"We shall follow her," they said, "but we shall not leave her first!"

A servant of the marquis made an unpleasant remark to Félicité, and she answered him, "Look at her! She is still the mistress here, and as long as she remains, I shall be here too!" And she ran to throw herself into the arms of her protectress. . . . Oh! If she could only have revived her! . . .

I went home, half dead, at midnight.

Fortune-blest nights! Happy era of my strength, you are no more! All the other losses could mend, could be forgotten—the Marquise made them unimportant— but her own shall be felt until my last sigh, which it will hasten! . . .

THE PLACE DAUPHINE

Happy the minister whose appointment to the ministry rouses universal rejoicing! A curse on the people, who always believe that the outgoing man is reprehensible! [1] . . . It was a Friday evening. I was on my way to the leading actor with a play which will perhaps have failed when this piece appears. I was filled with anxiety, deeply absorbed in the loss of the Marquise, in Du Hameauneuf's illness and in my private affairs. I saw illuminations on the Quai des Orfèvres; I knew the reason for them, and was greatly pleased. I continued, with my eyes turned to the right, when a chicken vendor's coop fell upon my head. "Have you nearly finished?" I asked goodnaturedly of a boy about twelve or thirteen years old.

"We haven't started yet!" he retorted. I went on, although I was somewhat tempted to punish him. But at that very moment I saw four big rascals seize an enormous coop and carry it like a shrine to a bonfire burning in the Place Dauphine. Others imitated them. When I reached the guardhouse I saw that the soldiers were disarmed and scattered. I was astonished! But I did not know whom to notify. A tall young man spoke of setting fire to the guardhouse. I took up his words, saying, "Only scoundrels could destroy the quarters of the men charged with watching over the citizens' safety!" The young man retreated at that. I saw the rifles tossed into the fire blazing in the middle of the Place Dauphine. I saw a jeweler maltreated for refusing to light up; I saw stones flung through his windows. I went on. I crossed the Palais-Royal,[2] where firecrackers resounded.

🎋 107 🎋

THE WALKS IN THE NEW PALAIS-ROYAL

What a different sight here! While the whole city stirs with unrest, perfidious and laughing pleasure struts in a hoop skirt, elegantly coiffed, and arrayed in all the fashion and allurement of opulence! It is no longer conspicuous, as it once was, for its incongruity; it has all the harmony of propriety. I stopped a moment and contemplated this bazaar.

. . . .

I proceeded to attend to some urgent business.

When I returned I found the Palais-Royal closed; but the garden was filled with artifice. Back on the Pont Neuf, I caught sight of the guardhouse in flames! I must confess—I was stricken with sorrow at the sight of that excess. I wanted to look at those who had committed it. I saw workers, idle because there was no night employment as yet. I saw children who committed this crime as though they were doing ordinary mischief. I saw irresponsibility, foolishness, ignorance, habitual insubordination infiltrating public affairs. But I discovered neither conspiracy nor design. On the contrary, I heard cries of "*Vive Henry IV!*[1] *Vive Louis XVI!*" It was a demonstration by undisciplined youngsters. . . . I went to supper at the home of a woman worthy to soothe the pain that the Marquise's death had caused me, but I wanted to

look in at my friend's house beforehand. A step away
from his door, I was accosted by three men who insulted me. I shouted threats at them. They stopped,
and I saw that they had mistaken me for one of the
members of a guild which had been attacked some
days earlier. I dealt very harshly with them! It seemed
to me I had regained my former agility. . . . I went
in to see Du Hameauneuf. His condition alarmed me.
. . . Oh, dear friend! Am I doomed to survive all those
I love? . . .

I went on to visit Mme. la Comtesse Fanny.[2] (. . .)
We did not leave her house until five o'clock. A
young lawyer asked if he could walk with me. He
accompanied me to the Pont Neuf, where we saw the
remains of the fire. In the Place Dauphine they were
drawing the rifle barrels out of the ashes. We were
told that various guardhouses had been attacked,
among them the one at the Grève, where the soldiers
had put up a courageous defense, and where a youth
of twenty-two had just been killed.

All public unrest is evil; whoever excites it commits
the crime of "lese society." I hold in contempt those
who are pleased by it, if there are persons so lacking in
humanity as to feel that hideous sentiment. I am in
favor of subordination: it must be complete. I would
obey the magistrate, and authority even if they be
wrong, just as my arm must always obey my head. Any
resistance by its members enfeebles a body politic. To
anyone who spoke to him of the provinces which were
demanding privileges, Du Hameauneuf replied, "*They
are poor brothers if they seek relief by shifting their
burden to our shoulders! I reproach them for it. . . .*"

He said as much in regard to the guilds that
claimed exemptions. But of course Du Hameauneuf
was known to be extreme.

What sad nights these are now! . . .

O heavenly De M***, you are no more! I would

not survive you if I had not found another you in the virtuous and lovely Fanny!

108

SUPPERS WITH FANNY

Immersed in an endless grief, I was vegetating. I had not even the heart to revise this *Night*, and extol in it the memory of a woman . . . nature's masterpiece! For a good and beautiful woman is someone well above the mass of humanity! . . . How many good ones I have known! My mother . . . the good Berthier de Joux . . . Mme. Parangon . . . the good Madelon Baron . . . and a host of others.

That good Sellier woman alone, so good that she . . . gave—shall I say it?—her honor, without regret, when she believed it necessary. . . . I do not suggest that she be emulated. But in her, the aberration had a cause and a purpose, which astounded me and forced me to esteem her, to . . . adore her, that good woman whose beautiful heart purified vice itself! . . . But what to say of the Marquise? The most beautiful soul and the most refined deportment, with the loveliest body. She gave the lie to Ovid: *Lis est magna cum pudicitia formae.* Her sincerity was that of a girl of sixteen. She loved goodness and beauty of soul; she would search for it in others of her sex and she would cling to it; her little society was the evidence of that. Once her heart had been stimulated by benefactions—and she needed only to be shown the way—she made no further idle expenditures; all her self-indulgence lay in bringing solace to unfortunate women of all kinds. What a future, O my Lord!—O Supreme Origin of all beings[1]—what a future you intended for her! She is in your Paternal bosom! . . .

A month after my supreme loss, I suffered another. M. du Hameauneuf died of pneumonia on September 20, 1788.

I was prostrate for a long while, when a warm and eager friend went to great pains to revive my shattered energies. Why should I not tell his name? It was M. Mercier,[2] author of so many worthy writings.

One day he told me, "I must introduce you to a remarkable woman. She has an interesting circle of friends. You'll go there on evenings when there are few visitors." I refused. . . . Unthinkable! . . . but true friendship is insistent. I yielded.

I must confess that when I saw Countess Fanny I felt spirited back to the Marquise's presence. If Fanny's surroundings had been the same, the illusion would have been total. For this reason I was thoughtful and absent-minded. But I was not long in discerning the virtues of this divine woman! My heart opened to friendship, friendship tempered grief, and grief turned to melancholy. Oh, heavenly de M***! You have a living reflection in the delicate and sensitive Fanny! How I love to listen to her! She reminds me of everything I have worshiped in the fair sex. I am accustomed to women like her; that is why I am so content when I join in one of her suppers, where the gracious candor, the wit and the kindliness of the guests match their intellects. One meets great men without pomposity there; foreigners who make one cherish and respect their homeland. The conversation of these latter cannot help but be highly beneficial! It teaches us about a very distant nation or a neighboring one. We listen; we compare; and we come to know men.

. . . .

Here I end this long and laborious work, which will one day serve as supplement to another, under way since 1783: *Monsieur Nicolas, or the Motives of the Human Heart Unveiled.* I had at first intended to include various of its sections in the *Nights.* But apart from the fact that this would have been duplication, I found no room for those passages although I had in fact read them to the Marquise, and am rereading them at present to the Countess.

. . . .

THE
NIGHTS
OF THE
REVOLUTION

❦ 109 ❦

July 12, 1789

We went out at six o'clock in the evening, and walked toward the Pont Neuf. As we reached the Quai du Louvre, we saw a terrified mob scattering. We asked what had happened.

"M. Necker[1] has been dismissed! . . . Foulon[2] is going to take his place! . . . The troops . . . the troops are moving. The prince . . . Lambesq!" These words were all we got for answer.

Just then a tall girl, dressed like the nymphs and well shaped like them, appeared from rue de l'Arbre-Sec and demanded: "Where are those men going off to?" She was told: "They are fleeing with their wives."

"Cowards!" she cried, seizing one escapee by the collar. "Let your wife go and come back yourself!" The young man smiled. "She is my sister," he replied. "Let me take her away and I shall return armed. . . ."

Another young man, who seemed to be the nymph's lover, came and took her by the hand; he played the woman's role, and led her away. The beauty turned back though, and, still seeing men in flight, she stamped the ground in rage with her delicate foot.

What had set the frightened Parisian to flight?

Drawn outdoors by a fine sky, the hard-working townsman had taken advantage of a day of rest and gone for a breath of fresh air in the gardens Le Nôtre designed. To relieve his pretty mate, the good-natured Parisian was carrying the child. He is stronger; the thought leads him back to Nature, though it would appear to set him farther from it. Reaching the lawn around the shaded ponds, the husband and his spouse sit down to rest, while the child they had carried darts off toward other little ones at play. He romps about and brings a smile to his mother's lips.

Meanwhile, on the terrace overlooking the river, some fools are provoking the soldiers, who have gathered for no special purpose. A stone is said to have glanced off Lambesq's helmet. Outraged, the commandant[3] bristles. He lets reckless counsel sway him; he moves, on horseback, into the garden of the Kings. . . . A sacred place meant for games, for laughter, for loves, where Mars must never appear but as a statue. . . . He advances, his saber in hand. . . . Shrill cries rise. The cries of the young mothers answer them. They all leap to their feet. They seize their children. This time it is not the fathers who carry them. The terrified mothers feel them safer in maternal arms. The children weep at being snatched from their innocent play. The wives call to their husbands, to escort them. Everyone flees: the women out of fright, the husbands to free themselves of their families.

Meanwhile, Lambesq is soon aware that he has made a mistake. He tries to turn back. Some rash old man dares to close off his retreat and cries, "Pull back the swing bridge!" The hapless wretch falls under Lambesq's blows! . . . Fateful act! But he should not have entered the garden on horseback; that is a crime Lambesq can never wash his hands of.

I learned all this from the dauntless nymph. . . . I went to the Palais-Royal, where since June 7 many assemblies had gathered, where motions were passed that became the origin of the districts or the municipality. . . . I found only some rough men with burning eyes, more intent on loot than on liberty. . . . I fled.

I ran on to the Tuileries. It was completely deserted. Those merry gardens had a melancholy look that brought an involuntary cry from me: "Oh, Kings! Without subjects, what are you?" Then I meditated on the puerile attitudes of the aristocrats, who make life so difficult for the people, and I saw them as fools who grow tired of too many blessings. "Everything belongs to the nation, everything is for the nation!" I thought. And the madman who adds to humanity's torments commits the crime of "lese nation," and he is guiltier than Lambesq.

Night fell as I continued to roam. I returned to the city. I went to the Palais d'Orléans.[4] Riotous groups there were recounting in fury what had happened in the course of the day. They shouted threats, they set bounties on heads! . . . And I—I shuddered. I saw a cloud of misfortune gathering over this luckless capital, once the most voluptuous city in the universe, the freest, the most pleasant, and consequently the happiest. . . . O London! despite your pride, I defy you to compare yourself to Paris. Even under the Saint-Florentins,[5] the Sartines and the Lenoirs, Paris offered the honest man more liberty than that smoke-ridden London, where the brigand strips you clean by virtue of that liberty which defies the police! . . . For twenty-five years I have lived in Paris freer than air! Two principles sufficed to make any man as free as I: to be honest, and not to write any pamphlets against the government. Everything else was permitted, and never was my freedom hampered. It is only since the Revolution that a scoundrel has succeeded in having me arrested twice!

At eleven o'clock in the evening, weary with watching and listening, I left the Palais-Royal. But what a frightful din! Wild shouts rose from every direction. Rue des Petits-Champs was filled with armed bandits. At the risk of my life, I wanted to see them more closely. I passed by the swords and the clubs. They were battling or pretending to battle. I observed them out of the corner of my eye. Lawlessness shone in the glittering eyes of those scoundrels.

At the top of rue des Vieux-Augustins, I was nearly killed by a pistol shot. I reached Les Halles. It was the very picture of hell. "Oh, my country!" I exclaimed—for the city where we have settled, where we are husbands and fathers, is our country. "Oh, my country! You are going to perish through these bastard offspring, who will slay your legitimate children!"

I escaped, amid increasing perils, and I reached rue des Prouvaires at midnight. There I was seized by the collar.

"It's a priest!"

"No, no, my friends, I am a father and a grandfather."

"He's too old!" said another. The brute who held me shoved me down into the mire, and let me alone.

I turned into rue du Roule, or rue de l'Ancienne Monnaie. The door of an armorer was being forced. A unit of the royal guard was advancing, with beating drum and fluttering banners. They carried the rammers off with them. I was at the corner of rue Betisi. A young man stopped there; he held his young and lovely wife by the hand. He was seized by the marching troops and forced to leave her. The young wife tried to keep him there; she cried out. A rough lout pushed her away with a blow of his fist, muttering these obscene words: "*Og evohs ti, ydal.*" [6] She fainted. I caught her in my arms, and that moment made all the evening's troubles worthwhile. I brought her to with the aid of her smelling salts.

"Courage!" I told her. "Your husband will take

advantage of the first street corner to slip off and come back to you. Don't fear for him! He pretended to join them willingly. If he is too long, I shall take you to your home. Say that I am your father. I have a daughter your age."

"Ah, you are a father! Monsieur, I entrust myself to you! Take me to my own father's house." He was a silk merchant near Les Halles. We set off in that direction.

At rue Tirechape we encountered someone running swiftly as a deer. He was being pursued by two louts armed with pikes. "It's my husband!" cried the young woman. I did not reply, but concerned myself only with saving him. "Help! Help!" I shouted with all my might. The two pursuers stopped and came over to us. That was what I had wanted. I solicited their help in "carrying my daughter to our home." They agreed. They formed a stretcher of their pikes, wound two waistcoats around it, seated her on it and carried her. The young husband had seen us. Finding himself no longer pursued, his fear vanished; he turned around, followed us, and joined us in his father-in-law's house. The sight of him brought his wife back to life. . . . I left them to go home. Brigands stopped me once more at the Pont Notre-Dame. My genial manner disarmed them, and I reached my house where I could assuage my family.

Such is the sketch I have to offer of the first night of the Revolution. I describe only the things I have seen.[7]

110

July 13, 1789

During the day, the bandits from the Faubourg Saint-Marcel went by my door, on their way to join the bandits of the Faubourg Saint-Antoine. These bandits were beggars born; together with the frightful thieves of floating lumber, they made up a formidable mob which seemed to say: "Today is the last day for the rich and the comfortable; tomorrow will be our turn. Tomorrow we shall lie on the featherbed, and those we have left alive can have our gloomy attics, if they want." All the women trembled; my own thought was: "Now or never is the time to form a national militia."

I did no work. I got up in the morning, for the first time in years, and went to see the workmen and artists of my acquaintance. "Friends," I told them, "hurry to your districts. Tell them that the ordinary citizens must take up arms to save themselves from the outlaws and brutes." (. . .) Each of them went to tell a hundred others the sad news that the brigands were taking advantage of the unrest and that they planned to plunder the city during the night.

Alarmed, the good burghers immediately gathered and deliberated. Others went directly into action and joined the patrols. At ten o'clock in the evening, as I came out of the Palais-Royal, I was overjoyed to see the first bourgeois patrol. A fine tall man in a white cloak and low boots was commanding; he moved with impressive dignity. He crossed the slimy gutter at Saint-Honoré, where there was already a guardpost, and

came to identify himself, thus from the outset giving
rise to the notion of detecting spurious patrols. I
should like to know this worthy citizen, and make him
generally known. He will recognize himself by this description; it was Monday, July 13, at ten o'clock in the
evening, when I saw him with his patrol across from
the Café Militaire.

The tocsin sounded. The Palais-Royal passed motions. All was unrest and consternation. During the day
some had gone to the Invalides for muskets, and the
following day they were to go with the same demand
to the Bastille . . . the Bastille whose lofty towers
still rested upon their deep foundations, moistened by
the tears of so many poor unfortunates. Reassured by
the sight of the bourgeois patrols, I ventured to roam
the streets of the capital. I cannot say why, but I did
not fear any outside conspiracies. Only the bandits
worried me, and I could see their vigilant repressors
bearing weapons. But alas—abuse slips in with the law,
and poison is cousin to the cure. Reaching the Marais,
I heard cries. Six armed men were pursuing a young
girl who seemed to be a chambermaid. As the partridge
in flight from the hawk sometimes throws itself to the
hunter's bosom, the girl darted into my arms. I had
no weapon. They snatched her from me. "We don't
mean to do you any harm!" the head of the band told
her, "but you must open the doors. We want to know
whether the man we're after is inside the house you
were about to enter, and whether he has arms or gun-
powder."

"Alas, messieurs! I'm alone. All the servants went
off this morning with my master and mistress. I knew
I would be afraid, so I was going to spend the night
with a friend when you saw me come out. I had forgotten something and was going back for it. I saw
you; I got scared and ran back the way I had come."

"That seems plausible. Nevertheless we want to

see the house." The girl was obliged to open the door.
They told me imperiously to leave, and I was obliged
to walk on.

I did not go far; despite the danger I ran, I hid
in the shadows and listened. I heard the girl scream.
But just then I caught sight of another patrol. "Messieurs," I told this one, "a patrol has gone into that
house; I think it is a false one, and what confirms my
suspicion is the cries of the young chambermaid they
forced to let them in. . . ." At my words the commander stepped to the door and tried to enter. A
fusilier who had been stationed there barred his way.
This resistance increased the suspicion. The patrol
forced the door. The sentinel fired into the air and
disappeared. We heard great commotion within the
house, as of people escaping through the garden. The
patrol fired on them, and they dropped what they
were carrying off. It was a false patrol of robbers, all
of them servants of neighboring houses who, on learning that the girl's employers were absent, had set
themselves up as a patrol in order to steal. They had
designated a stranger to speak to her. Finding themselves masters of the situation and presumably safe
from all interference, Josephine's beauty had tempted
them, and they decided to satisfy their lust; but she
had cried out. Their sentinel's shot warned them of
danger, and they had fled. Everything was restored to
its place. The true patrol conducted itself as became
decent citizens; the doors were properly locked, and the
girl went off to sleep with her friend.

This is only one of the many incidents that occurred during that terrible night which preceded a day
still more terrible—a day forever famous in the Annals
of France.

111

July 14, 1789

I rose late, to buy the *Tableaux de la Vie* which I was sending to Neuwied.[1] I left the house toward half past three, my head still heavy, and I set off like a drunkard toward the Pont Notre-Dame. The sky had cleared, and the bright daylight began to rouse me; I was breathing deeply, when I saw a tumultuous crowd before me. I was not surprised. I drew closer and . . . Oh, hideous sight! I saw two heads atop a pike! Horrified, I asked who they were. A butcher told me, "They are the heads of Flesselles[2] and Delaunai." [2] I shuddered at his words. I saw a cloud of misfortune rising over the poor capital of the French. I was misinformed, however, in part: Flesselles' head, mutilated by a pistol shot that had just put an end to his life, was rocking with the swells of the Seine. It was Delaunai and his major whom I saw abused.

I went on; a thousand voices sounded the report: "The Bastille has fallen!" I did not believe it, and I went to watch the siege. In the middle of the Grève, I found a body shorn of its head lying in the midst of the gutter. Five or six people were standing around, looking at it indifferently. I asked questions. It was the warden of the Bastille. . . .

I was thinking. . . . This man who in his time never responded to the despair of the hapless creatures buried alive under his care by despicable ministers— look at him now! . . . I went on without inquiring further; my soul was racked by too many sensations;

in its present raging turmoil it could never have absorbed any details.

Past the arcade at the Hôtel de Ville, I encountered cannibals; I saw one of them illustrate a horrible word, articulated since then: at the end of a *taillecime* (a top-chopper) he carried the bloody entrails of a victim of the furor, and that hideous bouquet did not cause a stir.

Further on, I encountered those killed, borne on stretchers; I saw five in all, including two wounded. Behind them were captured veterans and Swiss guards.[3] Young and pretty mouths—I still shudder at the memory!—were shouting after these unlucky creatures: "Hang them! Hang them!" But what disturbed me more was a big strong Swiss soldier on whose head they had put a butcher's long carrying-hood.[4] A roughneck whose full weight he supported kept tugging at it like reins; and that little beast, whom I was tempted to knock on the head, accompanied his atrocious insults with clubbings about the ankles and shins of his mount. This was not one of the victims, however; the two veterans already swung from the fateful lamppost.[5]

I had intended to watch the start of the siege of the Bastille, and it was already over; the place was taken. The rabid were flinging papers—papers invaluable to history—from the tops of the towers into the moats. A destructive spirit hovered over the city. I still see it, that fearsome Bastille—I had not had the courage to look at it when I walked every evening to rue Neuve-Saint-Gilles three years earlier; I saw it fall, with its last warden.

Oh, such reflections! I felt stifled by them, and I could scarcely untangle my thoughts. . . . I turned homeward. A sense of joy at seeing that hideous terror near its end mingled with the sense of horror that filled me. When I got back from the Grève, I made inquiries. It was then that I learned how Delaunai had been seized, and the reasons for the rage he had inspired; how the virtuous Delolme[6] perished, despite his defense by an ex-prisoner; how Delaunai, indecisive, had fallen victim to the courage of his major, who wanted to defend himself; how, in his indecision, he had ordered the drawbridge raised after having permitted entry; how someone other than himself had ordered guns turned on the people; how he had been seized by a grenadier, and on being taken to the Place de Grève for presentation to the city, a hooligan had dealt him a blow on his bald head that set his tears flowing and he cried, "I am lost!"; how this blow, with a thousand others after it, signaled his death; how his head had been cut off, at the first pile-houses near the port, and how it was borne on a pike; how he had been searched and his letters carried to the Hôtel de Ville; how they implicated the unfortunate Flesselles who was not told of the warden's death; how he had been forced to go down and how a stout strong man, calling him a traitor, blew his brains out; how the two artillery veterans had been hanged from the lamppost and then beheaded as well. . . .

I shuddered. "Oh, Lambesq," I thought, "your reckless acts have roused the darkest suspicions in the minds of the populace, and it is you who have murdered these five wretches!"

I roamed around for the rest of the evening. As I passed the Place Dauphine, I heard the drumroll. A handsomely dressed man was making a public announcement to the effect that there were tunnels in the Luxembourg that led to the Montrouge Plain. I calmed down; I felt it was a false alarm and that if there had been real news, they would not have contrived that one.

I went to the Palais-Royal. All its stalls were closed. The heads, like Medusa's, seemed to have petrified everything there. The groups in the garden no longer concerned themselves with emotions, as they had in preceding days; they spoke only of killing, of hanging, of beheading. My hair stood on end.

Suddenly a man appeared. "Gentlemen, we are in serious danger! There are only eight men at the most important post, the one at the end of the Pont Royal, and eight hundred are needed to guard the cannon. Let all good citizens show their zeal! Let them go and alert the Saint-Roch district,[7] while others go and tell the post that support is on its way!" I went to the Pont Royal.

I found, in fact, no more than eight men. I crossed the bridge and came back by the Quai des Quatre-Nations. Sentries were asking "Who goes there?" as in cities at war. False rumors kept everything at a high pitch. I went on. Here they were tearing up the pavement, to stop the cavalry. There they were stacking the church chairs into barricades over the protests of the women who rented them. Every avenue was patrolled, and sentries stationed about were challenging all the passers-by.

Such were the circumstances as I left my lodgings and set out for the Île Saint-Louis, where till that day I had never neglected to walk. In the middle of rue Saint-Louis I was interrogated. I related what I had seen, and that a moment earlier a horseman had appeared at a gallop, shouting "To arms!" An evil man caught sight of me and called to me. I gave my name and continued.

On my way home I was stopped with a great deal of sarcasm by the sentry at the head of the Pont de la Tournelle, a little man with a malicious manner, who forced me to enter the guardhouse. That would have been the end of me if the scoundrel [8] who had set a tough to do his work for him had dared to show himself!

That I had been singled out was borne out by

the fact that the sentry did not know me personally. The perfidious little man who had noticed me had described me only by my red garb, and in the guard-house I found another man in red who had been mis-taken for me. The insolent sentry, who looked to me like a river-bank fop from the Île, made some peculiar remarks to me, and wanted to search me—not im-mediately, but after he had stepped outside a moment. He had doubtless gone to consult the informer, who could see me from there. I demanded to see the officer in charge. I was taken to the sergeant, who paid me little attention. I was getting impatient. The man in red who had been taken for me was released. A small boy said a word to the sergeant, who left the room. When he returned, he was entirely different. "You re-leased the first," he said to the sentry, "I am releasing the second." The sentry seized me by the collar, say-ing, "I have information! I have information! This is the one who is a spy for the King!"

"Good heavens," I told him, "I spy on vice, but not for the King; I have never had the honor to be in direct contact with the head of the nation. How-ever," I added firmly, "the officer has set me free, sentry!" Pushing him aside: "Obey your officer!" And I succeeded in taking my leave. I repeat, it would have been the end of me if I had been taken to the Hôtel de Ville. The denunciatory monster would have sent up a cry and had me hanged from the fateful lamppost. That day no questions were asked.

But who had disposed the sergeant so kindly to-ward me? A young girl. While I was being detained, a pretty, dark-haired girl, who noticed me every day on the Île and who from her window had often seen me inscribe my dates, heard the informer counsel my ar-rest. The young lady immediately came down with her cook and managed to identify me more definitely from the outside, through the low window of the guardhouse. At that moment I was trying to set them straight. "Ah," she said, "it is that poor 'dater,' the one the children call 'Scribbler' ever since some vicious, ugly little man pointed him out to them! He is a good man. I took to following him and reading what he wrote. It is completely innocent, I assure you!" She called a little boy and sent him into the guardhouse to ask for the sergeant. The man came out, and the pretty girl spoke up on my behalf. It was this that made him change his mind.

As I went out I met her. Despite the reticence inherent in her sex, and despite the hour and the day, she approached me. "I should like to take you back to your home," she told me. "You have a cruel enemy, whom I heard denounce you. Give me your arm, I shall protect you." The sentry had returned to his post. That man was a dependent of the pretty lady's father.

"Who are you?" she asked me.

"I am the author of *Le Paysan Perverti.*"

"You? Ah, if my father were at home he would embrace you! . . . Come, Madelon! Let's take him home. I took an interest in him before I knew who he was. And you, wretch," she told the sentry, "watch your step!" We set out on our way. "I shall point you out to my father next time you come to carve your dates."

"I shall never return, mademoiselle! I cherished my island, but now it is profaned! I shall never return to it! Alas, it already was! A villain had my daughter arrested there—my daughter who was his wife by an evil twist of fortune. . . . I could not forgive my beloved island for that. And yet I loved it so dearly that I was unable to abandon it. But today, I renounce it. . . . It had me insulted by its children; I forgave it that, because its children had not yet become cruel. Now that they have, they would profane the island by hanging me from one of its sacred lampposts, which have so often shed their light on me in the silence and darkness of the night." (*Turning back and kissing the last stone of the Pont de la Tournelle.*) "Ah! my Île, my dear Île, where I have wept so many delicious tears! Farewell, I tell you—farewell forever! Every Frenchman shall be free, but I shall not. I am banished from my island! I shall never again have the freedom to stroll there, and the last pleasure of my life is forever abolished!" I had stopped. The young lady was moved. "You shall come back for our sake," she told me. "No, no! The villain who dragged my family through the slime would have me hanged before your eyes. I shall never return. . . ."

And I never did. July 14, 1789, is the last of my dates on the island. . . . Oh, July 14! It is you who, in 1751, saw me arrive in the city for the first time, as I am shown in the first engraving of *Le Paysan-Paysanne*. It is you who took me from the fields forever. And it is you who exile me from my island!" We proceeded in silence. At my house the young lady saw Marion,[9] my darling daughter, and she came to love her; she loves her still, they shall love one another until their last breath!

112

July 17, 1789

Amid the turbulence, there came a day of gaiety and joy. . . . O King! Head of the nation, in doing you honor it is herself she honors. In loving you, she gives the most powerful evidence of an encompassing brotherly love. Blessed art thou, good Louis XVI! Posterity will tell of you forever, and you are more immortal than ten kings together!

On the evening of the sixteenth, the same words were on all lips: "The King is coming to Paris! He is coming to prove to us that he holds no grudge against the capital for the taking of the Bastille!"

"Let him come, then!" cried the fanatics, "but he won't come!"

"He will come," the good citizens said calmly. (. . .) "He will come! We know the goodness of his heart."

"He will come!" cried a shrill voice. "And meanwhile, d'Artois[1] is off! He is sending the children away! The Polignacs[2] are escaping!"

"They are frightened of the hysteria! You have condemned them! Can any creature be denied the right to flee a cruel death?" (. . .)

Meanwhile Louis was preparing to come to the capital. There was great agitation at Versailles. The Queen was trembling, the princes were in flight. Only Louis girded himself with determination. The morning of the seventeenth dawned; Louis set out.

Two honorable men—Bailli,[3] the virtuous Bailli, and the young hero Lafayette[4]—had accepted the reins of municipal government, the former for civil affairs, the latter for the military. Lafayette hastened to meet the monarch. Bailli prepared the people to receive him, and brought the keys to the city; all good citizens brought him those to their hearts.

Louis arrived. Orders were given to pile ammunition around the lowered cannons along the route.

O Lafayette, blessings on you, for you only took command to serve your country worthily. You only took command to keep it from the hands of the intriguers, the perverse and the traitors.

Blessings on you, hero of the two worlds![5] And

you, Bailli, blessings on you, for you have brought humanity, knowledge, modesty and wisdom to replace the oppression, the ignorance, the impudence that pervaded the police system before you! We have all gained. But you, you have lost your tranquility, the sweet commerce of the Muses! [6] You exhaust your spirit! But what am I saying? You are expending a huge store of philosophy for the benefit of your country, and at last putting into practice what you have meditated for so long! Blessings on you!

I could not restrain that outpouring from my heart.

I shall not report what Bailli told the King; he described his people's feelings of love, for that was the general sentiment. Louis, deeply moved, replied only, "I shall always love my people!"

Cries of *Vive le roi!* had been forbidden on the monarch's arrival, but when he emerged from the Hôtel de Ville, the heart's barricades burst. *Vive le roi!* was the cry that was heard simultaneously from everyone's lips. The sound traveled from one to the next throughout the city, and those who had been detained in the most distant quarters took it up. Women and the sick flung open their windows and answered those in the street: *Vive le roi!*

There are many others who will recount what was said at court, or in the center of the city; history will lose none of it. I, the Nocturnal Spectator, go far afield to gather facts otherwise unknown. I have seen and heard what I have just reported. I have seen and heard what I have yet to tell.

Nonetheless, this fine day was to be marred by bloodstains set nearly midway between two scenes of horror. A pregnant woman was killed by the reckless shot of a musket. But at this instance the population of the capital regained its sense of humanity; they were extremely moved and swore to punish the first who dared to fire. You were nearly the victim of that vow, young Garneri—you whose name has become famous at the bottom of a hundred pamphlets. This bookseller put down his gun as he went in to dine. Instantly the crowd gathered and, spurred to new ferocity by humane feelings, it determined to hang him! Fortunately he was surrounded by friends, who added physical strength to that of reasoning. He was saved. His sweet and gentle sister, whose loveliness equals her virtue, would again be able to see her brother who had been like a father to her.

The presence of the King, like that of the beneficent sun, appeared to disperse the heavy clouds that had lain on our horizon. The storm rumbled now only at a distance. As for myself, I breathed more easily. I dared to cross my island. I looked around for the impudent sentry. My evil informer lay in hiding in the wreckage of the Bastille, from where he was soon chased off.

I was unaware that two no less terrible clouds were gathering—one at Viri,[7] the other at Compiègne[8]— which were to meet and burst over the capital.

As I crossed the island I saw the kind brunette who had saved my life. I was already on the bridge when she pointed me out to her father. They signaled to me, but I did not stop till I had reached the summit, a point which seemed to me the boundary between the island's territory and the Saint-Nicolas-du-Chardonnet district.[9] It was there that I awaited the father and daughter. They ran over to me and did their best to take me back to their house. I declined. I swore never again to return to my island. "When I was insulted for the first time," I told them, "at the instigation of that vicious character, I wrote to the magistrates: 'Beware! There is a pitch of ferment, of insubordination, which can lead to worse! Do not allow it!' The apathetic De C*** scorned to pay attention to my request, and I was affronted daily, but I had no reason to fear for my life. Today, when the shout of a child or the word of a streetpeddler can lead to the lamppost, I shall be careful not to give my countrymen an opportunity to commit a crime! I shall shun those beloved sites; my act of mourning shall be to deprive myself of them. But the island's decent folk shall be the dearer to me for it!" And I went on my way.

The King's arrival was balm to my state of mind; it assuaged the fears that I had felt for this beloved Paris, which had become my home. I was tempted to visit my island; an unforeseen event kept me from breaking my vow.

As I left my lodgings I saw six armed men walking in the shadow along the houses. At rue des Rats they said, "Here it is." They asked the fruitwoman for a certain lawyer. "He hasn't lived in this neighborhood for a long while," she told them. "I think he has rooms now on rue du Jardinet, near the Cordeliers." The armed men went on, and I followed them. (. . .) They proceeded to the Place Sorbonne; they took on more men there. They came next to rue Hautefeuille. They recruited still more there. Then they went to rue du Jardinet. The lawyer was at home, but alarmed at seeing thirty or forty men, he attempted to escape through the window. He fell and cracked his skull. He was carried to a surgeon, and thence to prison. And what had he done? Written a pamphlet in which he told the truth with humor, in which he exhorted the Parisians not to frighten their fellow countrymen, not to wreck their commerce, not to plunge themselves into poverty.

I felt no further longing to break my vow and go to see my island. I turned back to lock myself up at home.

. . . .

113

July 22, 1789

A general peace of mind began to return after the monarch's arrival in Paris. This monarch, adored and justly so, had come to tell his people that what had been done was directed not against him but against injustices. And Louis did not make common cause with those wrongs.

But meanwhile a faint rumor was spreading. *The Intendant of Paris has been arrested at Compiègne; his portfolio was seized; certain papers were found in it. . . .* What papers? They were never seen. Two hundred and fifty men of the Paris home guard had gone to fetch him. He was on his way, the unfortunate man!

This widespread rumor was disastrous to his father-in-law, who was already resented for his wealth, his unending good fortune, and perhaps a certain harshness. Foulon[1]—an unfortunate name, which should be changed when one enters high finance—Foulon had taken the precaution of passing for dead. He was secreted on an estate a few leagues from Paris. Faint rumors set him trembling. On the evening of the twenty-first, as he stood at a low window, he heard three peasants talking among themselves: "He's inside there. He said if we were hungry we could just eat hay. We ought to take him to Paris with a sheaf of fodder in his mouth." These words alarmed the unfortunate man. In the middle of the night he slipped out alone, soundlessly, unattended, at seventy-four years of age, and set off to seek shelter at Viri, in M. de Sartine's house.

But he was being watched. He was followed, and about midway some peasants arrested him. They wanted to hang him, but on further thought they refrained. They tied him up, and laid him out on the tail of a cart (his previous affluence rendered their hearts devoid of mercy). A gag of hay was forced into his mouth, thistles into his shirt, and he was taken off to Paris. Oh, unhappy old man! What cruel penance you did for your good fortune! But he had aspired to succeed the adored Necker; his name was Foulon, and it made his misery greater. He got to Paris. He was led into the Hôtel de Ville. The electors trembled. In those troubled times a man accused was always guilty. Foulon spent six hours in the Hôtel de Ville. His only crimes were his continuous good fortune, his ambition to be minister, and his immense wealth . . . which could not save him. He spoke, and was heard; and the man who only the day before still aroused envy had now become the lowest of the low. The zealots roared against him, and the terror they inspired stifled any compassion.

However, he was held there awaiting a moment of calm to send him off to prison. Suddenly the furor grew fiercer; the ferocious beasts who brought Foulon there demanded to see their victim. He was shown to them—they wanted to identify him themselves. The unhappy old man, to make himself seen, mounted one of the coffers that had been brought with him. It seems scarcely possible, but I have this from an eyewitness: a thick-set little man darted forward, scattered the guards, seized Foulon and flung him into the midst of those who were waiting for him; he was dragged off and beaten; they reached the fateful lamppost; he was caught in the noose; one man hoisted him up while others dragged on the pulley. The half-dead old man was strangled. The rope snapped. . . . The head was severed from the trunk which was trailed through the gutters, while the head, carried on a pitchfork to the Palais-Royal, the abode of pleasure and of horror, was doomed to an even more hideous treatment.

Oh, men of France! Oh, my fellow citizens of Paris! What monster's black soul raged in you during those moments? Ah! You would never of yourselves have committed such atrocities worthy of cannibals! Some monster impelled you, for the peasants themselves, despite their bitterness, are humane and compassionate. Some monster had poured its venom into their corroded hearts.

These were but preludes to that horrible night. You were soon to arrive, unfortunate Bertier! Let no one imagine at this point that I grieve for tyrants and oppressors! Ah, that baleful notion is the furthest thing from my mind! But I . . . grieve for man, and nothing human is alien to me! I retrace these hideous scenes, O my beloved countrymen! to set you on your guard against the future and against infernal impulses. Let us be men, first of all; afterwards we shall be what we like.

Bertier was at Versailles when they took his portfolio (of which there has been no further mention). One of his close associates hastened to warn him of the danger. The Intendant of Paris went to Soissons. While there, he learned that his orders were needed at Compiègne to start a shipment of wheat on its way. He could have sent his signature, but he went himself. He stepped out of his carriage. His deputy had moved and was living in a handsome house he had recently had built. The Intendant was obliged to ask the way. His manner betrayed him, although he wore a bobtail wig and a gray coat, and his shoebuckles were made of steel. The deputy's house was pointed out to him, and he entered. They sat down to lunch.

Meanwhile, the man he had asked for directions said to another, "I just talked to a man I think is the Intendant. Do you know him?"

"Let's go in on some pretext." They asked for the deputy, and he was notified. Since he felt he had to speak to them, under the circumstances, the deputy stepped out, and as he opened the door the Intendant was recognized. The men said something and left. "It's him," said the second. "If it is, we've got to arrest him." Thus began Bertier's sorry fate.

Nearby lived a carpenter, the owner of a house. The two men confided their plan to him. They found him eager to take part in their project; twenty others joined them. The house was surrounded. One of the deputy's servants warned his master of the uproar. "You're the one they're angry with!" the deputy told Bertier, shaking with terror. "We'll try to slip you out through the door at the end of the garden." The Intendant went down to it. It was opened stealthily; no one was in sight. But, anticipating this move, the villagers, were lying in ambush. They accosted the Intendant, and with that heavy humor which peasants affect more conspicuously than anyone else when they believe they have nothing to fear: "The Intendant! Well, well! Fancy meeting you here! Where are you off to?"

"I am just leaving."

"Oh no, you're not! You're going to stay with us." And they seized him. He was set under a guard of twenty men, not counting those who were outside, and they wrote to Paris.

The current municipality, made up of the electors, sent two hundred and fifty men to bring back the Intendant.

Meanwhile, the news of his imminent danger was spreading. His elder son hurried to Versailles to plead with the deputies for his father's life. But what could they do? Dispersed because the assembly hall was being set in order, there was no place for them to confer.

It was on the very day of his father-in-law's death that Bertier arrived. It was half past eight. The agents of cannibalism ripped off the stairboard of his coach; they tore off its canopy. Who did this—good citizens? Oh no, the good citizens moaned, timid and terrified; the enraged aristocrats were more delighted than saddened by the excess of evil; they hoped yet to turn it back upon the people.

All along rue Saint-Martin, young and pretty women shouted from the windows, "Hang him! Hang him! . . . To the lamppost!" Madwomen! . . . For at that terrible moment, a wretch in tatters presented Bertier with his father-in-law's skewered head, and one of those women fainted who a moment earlier had been shouting, "To the lamppost!" Another aborted. A third died of shock. I say this in the honor of humanity: Foulon's head exacted ten sacrificial victims for itself, when it was presented to his son-in-law. . . .

However, the unfortunate man did not see it. Utterly dejected, though he never suspected the fate that awaited him, he was proceeding with bent head and closed eyes.

He reached the Hôtel de Ville. At this point, I was an eyewitness. He was interrogated. He replied that he was not guilty of anything; that he only carried out orders. He was interrupted. He mentioned that he had gone without rest for four nights. He asked that the questioning be put off till the following day. He was informed that he was to be taken to the Abbaye.[2] After seven minutes he emerged from the Ville. Halfway down the steps, hearing cries of rage, he remarked, "What a strange crowd, with all that shouting!" Then, at the same moment, he added to a grenadier of the guards, "They frighten me! My friend, do not desert me!" The grenadier gave him his word. Did he do so ironically?

At the landing, a group of some thirty persons sprang upon the guards escorting the prisoner and pushed them aside; he was seized, dragged off and beaten. A hooligan of fifteen awaited him, straddling the bar of the lamppost. I saw the rope dangling. I should like to state unequivocally here that the demands for his death did not come, with fervor, from more than five or six persons; that some thirty ragged hooligans took them up with the laughter of hyper-hooliganism but not of fury. Though I did not see him, I was told it was a Saint-Louis Cross[3] who laid the first hand on the Intendant. Perhaps the emblem[4] in his buttonhole was misleading.

Reaching the fateful lamppost, and finally recognizing death, Bertier cried out: "The traitors! . . ." He offered resistance; he struggled with his hangmen. The noose was slipped around his neck and he was lifted up. He tried to support his body's weight with his hand. A soldier went to slice off his hand, and cut the cord. The victim fell, lunged at an executioner's cheek and scratched it. He was hoisted up again. But the rope snapped a second time and he was slaughtered at the foot of the lamppost; his belly was slashed open, and his head cut off. . . .

I shall say no more of all these events which I did not see, although I was present. They were hanging Bertier, they were cutting off his head, the rope danced —while I thought he was still inside the Hôtel de Ville. . . . All at once, I saw his disfigured head. I was horror-struck.

O you mighty! O all of you, mere men, who believe yourselves gods! Ponder the dreadful fate of Bertier, of Foulon, of Flesselles, of Delaunai, and of the other unfortunates who perished at the Bastille, and tremble! *Erudimini, qui judicatis terram!*[5] And you, O my countrymen! Ponder, in horror, those barbarous acts unjustified even by their purpose. Only necessity could excuse them. But were they necessary? This is what I dare not decide.

I hastened to the Palais-Royal, drawn along by my companion. Some seer must have preceded us, for all the details of Bertier's death were already known there, and heralds were announcing his severed head. We left to avoid seeing it again, and we took rue Dauphine, since we dreaded the quays, the way from the Place de Grève. At the Buci circle my companion left me, and I turned into rue Saint-André with confidence. I was walking with my head bent down, deep in thought, when at rue de l'Éperon I found myself in the midst of two dozen of those hooligans I had seen at the Grève: they were walking in fork formation and pulling a rope connected to the two feet of a trunk . . . shorn of its head. They were shouting, "Make way for the Intendant of Paris!" I stepped back, shuddering, so as not to tread on the blood-soaked corpse. I saw only the back. I have since heard that the chest was open, and that the heart had been ripped out. Three women died of shock and horror in rue Saint-André. I myself could not rid my eyes of that corpse, which I had been forced to look at to avoid trampling. I still saw its trailing hands, its livid pallor. . . . I fainted when I reached home, and my children were obliged to keep vigil over me.

Ah, how I deplore the scoundrels' tone the next day, laughing as they told of Bertier's death! I want to underscore the sense of horror. I am a patriot, true, but I say to myself, "If these were victims vital to the public good, let us honor them, not revile them! . . ."

. . . .

Other persons give a different description of M. Bertier's end, which I reported earlier according to the public accounts. I shall relate it now as I have it from a reliable witness.

The Intendant of Paris had taken grain on the government's account and had distributed it in the provinces, on the bonds of the deputies and of the other local administrators. Pressed to render his accounts, he gathered together all these various bonds. At Soissons, where he visited his daughter, Mme. de Blossac, he recalled that he had a forty-five-thousand-livre bond to collect at Compiègne. He was determined to go after it despite the counsel and the pleas of his daughter and son-in-law. His daughter clasped his knees. He set out, accompanied by a loyal servant. Reaching Compiègne, he had lunch at the deputy's house and decided to go to the château to see a seigneur Tierri, a gentleman in waiting to the King. The deputy's wife took his arm, and they went to the château. Tierri had left that same morning. The Intendant was returning with the lady when he was recognized by a guard. The man asked if he was the Intendant.

"Yes. Well then, what is it?"

"You are under arrest."

"By what right?"

"You are under arrest."

The dispute gathered a crowd. The Intendant was taken into the nearest house, a carpenter's. He was held there while a messenger was sent to Paris. He spent two days and two nights suffering discomfort, humiliating treatment and total insomnia. They went as far as refusing to dress his cautery ulcer.[6] A surgeon was called. The Intendant had, however, left his portfolio in his carriage. Someone remembered it three hours later. They hurried off for it. But the intelligent servant had vanished with the portfolio and set out for Soissons across the fields. He arrived there without being arrested. There the portfolio was opened. An

eyewitness asserts that nothing was found in it but a
sum in gold and forty-five thousand livres' worth of
those bonds which the Intendant was collecting when
he was arrested.

The rest is consistent with the first version.

❧ 114 ❧

October 5 to 6, 1789

I pass over all events of secondary importance
(. . .). I shall not describe the Saint-Germain or the
Poissy massacres, nor that of the Mayor of Saint-Denis,
still less the one at Troyes (. . .). Every day of my
life I shall bless Louis XVI. Every day of my life I
shall bless Bailli and Lafayette.

The reader will recall those turbulent sessions at
the Palais-Royal, where Saint-Huruge[1] played a supporting role, although he believed that he was the lead.
The ferment they inspired was more than temporary;
it smouldered under the ashes—until the early days of
October.

On October 4 the eruption began; it was a faint
rumble. On the fifth it exploded suddenly, with a
frightful roar, like the fiery mouths of Vesuvius
or Etna. It was the women who began the uprising.
The high cost of bread [2] was the pretext; the true motive was the plan formulated after the Saint-Huruge
motion of having the King and the National Assembly
in Paris. It is true that this was the sole means of avert-
ing famine and of reviving the commerce of Paris.
I am not going to criticize this plan; it brought with it

an advantage from which I benefit myself—and can you complain when you benefit?

In the morning, the market women gathered to go to Versailles. By themselves, these women are never to be feared—they are good and law-abiding—but two other elements mingled with them: men disguised as women, aware of the real purpose; and vile creatures, the refuse and bane of civilization, who were prostitutes in their youth and are procuresses and bawds in their old age. It was these last who generated the disturbance.

Together with these admixtures, the market women roamed the streets, stopping all persons of their sex and taking a malicious delight (we speak here of the mixed group) in sending dainty women and girls splashing into the mud. There were marquises and countesses in the filth, and among others a baroness who seemed to take some pleasure in her plight.

But, before we continue, let me report a tale from the *Courrier national*:

> "*Yesterday, at the Oeil-de-Boeuf, three of the Queen's ladies, having purchased white ribbons, used them to decorate the hats of our execrable enemies or of men weak enough to let themselves be seduced by the sweet tongues of these dangerous sirens. To receive the honor of being dubbed knights by these female aristocrats, they knelt down and in that posture humbly received the white cockade as the only one they might wear; to refuse it, according to these beauties, was to insult and betray the King. This irresponsible audacity ought to inspire more pity than rage in sensible people. However, since such pretty ways have a dangerous influence, under the unfortunate circumstances in which we find ourselves, these champions*

of the court should be sent to the Salpêtrière[3] to distribute their cockades."

Letter from a loyal citizen of Versailles on the Subject of the Black Cockades

Versailles, October 4, 1789

Gentlemen:

There is much talk in Paris of the shameful conduct of the Flanders regiment, but no one is better able than I to tell you about the scandalous orgy which gave rise to it. I witnessed it; it is important to the preservation of our liberty to bring the details into the open.

Last Thursday, as everyone knows, a great banquet was given the dragoons, the soldiers of the Flanders regiment and the Swiss guards, in the Versailles opera hall. Probably advised by enemies as careless as they are stupid, the King and Queen appeared at the banquet at the moment when everyone present was in high spirits from all the eating and drinking. Level-headed Frenchmen would let themselves be cut to ribbons for their sovereign when he draws close to them; inebriated soldiers are wont to pile folly on folly, indiscretion on indiscretion—that is what happened. The dauphin was passed from hand to hand, and by his simple amiability, the charming child inspired the rapture of love bordering on excess. The Queen, yielding perhaps too much to the devotion which her august husband and son inspired, took off a gold cross which she wore at her throat and made a gift of it—who knows why—to a grenadier. The King drank with them; they shouted "Vive le roi! Vive la reine!" and took care not to shout "Vive la liberté! Vive la sainte liberté!" But they showered the defenders of our rights, our rescuers—the Menoux, the Targets, the Chapeliers, the Rabauds,

*the Thourets, the Biauzats, the Barnaves, etc.—
with the most insulting epithets.*

*They sang the ballad of Richard the Lion-
Hearted:*[4]

O Richard. O mon Roi!
L'Univers t'abandonne!

*At these words they were seized with a mad
rapture which can only be excused with difficulty
by the exuberance of drunkenness, and everyone
shouted suddenly, in one guilty voice: "We acknowledge none but our King! We acknowledge
none but our King! We do not belong to the Nation. We will only belong to him!" Then, tearing
the national cockade from their caps—that emblem
of unity, of fraternity, of liberty—these infidels
trampled it underfoot. Since that time such culpable excesses, which should make us shudder, have
not ceased. Every day true citizens are shamefully
insulted—citizens who, at Versailles, as in Paris,
consider it the greatest honor to march under the
banner of the country and are proud to wear the
national uniform. Our humiliation, our misfortune
is at its peak if the sword of vengeance and of justice does not fall on the heads of our treacherous
enemies! . . .*

Citizens' Departure from Versailles

"The rumor spreading Sunday evening of the insult
done the Nation fermented during the night in the
minds of all. The general discontent, heightened by
the prolonged scarcity of food, exploded this morning
in every corner of the capital. The women of Les Halles
united, were soon followed by market porters and
other workers, spilled into the streets, beginning at
rue de la Ferronnerie, and forced all the women to
follow them, even going into the houses to increase

their number. Proceeding next to the Hôtel de Ville,
they pillaged the arms and ammunition stores. From
there these new Amazons marched for Versailles, dragging a cannon with them. The men were not long
in following, and tonight at five we saw an entire army
of national guards, both regular and mercenary, inter-
mixed with volunteers of all ages and ranks, proceed
with long strides along the route to Versailles, drums
rolling, flags flying, with an artillery train. These troops
were commanded by the young and noble warrior so
dear to French liberty.

"What will that formidable apparatus do? Nothing, probably. At least, so we hope and wish. The aristocracy, which, secure in time of peace, tried to raise its
ugly head, will retreat into the den of gloom where it
skulked; and this second lesson—this immediate agreement among the real friends of the country, their
promptness in checking our enemies' audacious efforts
—will perhaps impress them sufficiently so they will
not again dare to give themselves over to the hope of
subjugating us.

"At four-thirty the women of Les Halles reached
Versailles. The King was hunting; a courier went to
warn him to put himself out of harm's way. His Majesty arrived, but the women did not see him. They
were received with honor by the bourgeois guards—
the dragoons, our good friends—and the soldiers of
Flanders turned civilians again. The courage and discipline of these heroines of liberty cannot be praised
enough. It is thus written in the book of the great
destinies of this Empire that prideful grandeur will be
crushed forever.

"The bodyguards, scattered by these women, gal-
lantly made their decision: they fled without warning
along various routes. Only one was foolish enough to
take the crowded avenue de Paris, and a gunshot
brought him down.

"Yesterday, Sunday, the fourth of this month, the soldiers of the Flanders regiment gathered with a group of the bourgeois; they drank together "to the health of the King and the Nation"; they reviled the bodyguards and strolled along shouting: "Long live the Nation! The devil with the bodyguards! We drank their wine, but we say . . . to them! . . . And if they order us against the citizens, we'll not obey!"

Here I resume the interrupted account.

A group of armed women set out at noon, and even earlier. They were interspersed with men in disguise. Most of the bourgeois women attempted to slip away. The men carried weapons. The populace was urging M. de Lafayette to set off.[5] But outlaws, who are always at work in any uprising, had driven away all the representatives, and the commander needed his orders from the municipality. Meanwhile, the young hero was burning to start out. He knew how indispensable his presence was to the safety of the monarch and that of the National Assembly.

While the necessary measures were taken, the women streamed by in procession. There was a young, rather pretty one, mounted on a cannon drawn by two horses, who seemed to be the leader of the women. "Well, are you with me?" she cried constantly. "Keep moving, then, ladies! March, and no mercy!" she would call to those who faltered. . . . She displayed some of her charms and was not at all timid about it. It was even reported that when someone expressed admiration for a certain portion she replied: "That's for the grenadier who does his duty best!"

At half past four the commander general departed, followed by the national militia. The brigade was large, for at least half of it did not have commanding officers.

The elements seemed unleashed against the Parisians. The cold rain drenched them to the bone. Exhausted from the events of the night before and from dissipation, a number of the mercenary troops fell out en route. Others, tempted by the prospect of easy pleasure, talked love to the Amazons. But most of the latter, more bent on reaching Versailles than on pleasure, put off the covetous men until the return of the expedition.

The first women reached the château gate at five o'clock. The disguised men, the female panderers and the brigands were among this company. These two last elements were intent on plunder. They wanted to force the bodyguards standing sentry to dismantle the gate and open it for them. They refused; one does not open doors to rioters, to frenzied folk, and still less to frenzied women. I am far from being an aristocrat. I thank God for the presence of the monarch and the National Assembly in Paris. I say more: I do not reproach the courage of the decent market women; but the bodyguards would have been guilty of treason toward the King and the nation if they had promptly opened the gates to men in disguise, to women without scruples or restraint, provoked still further by former police spies—by those creatures vilest of all because police lieutenants, surrounded by these scoundrels exempt from law, never took the trouble to be selective. The harangues of the disguised informers and of the bawds soon proved how right the bodyguards had been. The one who first resisted was killed, however; his adherence to duty cost him his life. It has been said that the bourgeois guards of Versailles fired on the King's guards. No, no! It was a hooligan, a robber from the capital with a stolen rifle, who fired the first shot. All the efforts of one Bastille volunteer could not avail to save another. The volunteer left him for fear of being killed as well; the national uniform would not have been respected.

It may be said, however, that the bodyguards had been wrong in one respect; the banquet the preceding Thursday had been the occasion of certain behavior which was not only imprudent but criminal, if the rumor does not lie. The aria sung there, *Ô Richard, Ô mon Roi!* was an improper act of compassion, which tended to mislead the King as to his people's attitude. If it is true that ladies distributed black cockades there, then they deserved severe punishment. If it is true, and I cannot believe it, that the national cockade was trampled underfoot, that is a crime which deserved the penalty of death. But I do not believe it, unless drunkenness. . . . Ah! Drunkenness and great banquets should be avoided during times of civil unrest. Great banquets always have dire consequences. And you, bodyguards, were you completely innocent? Ah, the shameful Beauvais affair contributed more than you think to bring about the death of those among you who were slaughtered! Remember, you bodyguards . . . all of you, my fellow townsmen, never does crime go unpunished! When the man from Beauvais was killed in the parterre at the Comédie by a brute among you, and the laws were silent, you should have meted out punishment to the offenders yourselves. The entire kingdom would have applauded you, and at Versailles you would have been beloved. And consider, I beg you, that that Beauvais grocer was killed by your men after a banquet. Consider that his wife was in labor and that she had sent him away to spare him the sight of her sufferings. Imagine her, when her dying husband was carried back to her! In the midst of peace, to stab a man in the very sanctuary of diversion and delight—it is a terrible crime, and one that called for the dishonorable demotion of the whole guard which made no amends for it. But on October 5, you were doing your duty. . . .

Until Lafayette arrived, crime, insolence and brig-

andage rumbled at the gates of the château. Total
confusion reigned. It was scarcely possible to defend
oneself from violence, and the bodyguards, despite
their orders, were obliged to fire a few shots to save
their lives. But finally, at nine o'clock, Lafayette arrived. The hero was alarmed at the uproar. He attempted to calm the crowd. But to whom was he
speaking? The weapons of the righteous citizens behind him were more effective than his pleas. He rushed
to the monarch's side; he brought him assurances of
the loyalty of the Parisians; he informed him of their
will, and he had only to pronounce it for that best of
men and best of kings to accede to it.

The Queen was terrified by the cries, not of the
citizens, but of that vile mob of scoundrels and despicable women who assailed the apartment doors. But
reassured by the promise of the hero of the two worlds,
she returned to her bed, and a moment of calm allowed
sleep to come to her.

But what relief can be hoped for from an impatient, uneasy crowd grown quiet only to gather new
strength? After the fulfillment of certain promises
made en route by the women, the rioting burst out
again toward half past three. Shrill screams were heard.
What has been so often printed was seen to be true
then: that indolence undoes valor. Officers raised in
luxury and ease felt their courage flag. Wearied by the
long vigil and still more by the uproar, they lost heart.
These are no longer the steel-sheathed knights in the
time of Francis I; these are effeminate weaklings, with
less courage than women. And this is how the aristocrat, the rich man, finally pays for his insolence and
oppression of the poor man he has plundered. He is
by long habit incapable of doing without the services of those whom he degrades. The hour of insurrection comes; the rich man and the frail ecclesiastic
are reduced to trembling before a populace accustomed

to toil! Without the cannon, which someone else fires; without the soldier, whom they lead on horseback— for their own legs would not carry them—these officers, extolled in our foolish comedies as dashing from civilian pleasures to military glory, would go nowhere from the depletion of pleasure with their whores but to the shame of defeat.

I have said that they were trembling. I have it from a lieutenant colonel. The King had arisen. Lafayette was with him. Louis XVI felt no fear; he looked into his heart, which told him that a good father receives only respect from his children. But then, as he conferred with the general, there were shouts: "Save the Queen!"

Shall I tell the hideous truth here, or shall I hide it? But why should I stifle it, since I started by exonerating the nation? Why should I stifle it, since I have singled out the guilty—that scum of all peoples which is the reservoir of the very baseness and villainy of man? Antoinette—woman destined by nature even more than by birth to be a beloved queen—you, the paragon of your sex, who can be reproached only for being too enchanting! O Queen, know that in these stern times when the least licentious of writings were rigorously punished, the blasphemous writings against you were published by the police spies, the only ones brazen enough, with authority enough, to do so without fear! (. . .) Know that for this reason the guiltiest among them has an income of forty thousand pounds. O Queen! Do all that you can for the freedom of the press, for the freedom of the printers' estate, and the infamous libels will grow scarce; the authors, the scandalmongers will be readily discovered and the law will put its mark on them! . . . But to return. . . .

The informers disguised as women, those professional panderers who live by the vilest, the most atrocious crimes, were reduced to complete idleness by the new regime. Aided and abetted by blind tools, their pimps, they believed they could overthrow the State by demanding the most horrible of all crimes. The Queen, whom those blasphemous characters dared to threaten, woke terrified; she left her bed and ran half-naked to seek the safest refuge: the King's arms. In fact, the monarch's bosom was, in that terrible moment, the most sacred, the only refuge in the kingdom. She knocked. No one heard it. Her fear mounted. At last the uproar outside made the King think the Queen might be frightened; he was going to see her, and thus it was conjugal love that saved Antoinette. Scarcely was the door ajar when the Queen, with the dauphin in her arms, threw herself into her royal husband's embrace with a cry that chilled the men accustomed to fearing nothing. What a scene! But who brought it about?

The brigands, and the wanton women disguised as fishwives tried to force the doors to the Queen's apartment. The bodyguards thrust them back. But now, as objects of a general hatred because of a presumed wrong—that they had fired on the women— they were nearly overpowered. All at once the grenadiers of the royal guards, who felt their love for the King and all that concerned him quickening in their hearts, grew angry at the harlots' hideous cries; they rushed forward, joined the bodyguards, embraced them and said, "We support the same cause!" This was an immortal act. The royal family—indeed, all France— must cherish these brave grenadiers for it. In the circumstances, each of them was worth a hundred men. They drove back the savage beasts, whose horrible cries revealed their intentions. It is thus that reckless crime defeats itself.

With the Queen safe, Lafayette prepared to escort the King to Paris at daybreak. This was an anticipation of the monarch's own wishes—for he understood that the capital was in much need of his presence—and he hastened his departure. Still, he reached the Hôtel de Ville only by evening. I say this because I saw it: everyone was moved by the behavior of the King's guards, who mingled with the people, the national cockade in their hats, and cried, "*Vive le roi! Vive la nation!*" And the two cries were the same: the king is the head, and the nation the body; they are but one. In point of fact, during the tenure of the Estates General,[6] the king lets the nation make the laws it wants him to carry out; he recognizes himself to be their representative; he yields his position to the represented, but he reclaims it when, after the law has been put through, a single leader is needed to carry it out.

The Queen presented a still more touching picture. She showed the dauphin, whom she held on her knees; she showed him to the people whose hope he is. It is reported that the royal infant has spoken several times, but I am not certain of it.

At half past eight, the King had returned from the Hôtel de Ville to the Tuileries.

Let others concern themselves with useless details; my own intention is to tell only such things as are likely to yield some good. I have exonerated the nation. I have tried to enlighten certain individuals who believe that the Parisians did violence to the king in the National Assembly. Whereas the truth is that the presence in Paris of the King and the National Assembly was necessary to the advancement of business and to the good of the whole kingdom; Paris is the queen of cities, as the king is the ruler of men. There can be no prosperity, no national glory, unless there is unity between the French and their king, and unity between the cities and Paris. The capital has been pictured as a man-eater. This is an error. The city is the bestower of delights, the mistress of the kingdom; if she brings the people happiness, it cannot do too much to repay her. In any case, she returns all that the people gives her. Generous lover, do not regret your gifts! If there is no greater coquette than your mistress, there is none more charming either, and her very coquetry becomes one of her assets.

TWENTY
PARIS
NIGHTS

115

FEDERATION

July 13 to 14, 1790

Take up your darkling flight again, Night Owl; utter a few more funereal cries as you roam the lonely streets of this vast city, in the hope of striking terror in the hearts of the criminal and the perverse!

On July 13 I had set out along rue Saint-Honoré with the intent of crossing the new bridge to reach the Champ de la Fédération. I was walking along pensively, without a cloak. At the toll bar I saw the sentry standing in front of the gate, and, behind me, a man spat at me behind my back. I was astounded. I turned around sharply. Across from Travers' former confectioner's shop, I was assailed by three, four, or five young men, among whom I thought I recognized an engraver. They surrounded me and closed in, saying to one another in a low voice, "He has the mark on him!" One of them felt for my moneybag, another felt in the pockets of my suit, another in the jacket; all that in the wink of an eye. "Ah, my good robbers, I have nothing, nothing!" I told them. They left me, after having convinced themselves. The woman who hawked newspapers at the stocking merchant's door told them, "At least have a little respect for his calling!" She took me for a priest: I was wearing an old black garment with frog fastenings.

"Can't you see they're robbers?" I asked her.

"Them? Those are gentlemen!"

"Wipe off the spittle I have on my back, I beg you. That is their mark." And she removed it for me.

I continued on my way as far as the Palais-Royal where I saw shameless pilfering going on. I laid myself open to it, because I was unpilferable. I carried nothing on my person since the time when, wearing that same black garment, I was attacked on rue des Vieilles-Étuves by six men who had marked me and shoved me about. I had realized in time what they were up to and staved them off, examining them openly. But they were completely unconcerned. One of them followed me right into an alley. I darted out of it, and took up a position next to the sentry at the Médici column, in the new market.

At half past ten I left the garden, and at eleven I reached the Champ-de-Mars.[1] I examined this work by the citizens, and the Altar of the Nation[1] reminded me of the great days of Greece. Without being devout, I believe in a Supreme Being, the Only True Being, since nothing exists but through him, for he calls himself by the most eloquent and most philosophic of names: *I am that I am.*[2] I prostrated myself; my soul went out toward him, and I prayed to him for my nation's sake: "Wellspring of life! See the unity of thy children! Oh, bring it to pass that the sun, as it proceeds in its course, see nothing so great upon this earth as the name of France!" I rose and started to walk home. There were a few lanterns in whose flickering light I was observed. A sentry stopped me. "No, let him go," said another I had not seen, "he has just said the prayer for our nation that Horatius once said for Rome."[3] I was therefore left free to withdraw.

. . . .

116

February 27 to 28, 1791

The blow is struck, O nobility! You group of weak-lings who hope to return to those privileges which were only tolerated by the people from force of habit, how can you fail to sense that such privileges were only tenuously held, as by a line that holds a ship ready to be launched? The sledge's blow has set it free; no power in the world can bring it back to where it was. O nobles, the harm is done! It would have been better for you to have kept quiet or exposed yourselves to destruction in order to prevent the axe from falling; but it has fallen, all is lost for you, and the foreigners will pour oil on the flames. Your emigration served the Revolution in two ways: by your absence, which relieved it of enemies, and by your goods, whose sale gave it a subsidy. And if you had dealt with others than those whom your morals had corrupted, your end would have come two years earlier. O nobles, the calamity is great for everyone, but above all for you, because your alleged friends, if they entered France, would sacrifice you to win back the subjugated people. They do not need you, but they do need the farmer, the vine-grower, the bootmaker, the mason, the workmen of all trades, and it is to them that they will sacrifice you! And those of you noblemen who re-mained—you fine gentlemen of the robe, financiers, big merchants, licensed master printers—do you believe that it is for you that Leopold and William, as well as the English and Spaniards and the Piedmontese, would conquer France? You appeal to them with your promises, but they will pillage you first of all, and won't even deign to pity you afterwards. See how they have treated the emigrés themselves, since January 21, 1793. And would these emigrés not be your cruelest enemies? Consider then, blind men that you are, that your former position depended on the old order of things, on custom; that the line is severed; that in a state of war when men are desperately in need of things and are beset from all sides, you are but useless mouths to feed. . . . Ah! Louis XVI has ruined you! He has brought about the downfall of aristocrats and democrats alike. . . .

❦ 117 ❦

April 17 to 18, 1791

I had gone to the vicinity of the Tuileries, which I could not enter. I took a turn around the palace. I was peering through the courtyard gates which look out on the Place du Carrousel, when I noticed two women in the courtyard which adjoins the Louvre gallery. They had left the little stairway in the passage and were coming toward the gate. I stepped aside. Someone quietly opened it to them, and they passed through. The porter, or his assistant, peered around; he noticed me and gave me a large bundle, saying to me, "Don't follow them too closely, your comrade will leave in a few minutes." I took the package, and I walked forty paces behind the two women who proceeded quickly and silently. The older appeared about twenty-two—she was very shapely and attractive—the second seemed barely sixteen.

They arrived at the carriage office above the Pont Royal, where a chaise awaited them inside. I saw them turn around then, and I handed them the package. "Heavens, what's this?" the older of the two asked me. "Then where is my . . . ?" She caught herself.

"The second package will be here in a few minutes," I said.

"Who are you?"

"A stranger; but I didn't think I should refuse to carry the package."

"Oh, good heavens!"

"Don't be afraid, mesdames; two persons of your age and appearance could never be planning any wrong!" The older one offered me money—for my trouble, no doubt—but I left. My second arrived, out of breath, carrying the other package, which he flung at the ladies' feet, very surprised to see the first one there. He spoke to them too quietly for me to hear what he said except for the last few words: "I must find him."

He ran out toward the Pont Royal, but I had hidden near the door behind the carriages. I remained there until he returned. The ladies then climbed into the chaise, and left across the bridge. I saw no patrol. At midnight I went back by the Voltaire and the Vallée quays. We will see the two young ladies again.

The next day, excited by what I had learned in the evening and witnessed that night, I went to the Tuileries. Lafayette's policy had been to admit everyone. There was much noise, but only that of voices of people all speaking at the same time. However, I saw that those who were privy placed themselves in large groups around the King's carriage and along the roadway by the walls of the Tuileries; I conjectured from that moment on that Louis would not leave. Like many others, I had at the time confidence in Lafayette, whom I believed a partisan of the Revolution. Louis arrived—he even climbed into the carriage. Immediately, horrible cries were heard from the surrounding groups. The officer in charge and the mayor urged the people to let the monarch leave, but they were speaking to deaf ears.

"Oh, I'll say," said a woman. "We were caught napping, but not again. Everything is being made ready; the aunts have left, what with those fine decrees of the Assembly that give those who should stay the right to leave. We have our reasons! And where are they, those ladies? They are telling their beads in Rome. Couldn't they have told them as well in Paris? They were stopped in Moret. Their rotten troops fell on our national guard with sabers, and would have been perfectly happy to murder the people if the court had dared . . ."

"Good grief," a man replied to two women, "and he was the one who prevented all those court brigands from daring it. He's still the best of the four. So let him stay with us, and the others can run off if they wish. Come on, come on! Let's unhitch the horses! Unhitch the horses, unhitch the horses!"

Lafayette gave orders. He was threatened. He was furious, as much as a fair-haired man can be, but you could see that he was using restraint.

"Ah, you've sent the aunts away," a man shouted at him, "but you won't send the King away!"

"No, no!" screamed the women. A crowd of dissonant voices repeated "No, no" in every possible key. It was noise enough to deafen as well as to frighten. The troops, meanwhile, did not seem disposed to obey their superiors, who went from rank to rank to sound them out. The officers made their report to Lafayette, who, having heard them, went to speak through the coach window. It was then that the outcries against the fugitive aristocrats redoubled; they were showered with curses, which must have caused more alarm than anything else.

Thus ended the second attempt. Louis was obliged to step out of his carriage and return to his apartments. It was then that Louis said these beautiful words: "If it is to cost one drop of blood, I will not leave."

That morning the Jacobins saved him from a terrible imprudence. How good it would have been for the unfortunate man if his secret plans had always been so opportunely betrayed! For it is certain that he was only going to Saint-Cloud to escape: his perfidious friends were leading him to his ruin, and without knowing it, sealing their own. Yes, whatever happens: the lords, the noblemen, the aristocrats of every level are forever lost, not in France alone, but in all Europe —if not during the eighteenth century, then during the nineteenth. The shock has been imparted; a new order of things will begin, and then the French will be destroyed. I, the Night Owl, will not live to see it. But oh, those of you who will, give credit to my intuitive foresight!

So passed the day of April 18; it roused Louis' fury against the Parisians. He resolved more strongly than ever to leave them.

 118

June 20 to 21, 1791

Then came the terrible period that led up to that of January 21, 1793![1] A profound sense of security lay over the capital, brought about by Lafayette, whose only program for the moment was inactivity. At nine o'clock I was at the Café Robert-Manouri.[2] The Jacobin whom we have since called the Maratist appeared at ten-thirty, sullen and reflective. He ordered a lemonade and proceeded to harangue against Lafayette with a fervor which his beverage did nothing to temper. I remarked to Fabre, another Jacobin but a gentle one:

"Something is in the wind today. Our wild man is furious!"

"No, I have just come from the Jacobins, as he has; everything is quiet."

Something told me no. I left the café. I went toward the Tuileries, and when I reached the new stewards'-pantries,[3] I stopped. I heard a faint activity; I saw people walking singly, but not far apart. I felt a turbulent excitement within me; it was as if I were electrified by the agitation of those in flight. Might the physical sometimes replace the mental in man?

While a thousand chaotic ideas buffeted me, I heard a sound behind a large steward's-shed. I moved quietly closer to investigate. I saw a man in the uniform of the Swiss guard.[4] I was frightened, for, aside from the fact that those people do not listen to reason, he might, as the saying goes, be in his cups. I went a few steps farther to huddle behind another shed. I waited there nearly a quarter of an hour, which doubtless caused me to miss a more important event. I finally saw the Swiss emerge from behind the shed where the straw was kept; with him was a tall and handsome woman with a blindfold over her eyes. "Stay there," he told her in a harsh but low voice, "until me be far away. . . . And be good and careful! . . ." He went off toward the new archway. I did not follow him. The hope of speaking to the woman kept me.

In fact, no sooner was the Swiss through the archway than I approached her. "Madame," I said, "I saw everything. Is there something I can do to help you?"

"Yes, you seem to be a respectable man. Give me your arm, and carry the parcel my servant dropped when he was struck by the sword of the Swiss who just left me."

"But did he violate you?"

"I shall not conceal from you what you have seen; he held his bayonet against my throat; I yielded. . . . Let us go." She led me under the same archway through which the Swiss had disappeared. We were midway across the Place du Carrousel when we were blocked by a heavy carriage moving at a slow pace. The lady's servant came toward us and took the parcel from me. The lady thanked me, entreating me to hurry away and assuring me there was some danger. I followed her advice. I turned around a moment later to watch her leave. She had disappeared. But I think she must have climbed into the big coach. I saw nothing else which might have concealed her. Who was she? What carriage was it? A single word more might be a grave mistake; I must not say it. I noticed only that she did not take the blindfold from her eyes.

I returned home directly, quite put out at not having persuaded her to tell me who she was. Certain sounds I heard on the Pont Saint-Michel made me retrace my steps and take rue Gilles-Cœur,[5] which seemed perfectly calm. At the corner of rue de l'Hirondelle a woman of ill repute was standing in the doorway—the abbess[6] of the house. She called me over. I asked her what she was doing there so late, on a street where no one passed by. "Where are you coming from?" she asked me. "From the Tuileries, from the Place du Carrousel? Are you in on it?"

"In on what?"

"Oh, you can talk now, it must be all over."

"I was escorting a lady."

"Oh, then you were . . . I'm waiting here for a

Swiss who was in on it, too, and so he won't have to
go back to the barracks he is supposed to come here
to sleep; he is not sure which is my house, he only
knows the street. And who would he ask, at this time
of night?"

As she spoke we heard footsteps along the quay.
I left the woman immediately, and turned into the
rue de l'Hirondelle, but I took cover in the cranny
formed by the old free school of design. Someone appeared; it was the Swiss, the same one I had seen
coming from behind the shed. He went up into the
woman's house, and I promptly returned to the door.
They were talking loudly. The woman, who had heard
me walking, glanced through a casement window that
lighted the stairwell. She led the Swiss in and returned to me. "He's in the bedroom with a girl. But
perhaps you've got the same problem? If you want
to, I'll take you in." I agreed. She did me the honor
of giving me a bed in her own room, and fortunately it
was not hers. We lay down in silence, and I fell into
a deep sleep. Toward four or five o'clock, I was awakened by the noise the Swiss made as he got up, for his
bathroom was separated from ours only by a thin par-
tition. He began to converse with the abbess:

"Me not taste your girl one bit. I has good supper
off another one last night, worth lot more!"

"Is it all over, is it all over?"

"What you mean? If you know what you act like
you know, me chop off your head! Not know?"

"No, no!" the terrified abbess replied.

"You do right thing forgetting!" He left almost
immediately, and I went home, still having learned
nothing about these events. I knew only that they were
important ones.

119

THE KING'S FLIGHT

The first person to sound the alert was the Queen's pot-au-feu cook. At six o'clock—that is, at the time I was leaving the abbess's house—she set off to make her report to the section headquarters.[1]

"At eleven o'clock someone quietly locked me into my room; I had left my key in the door, on the outside. Next I heard a good deal of coming and going for an hour and a half. My door was unlocked without my hearing it; I discovered this only during another attempt to get out. I dressed immediately and stuck my nose outside. I asked the first sentry if anything had happened. He knew nothing. But when I went down to the gallery, I found some commotion. I even heard someone say softly, 'They believe the King is gone . . . but where did he go?' 'It could only be to Saint-Cloud.'

"When I heard this I understood why I had been locked in; I realized that the escape plan had indeed been premeditated. I've come to tell you the time, which must have been between midnight and one o'clock, to judge by the activity I heard. They could only have gone out through the alleyway that leads to the passage from the Tuileries to rue de l'Échelle, while other coaches tried to get stopped on the Place du Carrousel to divert attention." The woman's conjectures were correct.

I set to work on my return. I did not hear of the affair until I first went outdoors at noon. Even so, I

would not have learned of it until evening, except that
I heard a great chattering among the washerwomen
in my street, and a few words reached my ears directly.
"He leff lass night! Monsieur, too, and Madame.[2] The
King, the Queen, Madame Élisabeth, Madame, the
dauphin." I realized then that a most important event
had occurred. I dressed; I went out; the bad news
was confirmed. At the end of the Pont Neuf and
la Vallée, I ran into the astronomer Lalande, who
was pale and haggard. I concluded from this that he
was not an aristocrat. The confusion was widespread;
I went to the Tuileries, to the Palais-Royal; I returned
by rue Saint-Honoré. Everywhere I saw people tearing
down the royal coat of arms, and even the notaries[1]
official shingles. Thus, it was actually on that day that
royalty was annihilated in France. Three days of
turmoil and upheaval. Meanwhile, on the evening of
the twenty-second, there was news of the arrest at
Varennes of Louis and his family. It was reported that
the Sainte-Menehould postmaster[3] had told the coachmen: "Stop, or I'll fire into the carriage!"

Louis said, "In that case, stop." He was put into
the backroom of a tavern. That was his first prison.

June 23 to 24, 1791

A single idea preoccupied every mind on the twenty-
first, the twenty-second, the twenty-third, the twenty-
fourth. That was the day when Louis was to return to
Paris: but what a return! Two commissioners from the
Convention[1] [Constituent] had gone to meet him at

Varennes—Barnave[2] and Pétion[3]—and they were to bring him back. Paris awaited him on the night of the twenty-third, and I had gone, like everyone else, to the entrance of the Tuileries. Then it was learned that he would not arrive, and the crowd dispersed. Deep in thought, I was walking near Champs-Elysées and never noticed that I was straying. I went by the place where the short-lived Coliseum had stood—that transitory product of the last and the most insignificant member of the Phélipeaux family,[4] despite all the evil he did! [. . .]

I quoted these words from the Psalms: *"Transivi et non erat.* I passed by again, and he was already gone." * Farther on I walked on the square where Mme. de Pompadour's usurped garden[5] had lain. "Ah, think of the glories that are no more!" I cried. "All the rest will pass as well." I went as far as the Chaillot gate; and, reminiscing, I recalled a delightful evening I had spent there.

. . . .

But at that point I became aware that I had wandered far afield. I turned back; eleven o'clock was tolling. I took the way along the gardens, as being the least traveled path. Getting near rue de Marigny, I slackened my pace. A man and a woman were seated in a garden by the inner wall of the moat which separated them from me. I walked soundlessly, and the height of the hedge hid me from their view.

"What a terrible revolution!" the man was saying. "Where will it end? To emigrate is to abandon the field to the enemy. Yet, if I don't emigrate, I will be dishonored. They have already sent me a distaff. . . .[6] I replied that I was needed here. I had planned to leave tomorrow; but now they are bringing the King back.

* Restif either paraphrases or misquotes the Psalm: "Yet he passed away, and lo, he was not." (Transl. note)

Who knows what will happen? And in any case, how
could I get out?"

"You should have emigrated, monsieur," the lady
replied. "Duty is duty. What are you doing here,
with a weak king who is more your enemy than the
democrats are? . . . In fact, I hope he dies, now that
he has been recaptured! Do you realize, monsieur,
what an advantage it would be for us, and for all
decent people, if that weak Louis' head should fall?
Imagine all Europe rising, all the kings united! Imagine
the mercenary soldiers themselves carrying out our
revenge, like dogs set against dogs. We can hope for
no other salvation than the death of Louis XVI. So
long as he lives, so long as he preserves a semblance of
authority, we are lost and the great powers will do
virtually nothing."

"Ah, madame, how little you know them! I know
them better than you, these powers whom you expect
to help us regain our rights! They take secret joy in the
. . . heart-rending . . . condition of a powerful empire they envied; they are watching for the proper moment to throw themselves on us and crush everything,
noblemen and commoners alike. Do not deceive yourself, madame. Our position is a terrible one, and if I
were not guided more by hatred than by reason, I
would go over to the revolutionaries tomorrow." At
this, the lady rose angrily and left. The man called
after her. I heard only these words: "No, no! I never
want to see you again!" He followed her. I cried to
him, "No matter what your reasons, become a patriot!"
I hurried away. [. . .]

A hundred yards farther on, near rue du Faubourg-
Saint-Honoré, I came across three women, two of
whom were supporting the youngest by the arms. I
passed them. They called to me: "Help us, friend!"
they said. "No, no, he's too old!" said the one they
were holding up. It was easy to see that they were no

good. I walked away, and just then a very elegant man passed me. I turned to see if the three women would accost him. They certainly did. The man stopped, and I drew aside. Thereupon the young one began to moan: "Monsieur, take pity on me. . . . I was coming from Passy, with my mother and my aunt; in the middle of Champs-Elysées we were attacked by some hooligans who tried . . . who tried. . . . I resisted them . . . and they beat me, beat me . . . so badly that I can't stand up! . . . You live nearby—couldn't you take us in? . . . for we live in the Faubourg Saint-Marceau." The man agreed. He turned into a porte-cochere close by, with the three women. I knocked immediately. He came to the door himself. "Watch out for those dangerous guests of yours! I warn you they are frauds; you would do well to have them watched." I spoke in a very low voice, and left. I reached my own house at one o'clock, and did not encounter any patrols. [. . .]

🎸 121 🎸

THE KING'S RETURN

June, 1791

The following day the city was seething. The youths and the men under forty were armed. The fugitive was not to arrive until evening. I waited before visiting the elegant man from the night before. But before I reached his house I witnessed the return of Louis, whom I considered from that moment on as dethroned. From the boulevards to the Tuileries palace, the national guard formed a double file with arms reversed; a deep silence reigned or was disturbed only by a few muffled insults. He returned, preceded by a thousand false rumors; his coachmen were taken for noblemen in chains, although they were not. Louis was home again, with only the shame of a wrong move. However, he was not punished for it, not even in the natural course of events. The Constitutent Assembly, faithful to its decreed principle that France was a monarchy, pardoned the monarch and believed it had won his allegiance by granting him all the consideration it could still grant him. Then the Lameths[1] and Barnave[2] changed their views. Mirabeau,[3] the great Mirabeau, was no more—since early April. What would he have done at that point? According to the information concerning him that has come to light since, there is great likelihood that he would have done all he could to re-establish the monarchy, that he would have persuaded the foreign powers to accept his views, that he would have thwarted the internal forces, and that we should have had no war. But what would we have become? It is easy to conjecture from the knowledge everyone has of the despotic and harsh, even barbarous character of the great Mirabeau. Today he would be our Cardinal Richelieu, and Louis XVI, like Louis XIII, would be nothing but a chief slave. The Lameths, Barnave and a few others would have been set to work by the change in circumstances. Lafayette would probably have been commander-in-chief; but Mirabeau would have been palace minister and, were it not for the present balance of Europe, Pepin the Short.[4] D'Orléans, by all reports, was done for; Mirabeau would not have been overly scrupulous as to the means in disposing of him. I knew Mirabeau's intimate nature during his lifetime through one of his secretaries, a splendid young man, whom he treated like a slave laborer.

. . . .

✥ 122 ✥

July 16 to 17, 1791

Once inside the Égalité garden, where I often walked,
I looked for the viccs I was accustomed to see
there. In almost every arcade I was invited by the
most disreputable people to join their game. Farther
on, I saw a young girl, attractive though quite un-
developed, being escorted by a prostitute who intended
to sacrifice the girl's youth and health. A moment later
I saw an even greater horror: children of both sexes at
the age of the sweetest innocence, provocatively dressed,
entrusted to madams who profaned their childhood and
cut short their lives—as man's epicurean tastes require
our butchers to stock tender veal. Some prostitutes,
(as I have said before) walk around with children simply to give themselves the respectable appearance of
motherhood and titillate blasé old bachelors. But others
prostitute these tender victims for the depraved tastes
of modern Tiberiuses: girls, boys—it's all the same to
libertines at that age. The children's innocence and
questions amuse them, as does the shamelessness this
same innocence gives to their obscene petting. Once
the libertines have aroused their foul passions to the
extreme, they use the children's mouths instead of
other orifices so far denied by nature. Sometimes, however they force them, and often the little girls die.
The child is then paid for—as one would pay for an
exhausted animal—a price agreed upon in advance
between the adults and the procuress, who always makes
a profit on the deal; and thus it is to her interest to
sacrifice the children.

And who are these victims? Sometimes quite simply children of the greengrocer who lodges the tart; or children stolen at a very young age; or foundlings; or children purchased from the poorest people on the outskirts of the city. These last are sold outright to the prostitute, who does with them as she wishes, without being obliged to account for their fate.

This hellish traffic has existed since before the new Palais-Royal. It accounted for the most substantial portion of the income of the deputy inspector of prostitutes, who may have passed some on to the police official. It is too odious ever to have been denounced, made public, and punished. Mairobert the censor, the same who committed suicide at the Poitevin baths in 1779, knew of it, however, and was the first to give me some inkling of its existence. Never would I have discovered it for myself.

That evening, noticing two children—a girl and a boy—accompanied by a large woman of handsome enough countenance, I approached them. The woman asked if I wished to go up with them. I consented. Reaching the mezzanine under the arcade, she asked me which of the children I preferred, and before I could reply, enumerated their lewd talents. As she spoke, these unfortunate children, pretending to play together, fondled each other in the most obscene fashion. I was revolted, but I could visualize how exciting the vicious corruptress's display must be to libertines, for the children successively exhibited every part of their naked bodies. But one thing was repellent: it was easy to see that they were not really playing; rather, they seemed bored, tired, and pained. When the woman had finished listing the bill of fare, she repeated her question. I replied that I had seen enough and that I would pay her, but that, nevertheless, I would be interested in knowing a few details

about her business. I assured her that after I had
explained my reasons she would not be angry.

"Fine, fine," she said. "I recognize you anyway.
I have seen you at Saint-Brieux's. You're a good boy,
more stupid than malicious. You had a certain lady's
shoe, which you worshiped like a relic. You're an
author, but you don't write your own books, for several
of them amused me. Well, I bought these two children
from a . . . But I don't want to tell you, although
I'm in no danger now. You saw those four women
with children? Not to mention the ones you don't see.
. . . Well, one of them buys up all the foundlings
available. She has a woman who does it for her. They
are raised on nothing but goat's milk, and so success-
fully that she rarely loses any of them. She sells them
to the rest of us when they are ripe. The woman is very
useful. Often she gives money in advance to women
who are concealing their pregnancies from their husbands and who come to her to give birth. That's not
all; she prevents a great many girls of good family, as
well as housemaids, chambermaids and cooks, from
destroying their fruit by offering to attend their confinement and to keep the children.

"There are others who buy children, choosing the
prettiest ones, from poor folk who can't care for
them. If any among those bought in their mothers'
bellies are malformed at birth, they are taken to the
Foundling Home, but so belatedly that they all perish.
Sometimes we travel, or send someone else, to the
provinces, and find some superb children. You bribe
the nurse, who sells the child; she shows it to the
priest when it looks sick; she leaves; and then you make
up a shrouded bundle of rags, for which the priest
makes out a death certificate. The same little business
is carried on here sometimes, with servant girls and
governesses—but rarely, because it's a big risk. The

child falls ill, seems to languish for a few days, then dies. They bury rags in its place."

"But what is done with these children?"

The wretched woman enumerated for me the horrors I have sketched.

"We're happy," she added, "if a pretty child isn't broken or crippled on us. It's only half bad if a libertine does no more than give them smallpox. We have people to treat them. If a child is delicate, we just cover up the symptoms to keep him going six months, a year, during which time he's used for all he's worth."

I did not wish, I could not bear, to hear more. I was feeling ill and about to faint. I walked out, and I was already on the stairs when I put a three-livre note in the woman's outstretched hand. I went away horribly ill.

❦ 123 ❦

A NIGHT IN THE TUILERIES
September 26 to 27, 1791

I went to the Tuileries over the Pont Royal. By means of the irons I use to chisel my dates on the island, I have occasionally climbed into this garden after it has been closed. I chose the section of the river bank where there is no sentry, and I entered without difficulty. I noticed some people. I slipped down under the trees without being seen. A great number of people had gathered there in the most sheltered spots, sitting on chairs in separate groups. I dared neither to stop, nor to come too close. But finally, having taken up a position behind a thick tree rather near to the largest group and the one where the voices rose highest, I heard them discussing affairs of state.

"It's dangerous," a man was saying, "to call foreigners into France: look how delightedly they received the first proposal!"

"But what about us, monsieur le duc?" one woman said sharply. "What will become of us?"

"We must gamble everything, sacrifice everything," a younger woman declared, "to regain our rights."

"Caution, caution!" a second man said. "His Majesty has already regained a great deal; our turn will come." At that moment, a heavy man started to walk toward my tree to urinate. Fortunately for me, a woman remarked to him, "You're going too far," and he turned about to retort, "Would you rather I stayed right under your nose?" I slipped quietly away during that repartee, which brought a response it would serve no purpose to relate.

I felt that a position near that group was the most interesting, but too dangerous. I walked off to more secluded parts. There I came upon a tall, young and beautiful woman leaning tenderly toward a man as she walked with his arm around her waist. "I should be back there," she said, "they are discussing important things; but you make me forget the whole world. And yet, what a time for love-making! Perhaps on the eve of a departure, of a bloody war?"

"We know when we leave home, my sweet," the man replied, "but we can't tell when we will get back. If you leave, though, I shall follow you . . . to the end of the world. But without you, never!" And he kissed her; they sat down on a chair, and the seat snapped and broke; and the lady murmured something; and they sank down on the grass, a more solid couch. . . . Everything I saw them do was completely natural;

it was, after all, not commonplace things I was looking
for.

I reflected; I could see that some plot was
afoot, and I knew enough about it to try to find out
more. However, I was not fully informed until much
later. I realized then that it was the women who forced
the men to emigrate, and that it was they who endured
the Revolution with the greatest impatience.

❦ 124 ❦

August 9 to 10, 1792

. . . .

I was awakened early in the morning by the sound
of artillery. In the street I heard the people discussing
what was happening. I got out of bed then and hurried
out. . . . Reaching the end of the Pont Royal, I saw
the gunfire. I asked for information. I received only
garbled accounts. Finally I understood that on hearing
rumors of a new deputation from the faubourgs the
court had taken up a position of defense; that it had
called to the palace the noblemen commonly known as
the "Knights of the Dagger" [1] and all those whose loyalty it was sure of; that it was counting on part of the
national guard, whose general staff was on the court's
side, and on the Swiss guards with whom it had surrounded itself. . . . I learned that while the court was
sounding the alert at the Saint-Roch church to gather
its supporters, the volunteers from Marseilles were
ringing the bells at Saint-Sulpice to gather the patriots;
I learned that the Faubourg Saint-Marceau had taken
the Marseilles volunteers at the Cordeliers, that the

Henry IV battalion had turned its cannons on the latter, and that its commander Carle had just been killed. I saw Swiss guards with their throats slit open . . . the national guard in full muster. I was stupefied. I could not imagine how, on the eve of such great upheaval, I had seen so many calm persons. I asked about the court. Louis and his family took refuge in the National Assembly hall before the first shot was fired. I felt less apprehension then for the public welfare. I moved on. I saw piles of corpses. I turned onto the Quai du Louvre. I saw firing from the gallery windows. I stayed close to the walls, and a woman who had not taken this precaution was killed twenty yards from me. I saw a butcher boy fall at the Saint-Germain-l'Auxerrois passage, two hundred yards from the Louvre colonnade from where the shot came. These were some of the despicable acts of which the "Knights of the Dagger" were only too guilty.

. . . .

❊ 125 ❊

HOUSE INSPECTIONS

August 28 to 29, 1792

As two o'clock struck I was aware of someone going into my neighbors'. I opened my door. They finally came to me. I was unarmed, without even my sword, which my nephew had lost. They took down my name, my age. They asked if anyone lodged with me. I gave satisfactory answers to all their questions, and they left.

Sleep was far from my lids. I went out to walk as far as I could without being stopped. I saw a cartload of non-juring priests,[1] in every costume—as men of the world, as women, and even in uniform. But what made the greatest impression on me was a fishwife, fitted out with the greatest verisimilitude, who someone told me was a former canon of Notre Dame. The bacchic sot was so convincingly disguised in this apparel that I could not conceive how anyone had been able to recognize him. A guard told me that they would not have recognized him either, save for an altogether amusing accident. The fishwife's husband had returned home during the inspection. He was a merry fellow, still in good shape. Finding someone in his wife's clothing, he never suspected it wasn't she. Now, he used to say to his wife when he wanted to have a good time: "Jacqueline, bend over and give me something." And Jacqueline, who knew what he meant, always bent over. The canon bent over too. Then the fishmonger went over to grab hold of him. But imagine his surprise to see—black breeches! He cried out. The guards, who were leaving, came back up again. "Hey, messieurs, have you put the devil's curse on my wife? She's got a black rump!" They examined the woman. It was a man! The real fishwife, seeing the plot discovered, ran in at the commotion. The husband saw her and, without warning, "stabbed her in the back," as he called it. Which revealed to all present that the woman was no Negress under her skirt. The canon was led away in his fishwife's garb.

Such was the tale told me by one of the guards of the escort, which I accompanied as far as rue de la Parcheminerie. I repeat it, such stories have nothing distressing about them; but it would have been inhuman to laugh at them, had one known by what terrible catastrophe they were to end a few days later. A Carmelite priest complained to P. Manuel, procurator of the Commune, that they lacked many things. "That will be taken care of by Sunday or Monday," answered Pierre. He knew, apparently.

MASSACRES

September 2 to 5, 1792

August 10 had revived the Revolution and brought it
to its peak; September 2, 3, 4 and 5 cast a brooding
horror over it. Those dreadful events must be described
impartially, and the writer must remain cool while he
makes his reader shudder. No breath of passion must
stir him; otherwise, he becomes a demagogue instead
of a historian.

On Sunday at six or seven o'clock I went out, unaware as usual of what was happening. I set off for my
island—that beloved Île Saint-Louis, from which a
villain had forced the residents to oust me. Ah, how
evil a man without breeding can be! In this tranquil
refuge, where I entered unobserved, I heard nothing
except for a domestic who was saying to another
through the window: "But, Catherine, that sounds like
the alarm ringing! Is something else happening?"
Catherine answered, "I guess so. Master says to lock
up." I moved on, without seeming to listen. I did
not walk around the island completely; I left by the
Pont Marie and the Port au Blé. There was dancing
there. I found that reassuring. When I reached the
large restaurant with the stairs, at the end of the port,
I saw more dancing. But just then a passer-by exclaimed, "Will you stop your dancing! They're doing
another kind of dance in some places!" The dancing
stopped. I went on, with a heavy heart; without knowing exactly why, I followed the quays—Pelletier,
Gèvres, Mégisserie or Ferraille—and I reached the Café
Robert.

I knew a little man there, of Swiss extraction but born in Paris, who always knew what was going on in his neighborhood, the Théâtre-Français section. . . . "They're killing them in the prisons," he told me. "It began with my district, at the Abbaye. They say it started with a man put in the stocks at the Grève yesterday who said he didn't give a d. . . for the nation, and other insults. People got excited; they took him up to the Hôtel de Ville, and he was condemned to be hanged. He had said, earlier, that the prisons were full of people who thought as he did, and that they'd get their chance soon enough, that they had weapons, and that they would be left behind in the city when the volunteers went off. . . . The result is that today crowds gathered in front of the prisons, forced the doors, and they're killing everyone who's in for anything but debts." I became very upset and frightened as I listened to little Fragnières; the picture he described, however, was far from the truth. After I had read the newspapers I asked him if he was going my way. For I was frightened. "Gladly," he replied, "but let us go by the Abbaye. Then I'll take you to your door."

We set out together. Everything seemed in a kind of stupor in the noisy rue Dauphine, which still bore that name. We went as far as the prison gate without difficulty. There we found a group of spectators in a circle; the killers were at the gate, both inside and out. The judges were in the guardroom. The prisoners were brought before them. They were asked to give their names. The records of their arraignment were studied. The nature of the charge against them decided their fate. An eyewitness told me that often the killers inside pronounced the sentence before the judges did. A tall man, cool and sober in manner, was brought before them; he was accused of hostility and of aristocracy. They asked him whether he was guilty. "No, I have done nothing; only my feelings were under suspicion, and in the three months I have been in prison they have found nothing against me." At his words, the judges inclined toward clemency, but a voice cried in the Provençal accent, "An aristocrat! Off with him—to the Force! To the Force!"

"So be it, to the Force, then," the man replied, "I shall not be any guiltier for having changed prisons!" (He was unaware, the poor wretch, that the phrase "to the Force!" uttered at the Abbaye meant the death sentence; just as the cry "to the Abbaye," pronounced in the other prisons, sent a victim to the slaughterhouse.) He was shoved outside by the man who had shouted, and he passed through the fatal gateway. He was astonished by the first sword-thrust, but then he dropped his hands and let himself be killed, without a gesture of protest. . . .

I who could never bear the sight of blood—imagine my state when I found myself pushed right under the swords by that inquisitive Fragnières! I was shaking! I felt I was getting weak and threw myself to one side. A shrill scream from a prisoner more sensitive to death than the others instilled me with a wholesome rage, which strengthened my legs enough to leave the place. I did not see the rest. . . .

The killing had started at the Châtelet by then; the crowd moved on to the Force. But I did not go with them; I was hoping to escape these horrors by staying home. I went to bed. A sleep made fitful by the fury of the carnage yielded me only troubled rest, often interrupted by a terrified start. But that was not all. Toward two o'clock I heard a bunch of savages pass beneath my window, none of whom seemed to speak with a Parisian accent; they all sounded unfamiliar to me.[1] They were singing, roaring and howling. In the midst of it all, I heard: "Let's go to the Bernardins! Let's go to Saint-Firmin!" (Saint-Firmin was a priests' residence; the galley slaves were at the Bernardins at the time.) A few of these killers were shouting: "Long live the nation!" One of them—whom I would have liked to see in order to behold the hateful soul in his detestable face—was shouting furiously: "Long live death!" I do not have this second-hand; I heard it myself, and shuddered at it. They meant to kill both the convicts and the Saint-Firmin priests. Among the latter was Abbé Gros, an ex-delegate to the Constituent Assembly, once my priest at Saint-Nicolas-du-Chardonnet, at whose home I had dined with two ladies from Auxerre. He reproached me that evening, in fact, for having expressed some disapproval of priestly celibacy in *La Vie de Mon Père*. Among the killers Abbé Gros saw a man with whom he had had some connection. "Ah, my friend, so you're here too! Well—and what do you all want here at this hour?"

"Oh," the man replied, "we have come for no good. . . . You've been decent to me. . . . But why did you retract your oath?" The man turned his back on the priest, as the kings and Richelieu did to their victims, and gave a signal to his companions. Abbé Gros was not stabbed, he was granted a kinder death; they threw him out of the window. His brain splattered . . . he did not suffer. . . . I shall say nothing of the convicts. Those poor wretches saw an end put to lives that even they could not regret. But earlier in the evening, another horrendous scene—one I did not see, of which I was unaware at the time—had taken place at the Carmelite monastery near the Luxembourg garden. For a few days all the non-juring clergy, arrested either at the city tollgates or during house-visit night, had been brought together there. The bishop of Arles had joined them voluntarily to console and encourage his brethren. And do not think for a moment that I am taking the side of the fanatic priests just because I have related this moving incident! They are my sworn ene-

mies—in my eyes the most despicable beings. No, no, I
do not grieve for them! They have done too much harm
to the country; earlier, by their scandalous behavior
which removed all restraint from the people; later, by
their scheming. There is nothing either good or evil in
the will of the Society: when a Society, or its majority,
wishes something that calls down war and vengeance
upon the nation, it is a monster! He who hopes to
avenge God and His religion is an impious apostate, a
mad blasphemer, claiming to act as God's protector.
God loves but one thing: order. It is order which is
His protection, and order is always found in the will of
the majority; the minority is always in the wrong, even
if it is morally right. It takes only common sense to
see this truth. The priests fancy their creed is essential;
they are wrong; what is essential is fraternal love. They
violate it, even in saying mass. All evil is done to us,
here below, by the fools—specious reasoners, false and
obstinate minds—for these are what constitute the immense mob of fools. . . . But I digress.

The killers entered the monastery at about five
o'clock. The priests had no suspicion of the fate that
awaited them, and several engaged themselves in conversation with the new arrivals, whom they believed to
be an escort that was to accompany them to their destination. One of them, probably bribed, offered to save
the bishop of Arles. The bishop did not deign to listen
to him. "But, I tell you Monsieur l'abbé, I mean
what I say—" Another killer, who had not understood
his words, came over to play a vicious game with his
victim by pulling at his hair, wig or ear: "Come now,
don't act like a child, Monsieur l'abbé!" (A famous
remark, once made to a sham priest climbing the scaffold.) This evidently was too much for the bishop, for
he answered: "What did you say, you scum?" I report this according to someone who heard it. These
words were answered by a sword-thrust which felled

the bishop; he was finished off. Another priest called the executioners "scum" as well. He took more than twenty slashes, repeating all the while, "Scum! Scum! Scum!" Two or three escaped, probably out of the goodness of some killers' hearts.

. . . .

The killers were at the Conciergerie,[2] at the Force. They killed at those two prisons, and at the Châtelet, all through the night. It was at the Conciergerie that Montmorin de Fontainebleau[3] died, and perhaps Montmorin the minister. During that awful night the people played the role of the lords of earlier times, who in the silence and darkness of night slaughtered so many victims, innocent or guilty! It was the people who ruled that night and, through the hideous sacrilege on the part of those agitators, turned despot and tyrant.

Let us rest for a moment. Other scenes await us on the morning of the third at the Force. . . .

I rose from my bed, in a frenzy of fear. The night had not refreshed me at all; it had set my blood aflame. I went out. I listened. I followed the crowds running to see the "disasters"—for that was their term. As I passed the Conciergerie I saw a killer I was told was a sailor from Marseilles, whose wrist was swollen from overexertion. I went on. The front of the Châtelet was lined with mounds of corpses. I started to run off. And yet I followed the crowds. I reached rue Saint-Antoine at the end of rue des Ballets just as a poor wretch, who had seen the man in front of him get killed, set off at top speed as he emerged from the doorway instead of stopping dead in his tracks. A man who was not among the killers but one of those unthinking machines, of which there are so many, stopped him with a pike in the stomach. The poor creature was caught by his pursuers and slaughtered. The man with the pike remarked to us, unruffled, "I didn't know they meant to kill him."

This prelude had almost sent me home, when I was struck by another scene. I saw two women come out: one whom I have come to know since as the interesting Mme. de Saint-Brice, lady in waiting to the erstwhile prince royal;[4] and a young woman of sixteen: she was Mlle. de Tourzel.[5] They were led into the Saint-Antoine church. I followed them. I looked at them closely, as much as their veils would allow. The girl was weeping. Mme. de Saint-Brice was comforting her. They were kept prisoner there. I left after a while; I could not go back. . . . I returned to the end of rue des Ballets. There I saw two other women climbing into a carriage, and in a low voice someone told the driver, "To Sainte-Pélagie." [6] I may be mistaken, but I believe it was the municipal councilman Tallien who gave the order.

There was a pause in the slaughter: something was happening inside. . . . I talked myself into thinking that it was finished. Then a woman appeared, white as a sheet, supported by a doorkeeper. Brusquely she was told: "Shout 'Vive la nation!' "

"No! No!" she said. She was forced up onto a pile of corpses. One of the killers seized the doorkeeper and pulled him away. "Please," the pitiable woman cried, "don't hurt him!" She was told again to shout "Vive la nation!" She refused with disdain. With that, a killer grabbed her, tore off her dress and slit her belly open. She fell, and was finished off by the others. Never in my life had I imagined such atrocity. I wanted to run away but my legs failed. I fainted. When I came to, I saw the blood-soaked head. I was told that they had washed it, curled it, mounted it on the point of a pike and paraded it under the Temple prison windows. Futile cruelty! It could not be seen from there. That unlucky woman was Mme. de Lam-

balle.[7] On my way home I had the satisfaction of
seeing Mme. de Saint-Brice being escorted back to her
parents' house, along with Mlle. de Tourzel. They
were trembling; the fate of d'Angremont, Laporte and
Durosoi[8] had frightened everyone connected with the
court.

The massacre continued. On my way I learned
from a rather trustworthy stranger, who testified to it,
that the dregs of Paris had mingled with the killers
in order to help their comrades escape from prison.
They had control both inside and out, so that they
were masters of life and death. Occasionally, when
several of these felons came along in succession, and
the killers grew impatient with nothing to do, these
scoundrels would murder an innocent man, unbeknownst to the judges, and so it happened that several
patriots were slaughtered. I returned home, wracked
with sorrow and weariness, probably because I had had
no real rest for so long.

Have I forgotten anything of that terrible night
and the day that followed it? I cannot tell! It is too
distressing for me to turn my memory back upon those
atrocious deeds, deeds nonetheless ordered by someone, ordered in cold blood, without the knowledge of
Mayor Pétion or Minister Roland.[9] Then who ordered
them? The cowards are in hiding. They dare not show
themselves. But we can see them behind the veil that
conceals them. If they believe they did right, as their
spokesmen insinuate, then let them come forward and
set forth their reasons! We will lament their error, and
perhaps enlighten them!

What, then, was the true motive for this butchery?
Many people think it was actually done so that the
volunteers, when they set out for the frontiers, would
not have to leave their wives and children at the mercy
of criminals whom the tribunals might acquit and release, whom evildoers might help to escape, and so

on. I wanted to learn the truth, and I may perhaps have discovered it in the end. There was only one purpose—to eliminate the non-juring priests. Some even wanted to eliminate all priests. Now, it was felt that there was still some religious fanaticism, and that such an act, directed explicitly against the priests and against them alone, would arouse certain people. Far from fulfilling the purpose, deportation would only put the priests in the position of an emigrant community possibly more threatening than if they remained. What was to be done with them? Eliminate them. If it had been possible to do this by some means other than killing them, they would not have been killed. So they were killed, and, to camouflage that illegal action, the prison affair was devised. . . .

. . . .

❧ 127 ❧

THE SALPÊTRIÈRE

September 3 to 4, 1792

I kept to my house for the rest of the third, believing the massacre at an end for lack of victims. But in the evening, I learned that I was mistaken; it had only been interrupted for a few moments. I could not believe the report I heard, that eighty prisoners at the Force[1] had taken refuge in an underground passage, from which they were firing on the assailants, and that there was a plan to suffocate them with the smoke from damp straw set at the entrance. I went there. People were still being killed, but more were being saved, and this seemed to confirm what I had been told: that the thieves were rescuing all their comrades. But some

behaved differently: all the counterfeiters of government promissory notes[2] were sending their own kind
to death while pretending to try to save them. The
killing had stopped at the Abbaye, the Conciergerie,
the Châtelet, where there was no one left.

That evening, they fell upon Bicêtre. There the
most violent of the insane were brought out; but they
were judged less scrupulously than in the ordinary
prisons. They were scarcely examined, for two reasons:
the warden, killed first, could not order the registers
brought in; and then they were generally known to be
despicable characters whom the Revolution could not
release. They were shot in the courtyard. Those in the
prison section, on the street floor in the cell block for
the insane, had tried to defend themselves by taking
up arms, but they were wiped out. This is what happened in that prison, unwisely combined with an
asylum.

But one operation remained to be carried out,
which gratified the malefactors and brigands still more.
I learned that it was planned for the fourth, on the
return from Bicêtre. Every pimp and former spy in
Paris was preparing for this operation.

There was one pitiful woman, Desrues' wife,[3]
who after a long prison term during which she had
diverted herself and borne a child—by La Dixmerie,[4]
they say—had in the end been flogged and branded
with an iron on her shoulders, like the Lamotte
woman,[5] and sent to the Salpêtrière jail for life. She
was apparently the main reason for an expedition
against the women of a prison-asylum. It was claimed
she was a schemer, a wicked woman capable of
anything; that she had often declared how delighted
she would be to see Paris drenched in blood and to
set fire to it. What astounds me still is that everyone
knew about this plan, and that no one intervened.
On the contrary, the following morning at seven o'clock

the brigands were accompanied by two officials—to keep order, they said. They arrived—the officials wearing tricolor sashes. In the courtyard a man of the people was shouting his head off: "The Mother Superior! The Mother Superior! Start with her!" That was not part of the plan. The Mother Superior and the sisters, who had appeared, showed the fear this man was instilling in them. "Wait, wait," said a man from Marseilles (and this is accurate; I have it from an eyewitness). "I'll take care of him for you." And he split the man's skull with a sword-blow, then propped him against a wall.

They had the door opened to the women's quarters; as inmates had done at first in the prisons, the women were beside themselves with joy in the belief that they were to be liberated. Here, the register was followed. The women were called according to length of imprisonment. The reason for detention was read out, they were made to leave their own courtyard, and were killed in another. The Desrues woman was the fourth or fifth, and it was she who revealed their fate to all the others by her hideous screams, for the brigands amused themselves by subjecting her to indignities. Nor was her body spared after her death. Was it because they abhorred her husband's crime? No, no—such people feel no abhorrence of crime; but they had heard that she was once beautiful. . . . Ah! If the famous Lamotte had still been there, how *she* would have been treated! Forty women were killed.

But while this bloody scene was taking place in one section of the prison, all the others were overrun by the libertines, the reprobates of France and all Europe. First, the pimps set their harlots free; what a sight to see! It was not a bloody one, but there was never a more obscene. All those miserable women offered their liberators and anyone else what they called their maidenhead. But let us turn our gaze from this scene and cast it upon another, no more decent, no more reassuring, no more moral, but one which at least will not present the repellent spectacle of a double corruption.

The procurers and the coarse men of the mob had only gone into the prostitutes' prison. But other libertines, more fastidious although perhaps still more corrupt, had gone into the quarters of the girls in the poorhouse—that is, those who were raised as public charges. They lead a dismal life. Always in class, always under a mistress's rod, condemned to an eternal celibacy, to bad and disgusting food, they await no greater happiness than to be recruited by someone for work as servants or apprentices in some arduous trade. And, even then, what a life! At the least complaint by an unjust master or mistress, they are taken back into the house for punishment. It is easy to see how listless and unhappy these creatures are. These were the degraded beings, then, thrown haphazardly into society and always oppressed by it, to whom Europe's most immoral and vicious characters made their way. The libertines roamed all the dormitories just as the girls were getting out of bed; they selected those that pleased them and pushed them back on their cots, in the presence of their companions, and took them there.

None of these girls was raped, for none resisted.

Those who gave full satisfaction were taken away by the libertines. A few decent young men, who were merely curious, rescued some of them by taking them away, but only the prettiest.

Since many of these girls are children of poor married folk, it often happens that they have brothers and sisters in the town or country. A brewer's apprentice of Faubourg Saint-Marcel went looking in the dormitory. He noticed a girl being flung down by a heavy German. The girl tried to fight back. The brute threatened to beat her. Suddenly the brewer's boy threw himself on the German and beat him with a short club. Everyone in the crowd was against the lad. "My God! She's my sister! Do you want me to stand here and let her be raped before my eyes?" Then everyone was for him, and he led her away. . . .

One of the prettiest girls found herself pursued by a butcher's boy, who caught her as she was jumping over a cot. He grabbed her where he could; she cried out. The butcher, without troubling over it, was about to take advantage of her when she turned around. "My own brother!" she screamed. The butcher stopped, dressed, and led his sister away. An eyewitness claims that several others were less fortunate; they recognized their close relative only afterwards.

One, however, was very lucky—a young blonde, perhaps the only perfectly beautiful girl in the Hôpital. She seemed to sense her worth better than the others. At the sight of the ravishers, she covered her face with a plaster and smeared grime over the rest. Then she looked over everyone who entered. She singled out from the others a very hale man of some forty years, who was eyeing the girls and appeared to smile at the less ugly. Jacinte Gando—that is the girl's name— quickly cleaned herself, hid her face in a handkerchief, and ran over to the man. She threw herself at him, crying: "Papa, save me!" At the same time she showed him her charming face. The man covered her with his coat and led her off, saying: "She's my daughter!" When they got to his home, Jacinte threw herself around his neck: "Do with me as you wish, but don't ever send me back to the Hôpital!" The man asked if anything had happened to her and was reassured. Thereupon he treated her quite unscrupulously, for he made her sleep with him that very evening, to the knowledge of his servants, but he was no less attached to her for it. He found her to have an excellent disposition and as many good qualities as physical attributes.

When he dressed her as a lady, she was as pretty as any in Paris. What was the outcome? Having made her the mother of a son, born at the beginning of May, he has just married her . . .

The episode with the girls of the poorhouse cut short the pillage of the Salpêtrière. Let us leave this terrible September which will one day be quite famous in our history.

❧ 128 ❧

October 5 to 6, 1792

Meanwhile, the National Convention was in session. There were Marat, side by side with Pétion, and Collot next to Mercier; a grouping such as is expressly forbidden in the Book of Numbers. It may be true that we are not Jews but . . .

It had been noticed that women in hats, and men with the look and dress of the Old Régime were sending signals from neighboring houses to the prisoners in the Temple,[1] that letters arrived in bundles from the laundress, and so on. . . . To avoid these annoyances, the Commune of August 9 and 10 decided that the prisoners should be more strictly confined. The tower was prepared and Louis was transferred there, together with his family. This intensification of precautions made his fate clear to him. Meanwhile, Louis passed the time in reading. He became his son's teacher. His domestic life was in order and it would have been happy if not for the cruel prospect. Never had he been the husband and father he was then.

129

LOUIS' DEFENSE
December 25 to 26, 1792

From the moment Louis appeared before the tribunal of the Convention[1] all attention has turned
on his trial. Defenders were granted permission to
appear. Old Malesherbes[2] came out of retirement
and requested that difficult assignment, one well beyond his powers. Louis named Target,[3] who refused;
then Tronchet and Desèze,[4] who accepted. His counsel
joined him. They were informed of the accusations.
Twenty years earlier, perhaps, Malesherbes would have
known how to proceed. Desèze and Tronchet had not
the slightest idea. Were they to defend a king for his
efforts to regain his authority after his power had been
limited and diminished? No one doubted that he had
done all he could to that end, publicly as well as
privately. Ah, if Louis was guilty in that, he was guilty
of mistakes, of blindess! Guilty of not realizing that
there was only one sensible move to make: throw himself into the arms of his people and by his candor, his
zeal for a Constitution that protected him as it did
all citizens, win back what he had lost through the
bad counsel of the blind men and fools surrounding
him; of not having taken the proper steps either to keep
peace abroad or to force back the enemies. It was of
mistakes that Louis was guilty, of not having understood what fate the foreign powers were preparing for
him; how by helping his brothers and the aristocracy to
power he had fashioned tyrants for himself who hoped

to destroy his authority, as well as the rights of the people. Louis! Louis! Your interests were the same as those of the greater part of the nation, and you did not recognize it. . . . Once the Constitution was drawn, and accepted by you, your interest was no longer that of the nobility, of your brothers, nor of the clergy. If it was religious zeal that attached you to the interests of the latter, you were still in error; the Christian clergy ought not to be rich. You saw Catherine put her clergy on pension—did you treat her as an infidel? Oh, Louis! You were blinded, but you were not criminal. So it was not for a specific crime, known to everyone, that your clumsy, if not culpable, Counsel Desèze should have attempted to expiate you—he could not possibly do that—but he should have said what we all felt: he should have spoken of our political interest in sparing you. The arguments of those who wished your death should have been refuted by clear, luminous reasoning which would have persuaded all of France. But you were not the man for that; it would have taken genius, and you had none. Imagine Mirabeau in your place, or even Linguet, in his better days; he would have made the Convention, and all France, tremble. That is how the half-talented sometimes ruin everything.

I describe in advance the thoughts that occurred to me only during and after hearing Desèze's speeches. On January 16 I left my house to go to hear him, and I succeeded in entering. I glanced over that vast hall where seven hundred men sat in judgment on a king! I saw that guilty monarch, once so great, haled as a criminal before his judges. I could hardly believe it. But in the next instant I said to myself: "It's a man before men, the weakest before the strongest; a king before men who want to be done with kings. This one is in their way. What will they do with him?" These thoughts were a terrible strain to me. To ease my mind,

I visualized the succession of centuries; I saw the men of 1992[5] reading our tale; I strove to hear them, and I did hear them. The severity of their judgment frightened me. It seemed to me that some of them reproached us for having lacked humanity, while the extremists, of the sort that exists today, approved our actions. I seemed to see that all of Europe had adopted a new government; but I saw on history's pages what terrible shocks her peoples had undergone. I seemed to hear the readers remark to one another: "How fortunate we are not to have lived in those horrible times when men's lives counted for nothing!" One of their philosophers exclaimed, "These shocks are needed from time to time to make men realize the value of serenity, just as an illness is necessary to realize the value of health."

"But," asked one of his comrades, "would you have preferred to be the shocker or the shocked?"

"No, no, I would not want to be shocked, but I would not mind having been. Past affliction, when one has not died of it, is a cause for rejoicing."

"Ah, listen to them, the debaters!" cried a visionary skulking in a corner. "You were they; you were the men of two hundred years ago. You are made up of their organic molecules and you live in peace because those molecules are weary of having been at war. You'll get back to it, after a long rest."

Here Desèze woke me.

After the Desèze plea, to which I listened attentively, Louis and his defenders were told to withdraw. Complete calm reigned. There was none of that great agitation that eloquence brings on; Desèze's oration had stirred no one but himself and me (. . .). The assembly was long in dispersing, and night fell.

. . . .

130

January 20 to 21, 1793

I left the Café de Foi and went into the Café de Chartres, at the corner of rue Montansier. . . . I looked out through the window. Henriette and Adelaide saw me and beckoned to me. They were prettier than ever; yet, they seemed dejected. I went out to speak to them.

"We are lost!" they said to me.

"Oh . . . why?"

"Let's go into the garden," said Henriette, "there is no one there; we'll tell you." We went to the garden and took the most deserted paths.

"Since you last saw us, my sister and me, the luckiest thing happened to us. A man, formerly poor, who loved us like a father, suddenly became rich. He wished us as much good as you yourself do, and besides, he had the means to help us. He did. We became independent, my sister and I, not so as to misbehave, but to be . . . what we have always wanted. We were happy for several months."

"Ah, only too happy," exclaimed Adelaide, "it couldn't last."

"Imagine," resumed Henriette, "since we became independent by his daily kindnesses we had nothing to do but benefit from the instruction of our dancing and music teachers, then work on fashions for ourselves. Then we used to dine with him, then on to see a show from his box! After that, we had an ideal supper, ordering whatever we felt like. With our independence

—oh, what great happiness!—we could face the whole human race with pride. You know us, so judge if we neglected to! From there, we went home, braving every approach, shunning all offers, and looked forward to a night of repose and refreshing sleep. So much for our good fortune . . . here's the bad. Louis has been condemned: Louis—whom we neither loved nor hated, whom we didn't know—is going to die. And our protector has sworn . . . not to outlive him . . . or at the very least to emigrate. . . . We'll fall once more into the abyss! Imagine our despair! Oh, it's inexpressible, and we have already resolved to kill ourselves, in some manner . . . that is not too painful. Tell us, which way is the least painful?"

"I wouldn't know about such things, but may I not say a word to your protector?"

"I'll see about it, and tell him you are coming," replied Adelaide. She ran ahead of us. I walked slowly along in the same direction with Henriette.

Adelaide reappeared as we reached the door. "He would very much like to see you; let's go up." When I saw the man, on the second floor, I thought I recognized him. I told him the two girls had confided in me, and begged him to tell me the reasons for his sorrow.

"I have none, other than despair over the welfare of France."

"You don't mean it! We are prospering!"

"Don't credit that kind of prosperity! Dumouriez is in a rage. Dumouriez is playing a game which would make you tremble! . . . But I will die before those misfortunes. . . . My two girls know you; who are you?" I introduced myself.

"I know of you! One of our friends, a man from rue Bergère, has mentioned you; he saw you at Gemonville's. He spoke well of you at first; lately, his opinion has changed. What have you done to him?"

"Nothing."

"Be discreet about what my two children have told you, until my death; the secret won't burden you for long." I promised him. And, in fact, I had only to bear the weight of his secret for twenty-four hours. But he did provide for his two girls.

. . . .

At seven o'clock, we were at the Temple. At eight, Louis came out. . . . But I should report certain details here, which I have from an eyewitness.

After hearing the decree which condemned him to lose his life, Louis had eaten supper, had gone to bed and had slept soundly. However, alone for a moment after the fateful sentence, he had been heard pacing back and forth, exclaiming: "The murderers! The murderers!" As his confessor he had requested a nonjuring priest who lived on rue du Bac, and this was granted him. He closeted himself alone with him. He had made his will, with the help of that priest, on the evening of December 26. He saw his family and did not bid them farewell. In the morning he was awakened by Cléri, his personal valet, upon orders from the two officials sent by the Commune. He got up. When the two emissaries had presented themselves Louis asked one of them, Jacques Roux, a priest, to transmit a parcel to the municipal body. Jacques Roux said, "I cannot; I have been sent here to take you to the scaffold." Louis replied, "Of course," and he charged someone else with the packet, which was delivered to its destination.

He left at eight o'clock, in Mayor Chambon's carriage, alone with his confessor. Two nights before, his counsel had been dismissed. He traveled along the boulevards, between two files of national guards, who sent the people away from their windows. He proceeded slowly. He reached the Place des Tuileries, formerly Place Louis-XV, at quarter past nine. He left the coach. At the foot of the scaffold his hands were tied togther; free hands would impede an execution by guillotine. He stepped up. The military instruments sounded. He moved forward to speak from the edge of the scaffold, facing north. The instruments stopped for a moment, but an order from the officer in charge set them going again. Louis spoke; the word "Forgive" was the only one heard. On a signal, the executioners brought him back to the block, and in the wink of an eye he ceased to live. . . .

. . . .

I walked home, dazed; everyone was—yes, the stupefaction was universal. "He was only a man!" said the quasi-philosophical rationalists. Agreed: but that man had a direct relation with every individual in France. Each of us felt an intimate acquaintance with him—a man whose name resounded unceasingly in one's ears, and in whose name was accomplished all good and all evil for a long while. He was only a man, but he was the rallying point for twenty-four million men. This was why the stupefaction was universal. But now, justly condemned by the nation, Louis was nothing more than a criminal. He could finally be given the detestable name of tyrant, and he had done enough evil to deserve it. I am a good citizen, peaceable, humane, no federalist, much less an anarchist; convinced of the inadequacy of human laws, I still feel that a society cannot exist without them. I feel something more: that they must not be touched except with the greatest caution, as the shock resulting from any change in them always engenders the real and very palpable evil of depriving men of their customs.

NIGHT INSPECTION.
THE PALAIS-L'ÉGALITÉ
January 27 to 28, 1793

The evening of the twenty-seventh I went early to the Palais-Royal, and finding none of those men or women there who sometimes detain me, I was about to leave before nine o'clock, when all of a sudden I saw the national guards arrive and bar all exits. Contrary to the usual practice, they permitted people to enter, but let no one leave. I learned that this inspection of the Palais-l'Égalité took place on the orders of the Convention's surveillance committee which had just, by decree, reduced its previous number of twenty-four to twelve. The reason—or the pretext—was to find the assassin Pâris[1] who, it was said, was hidden there; to catch red-handed all the gamblers, and to find emigrés or suspect persons taking refuge in this chaotic center of a large city.

At first I had no desire to leave; I wanted to see the outcome of the inspection. Pâris was not there—at least not any longer—or else he escaped. But they found gamblers in abundance, and several emigrés. As I waited I spoke to various groups of citizens—men and women—who wanted very much to go home to bed. It had not yet occurred to us that you might leave by showing your card. In the meanwhile, at every minute we witnessed new episodes with various outcomes. Those inspected, and the inspectors as well, were of all kinds. Once it was a constitutional priest

sleeping with a tender lass about fourteen years old:
"Hey! Monsieur l'abbé, you can marry now!"

"That creates too many problems!"

"I understand: you're not chaste enough to take
an honest woman."

Then, inside, it was a secret lover who had followed his young paramour on her walk, unbeknownst
to her parents, who were aristocratic merchants from
rue Saint-Denis. He was dressed in the uniform of the
national guard; elegant and handsome, his martial appearance enthralled the young lady. They had hoped
only to catch a glimpse of each other, but in the commotion the pretty girl lost her parents and went off
. . . to lose something else. . . . Afterward, she
searched for them and found them by having them
paged by the hawkers. Ah, how the lover blesses the
surveillance committee! . . .

In another spot they were leading a very rich, fat
clockmaker out of a prostitute's room; the girl, who
feared arrest, followed half-dressed. Entering the garden, the two of them were met by the clockmaker's
wife, who had come with the most elegant of his apprentices: she rushed up to her husband. "Who's this
you're with, monsieur? A strumpet?"

"That is not so, madame; I am not a strumpet! I
am a kept woman!"

"What! The impertinence!"

"Be quiet, woman. Let's have no scandal. Do you
think I don't see who you're with?"

"Who I'm with! Who I'm with, monsieur! Why,
I took the arm of one of your helpers to come and find
you. Get rid of that girl."

"If he leaves me, what will become of me then,
I ask you? He took me from my mother's house; he
gave me a pretty room and a louis a week, and just
now a twenty-five-franc note! Do you think I can go

back to my mother? If it were only she . . . but my
father will put me in the workhouse!"

"Hussy!"

"Hussy yourself, madame! If your husband keeps
me, I'd wager that you keep that handsome man; for
he's a real fashion plate . . ."

A slap from the woman kept her from finishing.
There was a huge circle of scoffers. An officer of the
national guard, who knew the merchant, came over:
"For shame, Monsieur and Madame Bultel! The scene
you are making is scandalous! You, monsieur, take your
girl to her room: this inspection is neither for you nor
for her; and you, madame, who were so gay just a
short time ago at Ferrier's restaurant; go on back there
—you still have a bottle of champagne to finish." And
taking her by the arm, he led her aside and said to
her, "When a person is guilty, it takes real brass
to come and make a spectacle of herself!" Then the
officer sent for the girl's mother. It was apparent that
the woman had sold her daughter; she came quietly.
They sent her away and said to the merchant, "You
may keep the girl: you harm neither your wife, who
looks out for herself, nor the girl, whose mother would
ruin her without you anyway" . . .

🎄 132 🎄

LOOTING OF THE GROCERS

February 26 to 27, 1793

A dark melancholy had me in its grip; despite the
reports of our army's success, some uneasiness plagued
me. Was it a premonition of our misfortunes? The
city felt the same thing. A horde of agitators ran

rampant everywhere, sent and paid, rumor had it, by the English or by the court of England, for the two are not the same. I went out toward five o'clock, shortly before nightfall. Scarcely had I taken a few steps along the quay than I saw an assault upon the grocery across from the Pont de la Tournelle. The pretext, I gathered, was the cost of soap. I saw the common women of Paris—these people so different from those out in the country because they have been debased unwittingly, because they are insignificant and hidden, because formerly the rich man, through ancient and wrongful habit, always addressed them in a manner and tone they would use for a dog—I saw these women riotously attack and destroy, without a thought for the next day. . . . I reflected: "Here are two grocers under attack (for the one at the Grands-Degrés corner was too, and I had not noticed it). These are agitators who have come to stir up these stupid people—these boatwives embittered by hard lives who, like animals, see no further than the present place and time, who feel the same envy toward the grocer's wife with her finer dress and better grooming as a bourgeoise feels toward a solicitor's or a lawyer's wife, and which these latter in turn feel toward the wives of the financier and the nobleman! A common woman does not believe she can do too much to cut the grocer's wife down to her own level. She does not understand that if the grocer's wife is not better off, she will be in no position to keep merchandise always in stock and ready to be sold; that if there is no stock, she, a laundress, will often have to wait for the shopkeeper to go and get it; that she would waste her days, lose time and clients; that she would want for bread. None of this penetrates her stupid head; and the agitators, the traitors, who come to set her moving take heed not to tell her that she is acting against her own interests. But why do the sections not do so, instead of

busying themselves with so many trivial things during
their long, tiresome and noisy sessions? Because the
agitators are constantly at the sections."

I proceeded along the Pont de la Tournelle. On
the Île, the grocers had not yet been attacked, but at
the Port au Blé, on rue de la Mortellerie, it was plain
looting! A despicable bricklayer was coming out of
the shop at the corner of rue des Barres with seven
sugar loaves. I pointed him out to the women, who
divested him of them. I have always seen, thought, said
and written that the uninformed masses are the greatest
enemy of any government. Attired like them, the agitator addresses himself to those stupid creatures. I
know only one remedy for the ailment in a land where
the masses rule: not equal distribution of wealth—
that is impossible, and would have to be done over
again all the time—but a community of property, such
as I proposed in 1782, in my *Anthropographe* [An-
drographe]. That plan alone, wisely executed and per-
fected, could reconcile everything. If this is not accepted, then coercion must be exercised against the
people, and in that case there will be no more equality;
for the people will never understand that by the present system, wherein all property is separate, the
wealthy are necessary, for they are repositories of political power; that it would be the greatest disaster if
everyone were lazy, unskilled or without a livelihood
like the ancestors of the poor, or the poor themselves;
that with the present system, property must be protected, and excessive fortunes should be prohibited
only when they are in land, because those who have too
much land put some into luxury acreage, which is thus
lost to cultivation. This is the great, the eternal truth.
If anyone but I had written the *Anthropographe*, I
would preach it from the rooftops, and I would have
introduced it at the National Convention; but I do
not like to put myself forward.

The extent of the abuses and even crimes committed during the looting of the grocers could never be known. Our worst elements, joining forces with the foreign agitators, carried out a veritable sack, like the plundering of a city taken in war. There was one grocer, a very rich man but one who does not want to broadcast his misfortune; I was told how he was invaded by six scoundrels, allegedly from the neighborhood—three of them masters, and three servants. After they had robbed him of his silverware but left his bonds and certificates, they bound his wife and his two very lovely daughters by a first wife to the bedposts; they had raped them, that is, the masters had, while the servants stood present, swords in hand and pistols ready in their belts; this crime was committed with a degree of consideration which bespoke a certain passion, but in the presence of the grocer, bound hand and foot; they had repeated the act three times, allowing their victims to rest and caressing them, now gently, now excitedly; after this performance, they had untied them and urged them to calm themselves; then they withdrew, the masters backing off, escorted by their servants, pistols in hand and ready to fire; his wife and his daughters had turned first to unfetter him, which had given the three scoundrels the time to get away. "For," he said, "I do not count their cowardly servants as men!" How just it is that that class has not been admitted to the status of citizen!

In another shop of the same kind, three bandits lured the master and mistress into their bedroom on the second floor, bound them, and applied heat to their feet until they had shown where everything of value was—gold, silver, bonds, fine linen, laces, silken gowns. Everything was removed, and the two poor souls, more frightened than hurt, were tossed still bound onto their bed, where they were left.

I could go on endlessly reporting other tales of

plunder and thievery, but they would only be more of
the same. I must proceed now to what I saw.

That night I roamed rue Saint-Antoine, and thereabouts; the Pelletier, Gèvres, and Ferraille quays; rues
de l'Arbre-Sec, Saint-Honoré, la Nouvelle-Halle, rues
J.-J. Rousseau, Verdelet, des Vieux-Augustins, des
Petits-Champs, and thereabouts. In rue Montmartre
I saw two women, a daughter and her mother, emerge
from the doorway of a grocery under siege. They were
not the grocer's wife and daughter; the mother was
one of my old acquaintances, whom I had seen only
once since her marriage, in 1786—that is to say, after
six years, for she had been wed the 11th of July, 1780,
as it is inscribed on the Île.

"Madame! where are you off to?"

"Ah, monsieur! I am rushing to the section to tell
them the grocer is being murdered in his apartment
on the second floor! His wife and daughter are screaming horribly!"

"Go on, madame. You'll find me here; I shall use
your name and try to get in."

I went into the building; I got into the shop, and
took the inside stairway to the upper floor. Reaching
the bedroom, I saw three bandits gripping the grocer,
and three others holding his wife, his son and his
daughter. I knew one of them, who had worked for
me once. I drew back toward the door, and from there
I shouted, "So-and-so, I know you; you are done for,
you and your accomplices." At the same time, I
plunged down the stairs. I heard some clatter; they
were opening the stairway door. A moment later, the
grocer's son called: "Monsieur! Say, monsieur! They've
left!" I climbed the stairs again. The six robbers were
in fact gone. I was thanked as a liberator. Who were
those men? Six unemployed workmen who were taking
the opportunity to make a little extra money. Such is
the disastrous consequence of the excessive wages paid

the workers in certain trades. The ease of earning turns them into wastrels; the wretched holidays arrive; they demand extra pay for working on those days, and on the next they proceed to consume that bonus, and more; their gullet grows hot and their elbows bend; they utilize every means, up to and including crime, to obtain resources. I have said this before: "There is nothing more immoral, more foolish, than two holidays in succession; think of three! A midweek holiday in the large cities is a day of chaos provided by government and religion; it is a crime of 'lese society'!" Let them ask me, who knows the working class better than anyone else. I am amazed each day anew that the electors of Paris have not sought out the most enlightened laborer for the Convention, the most enlightened craftsman, the most enlightened merchant, the most upright from among the men of letters; for, if they exist, they constitute so rare a phenomenon that it should be made known. That would have been better than certain . . . It is perhaps not fitting to name them, despite the freedom of the press; as the proverb goes: "Not all truths are fit for telling."

I went back by way of rue Saint-Honoré, where I saw a crowd around the grocery shop on the corner of rue des Poulies. What caught my eye was a woman who was trying to spur the mob to break in the doors. I moved closer in order to ask the reasons for her fury. "Why, citizen," she said to me, "this man has a boot shop besides!"

"Then Madame is a bootmaker?"

"No," the man who accompanied her said curtly, "but Madame does not wish a man to have several trades."

"Monsieur is then a former official of his guild?" [1]

The man and the woman moved off.

"It's much worse than that!" a man who had

heard us said quite loudly to me. "He is an old commissioner! He's N—ch." He mentioned a well-known name. . . . "Aha!" I exclaimed. "I understand: Monsieur and Madame want to restore the Old Régime." At these words, you should have seen N—ch and his wife run. They disappeared in an instant. . . .

. . . .

❧ 133 ❧

RAVAGES

February 28, 1793

We have reached the eve of the worst calamities, and they have already begun without our knowledge. Alas, on the very day a piece of good news reaches us from afar, a disaster overwhelms us where the news had set out from some days earlier. The looting of the grocers proclaimed the movements of insurrection in the Vendée[1] and Loire-Inférieure departments, but it did not indicate our losses abroad. Just as Paris seemed to be settling down again, and the sections had sworn to protect property, an unexpected, inexplicable, inconceivable event wrought fear in every heart.

One Saturday at ten o'clock in the evening, eighty armed men appeared on rue Serpente. Twenty blocked off one end of the street, twenty barred the other. They wore the uniform of the dragoons. Forty entered the pressroom of the *Chronique,* a once patriotic newspaper which had fallen into questionable hands and turned federalist;[2] they wrecked the type and the presses, shredded the printed sheets even for other works, completed this destruction in five minutes, and vanished at the outcry of a private party whom they had kept from going about his business. A committee from the Théâtre-Français section assessed the damages. It would not be difficult to trace the source; someone from the corner of rue des Mathurins had known of the plunder plan a day before (he boasted of it.) Where had he learned of it? I cannot understand the lack of common sense in some people. They should be put to shame for it, for they should either prevent the crime or hold their tongues.

While that incident was taking place on rue Serpente, or after it was completed, it was repeated in the home of a man who was much guiltier yet, for he was a deputy, a charlatan and an untrustworthy character. This man was obliged to flee when he heard that his life was threatened. He slipped unrecognized through the band of marauders, with two pistols in hand, and since he feared he would be recognized at the door, he leaped over a garden wall.

Panckoucke,[3] for his *Moniteur*, and Prudhomme,[4] for his *Révolutions*, escaped the fate of the two others by taking up arms; the first even had a cannon in position in his courtyard. I was greatly astonished when I passed rue Serpente and found it blockaded. I did not know whom to ask about it. Why has there been no law put through to the effect that any military operation in the Republic carried out by day, and more especially by night, must be explained to any citizen who inquires? Then we would know when a crime is being committed by brigands, for if they did not come up with an answer they would be exposed. Why is it not forbidden to stop individuals walking alone from going through a street? The day the grocers were looted a sentry sergeant tried to stop me from returning home along rue des Vieilles-Étuves-Saint-Honoré. He told me brusquely that I had gone by three times already, and that I had not yet explained my presence. And what if I did pass by three times, as long as I was alone and peaceable? . . . But the brute told others the same thing; he was determined to take advantage of his moment of power to order someone about. A good many laws of detail remain to be formulated before free citizens can enjoy their freedom. . . . Thus, I went on none the wiser. Nor was I for the rest of the evening, as I did not return to that quarter. I went to the Café Robert-Manouri, whose large clientèle made it as entertaining as it was instructive. After a moment of relaxation, I visited the Palais-Égalité;[5] then I left there by rue Vivienne and went on to rue Saint-Fiacre.

SUPER-
NUMERARY
NIGHTS

❧ 134 ❧

SETBACKS

April 2, 3, 4, 1793

Our victories ceased at the end of February, 1793, and
our losses occurred so rapidly that they stagger the
imagination. But console yourself, O France! They
result neither from your weakness nor from your lack
of courage. . . . Cunning scoundrels are responsible
for your reverses, which they will pay for with their
heads.

The recapture of Frankfurt by the Prussians was
our first setback. It shocked the French. The tempest
which drove Truquet's ship from Sardinia was the
second. The third was frightful: we were basking in a
profound sense of security. Our armies, it was said,
were conquering Holland! This was impressed upon us;
and while we believed that a monster[1] was at the gates
of Amsterdam, which was eager to open them to him,
that infamous creature was meeting with the emissaries of Francis and Frederick William! May all
traitors perish! May all the aristocrats still within our
country perish who rejoice over their country's disasters!
. . . And the anarchists—those madmen who believe
we can exist in a state of events that is advantageous
solely to them—let them likewise perish!

Our fourth setback took place at Aix-la-Chapelle,
where our troops were surprised as a result of the

treason of the generals, most of them in conspiracy
with the most infamous of men, the immoral Dumouriez. . . . The commissioners of the Convention
at Liège made an about-face; they had the Treasure
removed from that city. Liège, our friend, our confeder-
ate, fell again under the power of its tyrants. O Liège,
I wept for you as for my own country! We were deceived; the traitor Dumouriez, who deliberately lingered
in Holland, proclaimed that he was going to protect
the rest of Belgium, and the traitor surrendered it!
Louvain, Malines, Brussels, Bruges—all have been surrendered as far as Antwerp and Ostend; there, even
the dubious Commodore Moreton was turned over
with his ships to the English and Dutch fleets. Breda
and Gertruydenberg are evacuated and left to the
wrath of the *Stadtholder*. Yes, Dumouriez saves our
honor; without his betrayal, which exonerates us, we
would be debased in the eyes of Europe, of the Universe, and we should have deserved the fate of unfortunate Poland! . . .

At last the traitor removed his mask! Not content
with disobeying the Convention, he carried out the
most despicable act and committed the most horrible
crime: he had the commissioners seized and sent them,
in a closed carriage, to Tournai, to the enemy general
—Cobourg—who, if he keeps them, is an infamous
monster like Dumouriez. I am writing this on April 5,
and I await the outcome.

The evening of the second we learned of the report issued by the commissioners of the executive
branch. No one believed it. By the evening of the
third, all that I have reported was known. Upon receipt
of this terrible news, all Paris collected in groups in
the streets. I approached everyone I saw, to learn the
reaction of the public. I noticed that one group at the
foot of the Pont Saint-Michel was gathered around a
paid agitator who was trying to mislead it. I spoke in

a low voice to several sensible citizens, who then left him and led others away with them. The group at the Place du Pont Neuf was much more favorably composed; I had only to second it. Its whole atmosphere was for union, agreement, while that agitator was encouraging the citizens to fall upon all suspected aristocrats and stab them. No doubt he was a brigand . . . The group at the Place des Trois-Maries was in a rage; but it didn't seem to me there were any brigands there; I only heard several of those undisciplined workers who wish to charge so much for labor that it would be impossible for anyone to hire workers unless there were only one nation in the world and, consequently, no competition; for when the cost of labor is too high, all the arts and professions in that country flag; the citizens procure what they need from abroad, and no foreign nation can buy from their country except at exorbitant prices. This is what the stupid laborer does not understand. Nothing irritates me more than ignoramuses and blockheads, despite the futility of getting upset over what comprises three quarters and a half of the world. Say that to them in a group, and they won't listen to you. You cannot make yourself understood by anyone because that would take a cool-headed discussion. However, in other respects this group showed good sense about public affairs.

The Palais-Égalité was full, but nothing compared to the Tuileries. Everywhere the same talk; agitators here, good people there. I enlisted five or six groups of the latter to go over to the opposition group to revile the malevolent, and I was successful enough in this. I was recognized in the Tuileries by a man who called me by name. I was not happy at this; his tone displeased me and he seemed to be up to no good. I said to a woman beside me who had spoken to me, "Do you know this man?" She glanced at him and nudged me with her elbow. I bent an ear toward her, and she said, "He's from my own ward, the Pikestaffs; I don't know his name, but I will know it by tomorrow. He speaks there sometimes and is not very well thought of."

The man noticed that she was speaking to me of him, and, thinking her my acquaintance, he went off. I followed him with my eyes. He moved near the door of a café which the court had prohibited in July, 1792, and he hid behind someone with whom he seemed to be speaking in a whisper. I pointed them out to the woman. "Well, I know the other," she said to me, "he was a clerk in the War Office. He was dismissed." Since I had no connection with men of that class, I grew calm. Nevertheless, I kept my eye on the two men. The one who had called me by name got up and came after me. I moved around as fast as he approached, and thus avoided him. He turned toward the other man and said, "He's gone now, it will have to wait until another time." I stood still, watching . . .

Again I found the woman who had spoken to me. "Do you know what strange thing happened on the Île Saint-Louis?" she said. "I'll tell you, for although I don't know you, I have often seen you. They've had a man under surveillance there. As he was described to me, he resembled you—your manner of dress, your face."

"I know what that is about," I replied. "It's Dupont de Nemours, an ex-Constituent, they have a grudge against. They killed a man who they mistook for him. I could have been that other man if I still walked on the Île every evening, as I used to do under the despots—it was my only consolation. I would inscribe my fears and my griefs there. At present, I no longer need that solace. But if I were to feel such a need again, I would have to do without it. The rabble, who should no longer be such since the Revolution, still exists; and it is more dangerous than ever.

Not until this generation is gone will the population be purified. I can't tell you what contempt I feel for the good-for-nothings who foul, distort, dishonor, and corrupt the best things. The common belief is that it was the ambition of the kings, of the mighty, that produced despotism. No! It was the insolence of the rabble! I believe that all men began by being equal, for why shouldn't they have been? But the rabble—the idlers, the gluttons, the malicious of every sort—have remained poor whereas the diligent, the painstaking and the hard-working have won themselves a good and plentiful life. The indigent rabble grew bitter: it jeered, it stole, it killed. So the haves united, gave themselves a leader, arms, soldiers. This led to royal or authoritarian government, and this to despotism itself —wealth and comfort preferring the domination of one man to the anarchy of the rabble. They considered no measure too extreme in suppressing that despicable mob, and in the end they found themselves enslaved. They moaned at the discovery, but they preferred their enslavement to the perpetual danger of pillage and massacre. Ah, how much we have to hold against the rabble—worthless, incompetent, undeserving, which has reduced us to this cruel extremity! Such is still the horrible fate that our anarchists are preparing for us today—the Brissots, the Guadets, the . . ."

"I think you are right," the woman replied.

135

MARAT'S TRIUMPH

April 24, 1793

Marat—the name says everything—had been indicted by a previous order. A warrant was issued for his arrest.

He didn't believe he had to obey. One would have thought he would have played the abject imitator of Socrates. Is it not more admirable to be a true original? He even claimed that it was magnanimity that kept him from submitting to the decree. *He wanted to prevent his enemies from committing a crime!* He was right. From the outcome, one saw that it was indeed a crime, for Marat was a true patriot. What resources Innocence has when it wishes to avoid a false proceeding which is displeasing to it!

The Revolutionary Tribunal did not let the patriot Marat languish. His turn came quickly. It was not a trial, it was a triumph. The accused arrived surrounded by guards; women known for their patriotism covered him with flowers and escorted him into the courtroom. There, Marat sat down where he pleased, answered as he pleased; he even questioned the judges. All that he did was well done; all that he said was well said. Everything that he had written had shown profound wisdom; and whatever he might have seemed to exaggerate was verified by subsequent events. He cleared himself of the charge and an honorary wreath was bestowed upon him. He returned in triumph, led through the streets like Mordecai; and his accusers very nearly suffered Haman's fate . . . which won't be long in coming. . . . How can it be forgiven the *Journal du soir* for having reported his plea in such a way as to weaken it! What perfidy! Is this the way to treat a patriot? . . . As for me, I dedicate this chapter to Marat's triumph, and if I wished, I could add what I said to his friend, Citizen Dubois. But at the moment, suffice it to know that this famous man would have become so under any circumstances, thanks to his rare abilities.

On May 31 and on June 1 and 2, when the issue will be the seizure and the expulsion of twenty-two or thirty-two members from the Convention, Marat will

not jeer at the fate of the punished. He will no doubt
expel himself voluntarily from the Assembly, and in
an action without precedent fuse the role of accused
with that of accuser. Never has there been anything
like this! He continued to play this role for the remain-
der of his admirable life.

On May 1 something happened of a nature quite
different from those things which occupied my attention only too much. I had gone out early to celebrate
on my Île the first day of the most beautiful month of
the year. I was strolling quietly along, carefully avoid-
ing any encounter with the children of the people,
when I saw before me two women chattering gaily.
I listened to them for about half an hour, and I shall
relate the tale one of them told, as closely as I can.

The ci-devant[1] who married a sans-culotte[2]

A rich nobleman—when there still were some—
who had not so far wished to marry, was alarmed at
the threats being made to the aristocrats. He resolved
to take a wife and to put himself under the protection
of the sans-culottes by allying himself with them.
However, this way seemed difficult to him, for although they were not haughty, he didn't know how
to approach them. While he was pondering the problem one day, as he walked along rue de la Bûcherie,
he noticed a young sans-culotte nymph passing by
with her mother; she was dressed in red linen, but
smart as a sou, in the days when there were any. Quite
apart from any other motive, he found her charming
and felt that happiness would consist of being loved
by her. In another time, had he been sufficiently
enamored and the girl virtuous enough, he would have
revealed his intentions immediately and offered his
fortune. Today, however, the ci-devant keeps his status
secret. Luckily he wore the uniform of the national

guard. He followed them to the doorstep of their little one-story house. There he greeted the mother pleasantly.

"You seem to know me, citizen," she said, "but I can't say that I know you."

"Perhaps I'm mistaken," replied the ci-devant. "I took you for . . ." He was about to mention a name when a laundress with a little basket on her arm came up to them, and assuming the right of any pretty girl to interrupt the conversation, she said, "Madame Chantocé, here are your bonnets and yokes. . . . Good day, Marie Louise. Don't tell me you're interested in that . . . whatever-he-is . . . painter, engraver, draftsman?"

"No, no," answered Madame Chantocé. "That would be a fine thing in these times. Who wants to die of hunger? I'd prefer a soldier with a good character."

"I want none such either," said Marie Louise modestly. "But, Mama, the citizen is speaking to you. Answer him while I go sort our things."

"Do that, daughter," said Mother Chantocé. "Citizen, you were saying . . . you took me for whom?"

"For a Breton, from Vanade, four leagues from Chantocé and three from Ancenis."

"Well, you know my country at least! My family is from Oudon; but my man was from Chantocé, thus his name."

"Madame, I am happy to know you. Allow me to come in with you and we'll talk."

"Gladly, citizen! What's your name?"

"Gemonville, at your service. I lived for a long while in Nantes, then in La Roche-Bernard, called today La Roche-Sauveur, after that brave patriot Sauveur whom the rebels murdered because he wasn't of their mind."

"Well, I see you are a patriot and a good Breton."

"Haven't I seen you in Marillac, madame?"

"No, I have always lived in Paris, where I was born; but my father was from Pontchâteau, three leagues from La Roche-Sauveur—as you say it's now called."

"Well, then we really are among friends, Citizen Chantocé; so much so that . . . well, here I am all of a sudden in love with your lovely daughter, whose hand in marriage I will ask as soon as you know me better."

"Heavens, Citizen Gemonville, I like the way you lead up to that! Isn't he a scream, Marie Louise?" Marie Louise blushed without answering. "Come, come, citizen—when we know each other. . . ."

"Yes," resumed Gemonville, "that's all I ask, to have the chance to know you better, Citizen Chantocé; and your lovely daughter Marie Louise as well; for since I have been ready for marriage I have seen no one else I wanted for a life's companion. It seems to me that one could not help but be happy, coming home in the evening, or at any other hour, to find such a pretty welcomer as she, and as good a mother as you, Citizen Chantocé."

"Ah, listen to him! Come now, citizen, one would almost think you were serious."

"So serious that I propose marriage however you'd like it—performed before the municipality, or even in a church if you think it more binding, citizen."

"You know, Marie Louise, he's a handsome lad. Well, citizen, to begin the acquaintanceship: my daughter has her trousseau; she's an only child; she'll get everything. We had a little property in Brittany in Pontchâteau, which brought in three hundred livres of rent, taking one year with the next, but we don't have it any longer. What do you have, citizen?"

"I, citizen? I had four houses in Lorient bringing in three thousand livres, taking one year with the next; in Nantes, two houses let for storage bringing in four thousand livres—I will prove it to you before the wedding, Citizen Chantocé."

"It's obvious, citizen, that you *were* wealthy, but are you now?"

"Yes, citizen, and if I weren't in a position to provide for such a pretty girl as your daughter, I would not have offered myself outright. I will show you proof of all this whenever you wish."

"Indeed! Well then, Marie Louise? . . . We will see about this, citizen. In the meantime, there are some peas on the fire; if you wish to join us, you're welcome."

"So that's what smells so good," said Gemonville ingenuously. And he thought to himself: "I will see by the speed with which Marie Louise sets the table if I please her."

Marie Louise, red as a rose, or like a pretty cherry still on the tree, set the table in the twinkling of an eye. On the table she placed three silver goblets that had been wrapped in cloth and their best saltcellar; the soup was poured into a flowered tureen, which wasn't usually used, and fine faïence plates were taken from the buffet. She went to the cellar, and the two bottles she brought out had been silted up.

"Good," said Gemonville, "it will be all right."

They dined gaily, that is to say, the suitor and Citizen Chantocé, for the girl was a bit uneasy. Gemonville asked permission to return the next day with his papers, and asked Citizen Chantocé to have someone present whom she trusted. She agreed, and he went away lest they tire of him.

Mother and daughter spoke only of him. Marie Louise agreed that he was pleasing, had wit, and wasn't self-seeking; her mother that he was handsome and polite. "We shall see what comes of this," she added. "But he's very rich! . . . For the rest, as one always exaggerates we will be lucky enough if he has a third as much as he says the day after the marriage."

As for Gemonville, he was enchanted with Marie Louise, and very pleased with her mother. He resolved even more strongly to marry her and so surround himself with all the sans-culottes of his wife's acquaintance.

He returned the next day and found Citizen Chantocé surrounded by her family, as well as a solicitor summoned to discuss business. Gemonville impressed everyone with his courtesy and candor—without speaking of his former status. He showed himself a good Breton, a patriot and ready to sacrifice himself for it. He withheld his landed name, and used only the name of Gemonville. Because he was pressing, Madame Chantocé drew up a list of terms then and there. He offered the future bride even more than they had asked; in short, he showed such uprightness and good will towards Marie Louise that everyone congratulated her. Afterwards, there was a sumptuous dinner. Gemonville asked permission to contribute to it, and the rest of the day was spent joyfully. That evening, before parting, the mother allowed a moment of *tête-à-tête* to the couple. Gemonville used it well. He showed such tender, generous, decent feelings that he touched the heart that his good appearance had already disposed in his favor.

He came by in the morning to invite the ladies to honor him with a visit. His lodgings were unpretentious, which was fitting for an aristocrat who wished to become a sans-culotte. They accepted his invitation, and he promised to fetch them and two of their closest friends in a carriage. Thus there were five in the carriage, and Marie Louise sat on her intended's lap. When they arrived Mother Chantocé, with her two friends, explored the house, exclaiming at its comfort and the number of things it contained. During this time, Gemonville showed Marie Louise the little apart-

ment which would be hers when she was his wife. . . .
Dinner was delicious. The three older ladies were beside themselves; Marie Louise remained modest and
reserved; Gemonville, respectful. "They have taught us
how to live, these two youngsters," Madame Chantocé
said at the end of the evening.

Gemonville saw his paramour every day and married her ten days later. Once married, it was even better. He developed the sensibility and taste of his wife,
who had excellent natural aptitudes. Their happiness
delighted all Citizen Chantocé's acquaintances. She
now had at her disposal a large garden in the Faubourg
Saint-Marcel, where she was charged with preparing
a good dinner every Sunday for as many people as she
wished to invite: her son-in-law begged her not to worry
over a few sous more or less. These dinners surrounded
Gemonville with an imposing number of people, which
reassured him. He was president of his delegation; he
composed addresses to the Convention, heard them
applauded, and his name was on everybody's lips.
When it was a question of patriotic donations, his was
always the first. "I owe my happiness to the Revolution," he used to say, "without it, I would have married
my equal, and never would I have suspected the good
qualities present in the hitherto lower stations. No, it's
only in the middle class one finds a woman's heart like
that of my wife, and a joyous and pleasant disposition
like her mother's. But I never even knew of the kind
of happiness these two women have brought me; it is
too alien to the customs and the manners of the late
aristocracy."

136

May 6 and 23, 1793

In the evening, toward seven o'clock, I crossed over the Pont Neuf. In the center of the Place de Trois-Maries I saw a group of young men from all walks of life. I approached to listen. An orator was speaking. This is what he said:

"It had been decided that Paris should provide twelve thousand men to send against the rebels in the Vendée province[1]. The rolls were opened to receive voluntary military conscription. But it quickly became apparent that some other means would be necessary. . . . It was decided that no one should be exempt, neither bookkeepers nor law clerks. Who would believe that these latter have the blind insolence to incite trouble, by claiming . . . what? Privilege in a republic which has abolished all privilege! They assembled—without stopping to think that to assemble against the decree of the legally convened delegations is a punishable insurrection—to discuss among themselves whether or not they will obey the law of forced recruitment. The frail clerks, and even their errand boys, claimed that they are accustomed to a soft life, which makes them incapable of withstanding the hardships of war. The women find these reasons excellent. The bookkeepers raised the objection that they are indispensable to their offices. They were about to turn to politics when the armed force of the delegations arrived. The clerks feared for their delicate limbs, the bookkeepers for their curls; all fled; only a few stragglers were arrested, errand boys and supernumeraries, more manly than the others.

" 'All right,' " said a man seeing them run, 'leave the cowards to our women and the whores; they aren't good enough to be soldiers!' And the next day, those who had been arrested were released, and the entire class was then regarded as worthless men. Honor to good soldiers! And eternal infamy to the clerks, to the bookkeepers, to all cowards!" Here the orator was interrupted.

"Coward yourself!" a clerk said to him. "One of us, General Salomon, has distinguished himself and shown that one needn't be a giant to have courage . . ." Seeing that they were going to fight, I moved on. . . .

🕸 137 🕸

July 13 to 16, 1793

Let us pass lightly over the known incidents: the blind revolt—greatly repented—by several provinces, the flight of several arrested constituents, their maneuvers in the provinces to which they fled, the inspection made during the day of the Palais-Égalité, etc. . . . Let us likewise leave anything pertaining to our armies, which is not within the scope of the Night Owl in the streets of Paris. It is now July 13.

I went out in the evening at eight. I entered the bookshop of the citizen who sells the *Nights*. No one there knew anything of the sinister event. Reaching the Pont Neuf I heard a watchman tell a merchant woman: "She was running away. They stopped her at the door. He is dead." I didn't know what was meant. Furthermore, the first item was untrue. . . . I went to the Café Robert-Manouri. There everyone was speaking of the terrible event. But let us catch our breath a moment.

Since 1789, I had heard people talk of Citizen Marat. I had supped on rue de Tournon with people who knew him. An able chemist as well as physicist, he had made discoveries in a difficult field and had opened up new vistas. Through natural science he had achieved, in Paris, his first successes in medicine. He followed nature's methods, and his reputation was such, the second year of his practice, that he earned 40,000 francs. But nature unadorned by charlatanism is considered tiresome in Paris. So he was discharged the third year, and the fourth began his newspaper, the *Ami du Peuple*. What happened to him since is well known—how he was persecuted by Lafayette, who, supported by the whole army, was unable to lay a hand on this lone man. They contented themselves with wrecking his printing plant, and that was the first violation of the freedom of the press. Thereafter Marat kept himself so well hidden that three quarters of the population thought he did not exist. Finally he appeared in the open at the National Convention. It was no longer possible then to doubt his existence. The prejudice against him was general, and his own friends saw themselves temporarily forced to abandon him. He survived nonetheless. Finally the Committee of Twelve indicted him as I have reported . . . in an article written, and even printed, at the time of his triumph. He extricated himself; but certain factions of the public held his triumph up to ridicule. And what has it taken to return to Marat—able physicist, clever doctor, ardent patriot—the purity of his reputation? Death! The patriotic death he met on July 13, between seven and eight o'clock in the evening.

There are few deaths as glorious . . . Lepeletier was assassinated by an ugly character, a bully, an infamous ruffian, universally despised: the profligate Pâris. Marat, however, had inflamed an appealing young lady who, had she know him better, would have admired and defended him. His days were not cut short by an infamous, depraved hand: the monster was a girl, virtuous with a woman's virtue—that is to say, chaste. It was as if this man, devoured by the sacred fire of patriotism, was destined to see his days cut short by the hand of none but a virgin.

At seven o'clock Marie Anne Charlotte Corday went to the home of Citizen Marat, to whom she had written a letter which, if it is authentic, is proof of the crime, because she shows deceit in it. It was with infinite difficulty, and only on the orders of Marat himself, that she was admitted into his presence. Her manner, her discourse, everything about her was so reassuring that the women left her alone with the sick man in his bath. Seeing her chance, Marie Anne Charlotte pulled out a slender little knife, purchased that morning at the Palais-Égalité, and plunged it into the chest of the patriot, who uttered a sharp cry and survived but a few minutes. People hurried in. In a moment of panic Marie Anne Charlotte enveloped herself in a heavy window drape, where she was easily discovered. The guard rushed in; an eyewitness, Citizen Laferté, present later at the hearing, and in the escort to the Abbaye, heard her admit everything. On her way to prison she fainted. When she was coming to, the wretched girl said in amazement, "I am still alive! I thought the people would have torn me to ribbons."

She remained in prison from the night of the thirteenth to the evening of the nineteenth, when she was executed. Two days after Marat's funeral, she had written her father to beg his forgiveness for having deceived him by saying she was going to London. This letter

was regarded simply as an exonerating precaution. . . .
The girl deserved to die. She felt it and did herself
credit. But whence comes such resolute conduct, regarded with horror by the entire capital after the crime?
Is it not a manifestation of virtue? How is it that in
this century of Amazons she did not understand that
a female assassin is the most frightful of monsters? Oh,
you women who wish to be men, and you feeble men
who encourage them, the crime of Marie Anne Charlotte is yours as much as hers. . . . The executioner
struck her severed head; he was punished for it and imprisoned. It is not for the executioner to add to the
sentence.

🕸 138 🕸

THE PRETTY PATRIOT FROM CALVADOS

August 10 to 28, 1793

I am attempting to collect all extraordinary facts in
order to record them in this work, which will one day
be of the greatest importance.

A young lady from Caen, a true patriot, but somewhat fanatic, came to Paris with the intention of aton-
ing for the wrong done the Republic by the temporary
deviation of her province and by the crime of Marie
Anne Charlotte. The means she wished to use were
singular; she was a passionate brunette about twenty-
six years old. Like the ancient Gallic druidesses, who
each year solemnly conferred their favors on the most
distinguished warriors, she intended to bestow the
pleasures of love on patriotic heroes. In pursuance of
this noble project, she made inquiries. Then she wanted
to see and learn. Her investigations were quite thor-

ough. But one man was newly married to a pretty young girl whom he adored; another one had a jealous mistress or two; and still another disdained women and never stooped before them, although he used another word, which caused some amusement. Several others . . . etc. etc. Briefly, she could not find whom to favor in giving herself, nor to whom to give herself in favoring him . . . however one wishes.

She was in the midst of these fluctuations, when I encountered her by chance. I don't know what I seemed to be but, in short, she thought me the kind to be favored, and also that there would be much courage in this act of devotion. She approached me. I mistook her for a girl from rue de l'Arbre-Sec, who accosts me sometimes, and my reply was in keeping with this idea.

"I see that you misunderstand," Félicité Prodiguer told me then, "and I myself am perhaps in error. Who are you?" I told her about myself. The young lady reflected. "You are perhaps as good as another, but first of all I think I must ask your advice." She thereupon related to me how she had come to Paris to repair—with a zeal in the style of the ancients—the wrongs of her province. She revealed to me the state of her fortune, etc. I listened attentively.

"I think, citizen," I finally said to her, "that it would be more appropriate to dedicate your pretty person and your considerable fortune to a young patriot whose happiness you would assure and who would assure yours, thus providing two good subjects for the State. What do you say? And to suit your purposes, I advise you to choose a Parisian who has already served with distinction; that will make you resemble the ancient druidesses more closely." I explained to her what I meant by that. She begged me then to take her to a few public places such as the spectacles, the cafés, the ward headquarters. I consented, and we left at once.

We entered the Café Robert-Manouri, where she made her first observations. From there, we went to my ward headquarters, where she took great interest in a young man from the office. Appointment for the next day. We went to the Italian players, since the French Theater had just been suppressed for having performed various plays in which elements of aristocratic taste appeared, and for having shown inclinations in keeping with it. They finished on the [?] of September with *Paméla*, by the ex-legislator François Neufchâteau. Tuesday we went to the Opéra. Wednesday to the Théâtre-National on rue Richelieu; Thursday to the *République*; Friday to the *Variétés du Palais*; Saturday to the *Théâtre de Molière*; finally Sunday we returned to my delegation, where she dropped her handkerchief in front of the young man in the office. They were married, for she suited him well, and I believe they will be happy.

🎉 139 🎉

DECLARATION OF THE AUTHOR'S POLITICAL BELIEFS

As I said at the outset, I have written this work as incidents were actually happening. It has been very long in the printing. I included more of the public sentiment at the time than my own. But here I must present the latter in all its purity.

I believe that the true national representation is in the Mountain[1] party; that the Jacobins and the patriotic clubs of the same sort, those who think as they do, are the true patriots; that the Pétions, etc., praised a year ago, were traitors; that Marat, Robespierre, etc., have saved the country; that the executions of September 2, 3, 4 and 5 were unfortunately necessary, above all as regards non-juring priests, the laity, the counter-revolutionaries, etc.;' that the death of Louis Capet[2] was just and necessary and that the proper aim of his defense, as I have said in this work, was not to save him but to show the Nation that it was in her interest that the last tyrant of the French should perish; that when I said he was not a tyrant—having been born to the throne—I meant only that he did not ascend to it through violence. I maintain that at present all the old French kings must be named tyrants; that the days of May 31, June 1, 2, 3, 4, etc., October 3 and oo [*sic*], which resulted, saved the country; that the crimes of Marie Antoinette, of Brissot,[3] etc., are clearly established; and that with its vigor, its zeal and its fiery patriotism the Paris Commune has served the entire Republic exceedingly well.

P.S. The events which occurred since that time are: the evening of the sixth, the arrest of the ex-deputy Gorsas—author of the *Âne-promeneur,* then of the *Courier de Versailles à Paris,* later the *Courier des départements*—who had usurped, who knows how, a kind of reputation in these same departments. After August 19, 1792, he joined the Brissotine sect. The day after, the seventh, he was led before the Revolutionary Tribunal, with three witnesses to confirm that he really was Gorsas. His name was testimony enough; he was declared an outlaw, he was told they were applying a decree which condemned him to death. . . . He tried to speak. He said, it is believed, that his death would soon be avenged. The president replied with only four words: "Take away the accused." He was executed at three o'clock.

The morning of the same day a pair of twins were executed for the crime of counter-revolution. With them, but not as their accomplice, although guilty of

the same crime, Charlotte Vautant, a young woman of
twenty-two, whose death without a confessor had been
met with dignity. The true French patriots must be
very admirable, for those who falsely call themselves
such try to imitate them. I only mention the curé of
Saint-Barthélemy, a constitutional priest, to repeat
what I have already said: that priests cannot eradicate
the aristocratic filth from their souls. It sticks to them
like the paint encrusted on the bodies of savages.

On the second day of the third decade of the
first month (Saturday, October 12) Marie Antoinette
underwent secret interrogation.

On the third day of the third decade we received
the news of the surrender of Lyons. Four thousand
aristocrats escaped through the Vèze quarter, but they
were pursued and fifteen hundred were cut to ribbons.
The treasure which they were carrying away with them
was captured, and one hopes that the inhabitants of
the area will destroy the rest. A victory was won in
Vendée, where Châtillon was retaken. Deputies from
Nantes came to state the reasons for the all-too-slow
progress of the Republican army in Vendée.

The fourth of the third: Marie Antoinette was before the Revolutionary Tribunal. This haughty woman
finally felt the full power of these words from an ancient: *Nil humani a me alienum.* . . . Nothing human
is alien to me, not even unhappiness or shame. . . .
And she has deserved it.

Under interrogation, Marie Antoinette d'Autriche
de Lorraine added to her given names her title, which
made no impression. Her answers were short—yes and
no. Sometimes she added: "That is not so." She also
gave a written response. The president pointed out
that this was not customary and returned the note
to her through her unofficial counsel. Then she said it
aloud, without reading it. It was in response to a serious charge which related to her son.

I. Her interrogation, which began the third, continued through the fourth, and ended at three o'clock in the morning on the fifth. She was sentenced at four o'clock. They led her off to prison. She asked her two counsels if she had perhaps shown too much superiority in her answers.

II. Vouland, on behalf of the Committee of General Security,[4] asked that the two counsels be detained in order to learn if she had confided anything to them. They assured the Committee that she had divulged nothing. She went to bed and slept for about two hours. She took some chocolate. She spent two hours with the priest. She was dressed in white, and a little black ribbon fastened her bonnet. She did not ask to see her children. She left the Palais de Justice at eleven-thirty. She had requested a carriage. She was put into it with a confessor, a white-haired old man. She held herself erect, and did not make a point of speaking to the priest, although she answered him several times. She must have been pale, as any woman must who puts on a great deal of rouge and who has endured great anguish. She was executed on the Place de la Révolution, opposite the Statue of Liberty, at a quarter after twelve noon, for having consistently worked against the Revolution, for having maintained a party of Austrians in Paris, for having persuaded her husband to flee to Varennes, for having herself opened and shut all doors, for having continued to plot upon her return, for having bribed constituents so as to revise the Constitution in order to destroy its effectiveness, etc. . . . She was furthermore accused of a horrendous crime, which was indicated above.* It was said that a young gendarme in the prison . . . But that is

---

* Called upon to reply, she denied it, adding with a glance toward the people: "That is impossible; I appeal to all mothers." She did not, like Mary Stuart, refuse to acknowledge the Tribunal. (Restif's note)

not proven. More will be known about all these things in time. Her body was taken away at once and put in lime. May all tyrants perish—Kings, Queens, Electors, Landgraves, Margraves, Czars, Sultans, Lamas, Popes, etc., etc. . . . Amen! Amen!

P.P.S. They say she fainted at the moment when the blade fell.

They arrested an ex-gendarme who soaked his handkerchief in the blood. Exaltation, crazed mind.

On the eighth of the third, we received the news that the blockade of Maubeuge had been lifted.

Since this book went off press, events have come in rapid succession. The rebels of Vendée, having been defeated at Mortagne and at Cholet, repaired to the Île de Noirmoutier, where they were received by the perfidious inhabitants. Driven from Beaupréau and from Ancénis, they had only that asylum, where they have perhaps been taken by now, so that Vendée is destroyed. That fertile land, inhabited by superstitious and coarse folk, easily led astray, is now but a heap of ruins and ashes. Thus counter-revolutionaries no longer hold Lyons or Vendée. Bordeaux has just given evidence of the most ardent patriotism. Our army of the North, having driven the enemy from the vicinity of Maubeuge, is vigorously pursuing it, while another column which took Furnes is advancing toward Niewport and will perhaps take Ostend. In the Rhine area they attempted to repair the setback that resulted from an officer's treason.

The twenty-two indicted deputies have been before the Revolutionary Tribunal for three days as of today, sextidi—the sixth day of the first decade of the second month—October 27, old calendar. Vergniaud delivered a very vehement speech of an hour and a

quarter yesterday, quintidi—the fifth day of the decade
—but as of now I have no information about it, not
having been able to hear it. . . .

The anti-civic mobs continue at the bakery doors;
it seems a certain class of people takes pleasure in the
difficulty over getting its bread.

On October 22, old calendar, General Gartaud
gained a considerable advantage over the Toulon
rebels; six English vessels were damaged by cannon and
are under repair. About five hundred of their men were
killed. Thus we are on the brink of recapturing that
important place, forever the shame of the traitors who
govern England.

The King of Prussia has quit his army, leaving it
under the command of Brunswick, and has gone to
lead the one that will assure him the theft of part of
Poland.

Cobourg was taken at Maubeuge with his troops.
"If the French Republicans take me here, I shall become a Republican myself." He was taken, and he is
still the coward who received four deputies whom he
holds prisoner from the hands of the perfidious Dumouriez.

The new calendar of the Republic was established
for the first month, to begin September 22, old style,
which became the first of the first decade of the year
Two of the Republic, that is, the first of Vendémiaire.
It is well known that in *Les Nuits de Paris* I proposed a
reform of the year and the months; I proposed to
have the year begin on December 21 or 22, at the time
of the winter solstice. I proposed then to change the
names of the months, and to make them equal to each
other, etc. The names I gave them were: Primobre,
from December 22 to January 22; Duobre, Triobre,
Quartile, Quintile, Sextile, Septembre, from July 22
to August 22; Octobre, Novembre, Décembre, Un-
zobre, Douzobre—the last from November 22 to De-

cember 22. The names given in the new calendar are more felicitous. They are: Vendémiaire, from September 22 to October 22; Brumaire, Frimaire, Nivos, Ventos, Pluvios, Germinal, Floréal, Préréal, Messidore, Fervidore, Fructidore. Since the months were divided into decades, names were likewise given to the days of the decade which stand in place of the week. They are: Primidi, Duodi, Tridi, Quartidi, Quintidi, Sextidi, Septidi, Octidi, Nonidi, and Decadi, which is the day of rest. . . . Drums were beaten yesterday, sextidi, the sixth of Brumaire, to force open the shops which the partisans of the old Sunday kept closed.

I have now only to report the sentencing by the Revolutionary Tribunal of the twenty-two deputies who were before it. The twenty-two traitorous deputies condemned to death yesterday, nonidi, at ten-thirty in the evening, October 30, old calendar, were executed at midnight: Valazé, one of them, committed suicide on hearing the sentence; the others arose in a passion and threw away their promissory notes. They marched to their death with a false cheerfulness. Carra wore a look of dumb surprise; Silleri and Fauchet had a confessor. At the moment of the execution Vergniaud tried to speak; the rolling of drums prevented him. Such was the end of those who had not marched straight and unhesitatingly in the direction of the Revolution.

It is being announced, this first decadi of Brumaire, at eight o'clock, that our troops are in Mons, and that preparations to return to Toulon are being accelerated. Long live the Republic and the Mountain!

NOTES

THE NOCTURNAL SPECTATOR

1 THE POOR FOLKS' POCKETBOOK

1. *The useless people*: in Restif's view, those not directly useful to society.

2. *Les Halles*: since the twelfth century the wholesale market was at the Champeaux, in the same location as today.

2 THE HOLE IN THE WALL

1. *Watch*: a squad of armed men, on foot or on horseback, charged with policing the streets at night.

2. Lumber from Morvan was floated down the river to Paris.

3 THE DRUNKEN MAN

1. *The C.D.C.T.*: perhaps the Count de Clermont-Tonnerre?

2. *Hôtel-Dieu*: the oldest hospital in Paris, near Notre Dame.

4 THE BROKEN MAN

1. *Place de Grève*: (or, simply, *the Grève*): a large open area on the banks of the Seine, in front of the Hôtel de Ville (city hall); until 1830 public executions were performed there.

2. *Interrogation:* until 1789, this torture was practiced on persons accused of civil or criminal offenses, to provoke confessions or naming of accomplices.

3. *Blows:* the torture of the wheel involved beating the victim with a club to break his limbs, then leaving him exposed on the wheel to die. Introduced in France about 1539.

6   THE IMPRUDENT GIRL

1. *The Marquise:* the theme of the *Nights* rests on fiction: in the second *Night*, Restif relates that one night, at the window of a house on rue Payenne, he saw a still-lovely woman leaning out on her balcony. Although it was not the Marquise de Montalembert, a beautiful and charming woman he had met some time before and not seen since, he conceived the following device to be used for the *Nights*: The woman on the balcony confides to him that, married, wealthy, surfeited in all things, she is weary of it all, and subject to vapors. Restif leaves this *vaporeuse*; he sees her again the next night; she passes him a letter and begs him to answer it, and "each night I shall read what you bring me." Restif, the night wanderer, thus continues for many years to see this woman, and tells her the story of what he has seen in the course of his nocturnal walks through the city, either in writing or in person at her house. He calls her the Marquise de M*** (thus assimilating her with the Marquise de Montalembert). He brings to her house young women he rescues from corruption; she takes them in and helps them change their way of life. He later tells how this new cause gives her energy and life.

2. *Bretonvilliers:* this building housed the administration charged with collection of indirect taxes.

9   THE STREETWALKER

1. *Savoyard:* inhabitants of the duchy of Savoy (capital: Turin) settled in Paris in the eighteenth century and worked as water carriers, chimney sweeps, ferrymen; they had a reputation for being crude and ill-bred. See further: Note 1 under THE BRUTE.

11 THE RAGWOMAN

1. *Maison-Blanche:* at that time a small village outside the Fontainebleau gate.

14 THE RAID

1. *Saint-Martin-des-Champs:* prison for prostitutes until 1785, when they were transferred to the Petite Force jail, near rue Saint-Antoine.

15 THE RAID, *continued*

1. *Victoire:* one of Restif's girl friends, Victoire Dorneval, who lived in a brothel. Her father, an attorney, managed to find her and had her locked up in a convent.

16 THE DISMEMBERED CORPSES

1. *Cagnard* or *caignard:* crannies used as shelter by derelicts, around the bridges in this neighborhood and in the vestibules to the Hôtel-Dieu.

2. The Academy of Surgery which dated from Saint Louis (Louis IX) was relocated from rue des Cordeliers to the present rue de l'École-de-Médecine. There were dissecting rooms on rue de la Bûcherie and rue de la Harpe.

19 FESTIVITIES

1. *Feast days:* before 1789 there were 32 days of rest aside from Sundays, and the Parisian worker was free on Mondays (cf. Charles Kunstler, *La Vie Quotidienne sous Louis XVI,* Hachette).

20 THE DANCE HALL

1. *Monsieur Nicolas or The Human Heart Unveiled by Itself,* Restif's sixteen-volume autobiography published during his lifetime, 1794-97.

2. *Collège de Saint-Côme:* surgeons' society, at the corner of rue des Cordeliers and rue de la Harpe.

23 THE ESCAPING PRISONER

1. *Grands-Degrés:* see Note 1 under THE BATHS.

25 THE "WELL-LIGHTED" BLIND MAN

1. Restif refers to her attack of boredom and lethargy.

2. *Le Marais:* this district, on the bogs along the Seine, had hitherto (seventeenth century) been a focus of aristo-

cratic life in Paris; in the eighteenth century the center had moved and the neighborhoods to the west (Saint-Honoré) became fashionable.

26 THE SAINT JOHN'S DAY BONFIRE

1. Each year on the night of June 23, faggots were piled in the Place de Grève and the king would come to set them afire, signaling the start of popular celebration. After the death of Louis XIV it was the mayor of Paris and other public officials who started proceedings.

2. *The original:* Du Hameauneuf, another nightwalker like Restif. The name applied to the Comte de Villeneuve whom Restif had met at the house of Fanny de Beauharnais in 1787.

3. It is not surprising that such reckless talk should have brought suspicion on Restif as a police informer and, during the revolutionary period, as a spy for the King.

29 THE PLACE LOUIS-XV

1. *The Tuileries:* the gardens laid out by order of Catherine de' Medici, by Le Nôtre the elder; they culminated in terraces on the Seine and at the Place Louis-XV (the present Place de la Concorde).

30 THE SOUBISE GARDEN

1. At the time there were 30,000 Jews in France, in a population of 26 million (Charles Kunstler, *op. cit.*).

31 THE REAL MAGUELONE

1. *Nicolet Theater:* Jean-Baptiste Nicolet (1728-1796) presented pantomimes and opéra comique scenes on boulevard du Temple and at the large fairs. He had his own theater, became famous, and even received the title of *grand danseur du roi.*

2. *Bavaroise:* a beverage made of hot water or tea, sweetened with sugar or syrups and often flavored with rum, brandy, etc.

3. *Colas:* nickname for Nicolas, used for: a fool, a simpleton.

4. *Demerup:* an anagrammatic pseudonym, perhaps for the Demoiselles de Pumer.

32 THE SAINT-LAURENT FAIR

1. Renowned in the eighteenth century, this fair was held from June 28 to September 30. The public enjoyed marionettes, tightrope dancers, a great display of merchandise, and cafés. It was closed in 1775, reopened in 1778, then abandoned.

2. *Lazarists:* priests of the congregation of the mission founded by Vincent de Paul in 1625. The immense Saint-Lazare convent was a onetime leper home; it stood on the present rue du Faubourg-Saint-Denis.

3. *Candles:* apprentices were not paid for their work and even had to furnish their own candles.

33 THE MAN WHO LEAPED FROM THE WINDOW

1. *Pinolet:* the blind man of an earlier episode.

34 THE BRUTE

1. *Water carrier:* Savoyards or Auvergnats who brought water up to private apartments for bathing and household purposes. They were paid two sous a trip, that is, for two buckets, or eight gallons of water. There were 20,000 water carriers in Paris.

35 THE DOORSTEPS

1. *Shoe:* there are frequent references in Restif's works to shoe fetishism.

2. *Argus:* in Greek legend, Argus was a monster with a hundred eyes, fifty of which were always open for surveillance; here, the parents or the husband of the lady.

37 THE TWO WORKMEN

1. *La Courtille:* a famous cabaret and dance hall at Belleville.

2. *Nero's apologist:* Simon Linguet, guillotined in 1794. In his *History of the Revolutions of the Roman Empire,* he questioned the accounts of Tacitus and Suetonius and justified the tyrants.

40 THE BILLBOARD STRIPPER

1. *The Lazy Man's Labor:* perhaps the title of an earlier publication.

41 ACCOUNT OF A FIRE

1. April 6, 1763. The Opéra was then located in a part of the Palais-Royal.

2. The fire on the Pont au Change: the bridge leading from the Quai de l'Horloge (the clock tower on the Île de la Cité) to the Châtelet. It was lined with inhabited houses; they were demolished in 1788.

42 THE DEN OF INIQUITY

1. *Paysan-Paysanne: Le paysan et la paysanne pervertis* or *Les dangers de la ville* (The Hague, 1784). This appeared in Paris in 1787 before the first book of the *Nights* (1788). It was the resetting in four volumes of the *Paysan perverti* (1775) and the *Paysanne pervertie* (1784).

2. *Les Françaises:* the daughters, women, wives and mothers. (Paris, 1786; 4 volumes.)

3. *Recruiting agent:* these criminal methods of enlistment were common in the professional (mercenary) armies.

4. *Lavater* (1741-1801): published a *Memoir on the Art of Studying the Physiognomy* in 1772. Balzac made frequent use of his science of facial characteristics.

5. *Hôpital:* a prison/workhouse/hospital/shelter (detention-ward) for loose women. The word will often appear in its French form throughout this translation.

43 THE RAINSPOUTS

1. *Échené:* from the Burgundian word *échenet* for "conduit."

2. *Corneille's poverty:* this tradition has been discredited. Corneille lived to the age of seventy-eight and suffered many family difficulties in his last years. *Théodore, Agésilas,* and *Attila* met with no success.

3. *Church Council (conseil de fabrique):* until 1905, a vestry or parochial council managed the temporal aspects of each parish.

4. *Cabriolets:* these swift, light carriages caused many accidents in the narrow Paris streets.

48 NOCTURNAL IMPROPRIETIES

1. Tax which supported a constabulary of men who guided people through the muddy streets at night with lanterns.

52 THE LOCAL MAIL SERVICE

1. Established in Paris in 1758. The national post office had been set up for all of France in 1464, by Louis XI.

57 THE BATHS

1. *Grands-Degrés:* steps down to the Seine at rue des Bernardins. A street near the quay still bears this name.

2. *Port au Blé* (the wheat port): upstream from the Place de Grève.

3. *The Augustins:* a convent of this order stood at the location of today's Quai des Grands-Augustins and rues Dauphine and Pont-de-Lodi.

4. *Cabin* or *cabanes:* reference to the living quarters atop river barges, long called *cabanes.*

5. *Terrain* or *La motte aux papelards* were the names given to the eastern end of the Île de la Cité, which had formed gradually by deposits of earth, sand, mud, etc., and rubble of all kinds.

6. Restif explains here the meaning he has given the word.

7. *Sycophant:* informer and, by extension, sneak, sly; from those who informed on the illegal traffic in figs (sukon) in ancient Greece.

58 BILLIARDS: PLAYERS

1. *Bicêtre* "seminary": Bicêtre was a prison; sardonic allusion is made to the incarceration and stern lesson of life there.

60 THE HIGH HEELS

1. *Night Owl:* see Note 5 under THE CAFÉ.

61 BILLIARDS: THE RETURN MATCH

1. *The Châtelet:* fortress and prison built under Louis VI (1081-1137) north of the Pont au Change; closed by Louis XVI in 1780; destroyed in 1802.

65 THE CAFÉ

1. *Café de la Régence:* a celebrated café on the Place du Palais-Royal; Diderot set his *Rameau's Nephew* there.

2. *A Thousand and One Kinds:* Restif draws parallel between the fantasy of the classic tale and the fantastic nature of the news in these journals.

3. *Le Mercure galant:* a weekly begun in 1672; it became the *Mercure de France* in 1724.

4. *Madame Parangon:* a pseudonym Restif invents to disguise the wife of his first employer, under whom he served his apprenticeship in Auxerre. In two other works he recounts a supposed adventure with her. *Parangon* (paragon) is a typographical term meaning "line justification."

5. *Owl:* because of his hooked nose, Restif was so nicknamed in the workshops; it occurred to him to use the title of *Night Owl* for his nocturnal spectator's account, but he decided instead on *Les Nuits de Paris.*

67 AT THE HAIR- AND WIG-DRESSER'S

1. See Note 3, etc., of THEATER.

68 THE O FILII

1. *O filii:* part of the Easter liturgy.

2. *Carmelites:* their convent was near the Luxembourg gardens.

3. *Rapenot:* a Jansenist bookseller.

4. *Convulsionary:* from 1727 till the Revolution, extraordinary scenes took place in the Saint-Médard cemetery around the grave of the Deacon Pâris, a Jansenist: his followers were seized by collective convulsions. The cemetery was finally closed.

70 THE CLOUDY EVENING

1. *Hapless girl:* a girl who had wanted to drown her child, and whom Restif persuaded against the act.

76 THE DAINTY SLIPPERS

1. *Rue des Lombards:* so called for the North Italian (Lombard) settlers who acted as moneylenders, in the Saint-Merri quarter.

2. *The Grand Dauphin:* the son of Louis XIV who died in 1711.

3. *Perrault, Charles* (1628-1703): author of *Contes de ma mère l'Oye,* or *Mother Goose* (1697).

78 THE DRUNKARD'S REBUKE

1. *Sara's mother:* Restif's landlady, Mme. Debée, was

the mother of Sara Leeman, a young Jewess who was one of his sweethearts during his forties, and who left him.

81 ANATOMY OF THE HUMAN HEART

1. *Émile:* a treatise on education by Jean-Jacques Rousseau, and published in 1762.

85 MY DATES ON THE ÎLE SAINT-LOUIS

1. From 1774 on, Restif took to carving dates of special personal significance on the parapets or walls on the Île Saint-Louis, together with names and notes in French or Latin.

2. *Malum:* "misfortune."

3. "Despair! The divine lady called to heaven September 25. Sylvie dead August 29. Word of the Marquise, ill, September 29. The Marquise recovered today November 22. She is an angel." Restif collected his inscriptions himself, and long after his death (1889) they were published.

87 TUILERIES: PLEASURE PARTIES

1. An allusion to another incident: a young prostitute pursued by two Swiss guards of the Tuileries eludes them by hiding among the chairs piled together by the canteen-keeper.

88 A NIGHT IN THE LUXEMBOURG GARDENS

1. *Cavalier:* an official escort to a fashionable Italian lady.

2. *Melibeus, Corydon, Alexis:* shepherds in Vergil's *Eclogues.*

3. *Anacreon:* Greek poet known for his odes on life's pleasures.

4. *Quae te dementia cepit:* "What madness has overtaken you!"

5. *Galatea:* shepherdess in *Eclogues.*

6. *Élise:* one of the girls Restif's fictitious Marquise rescued.

89 THE OPÉRA

1. After the fire on June 8, 1781, a building was quickly constructed for the Opéra. This later became the Théâtre de la Porte-Saint-Martin.

2. *Rosalie Levasseur:* foremost interpreter of Gluck's operas between 1766 and 1785.

94 AN EVENING IN THE NEW PALAIS-ROYAL

1. Du Hameauneuf had earlier disappeared for a time, whimsically pretending to be dead.

95 FIGARO

1. *Figaro:* written by Pierre Augustin Caron de Beaumarchais (later made into an opera by Mozart). It ridiculed the selfishness and extravagance of the aristocracy.

97 THEATER. JUSTICE

1. This tirade is addressed to the French from the lips of Du Hameauneuf; he addresses the people as "Your Honor," with irony.

2. *Athalie,* killed in the name of Joash at Jehoida's instigation; *Le Cid,* etc.

3. *Variétés:* popular theater (1779), on boulevard du Temple.

4. *Petits Beaujolais:* founded in 1784; it substituted children for puppets.

5. *Ambigu-Comique:* on boulevard du Temple.

6. *Audinot:* manager of the Ambigu-Comique theater.

98 THE BALLOONS

1. The *Montgolfier* brothers built an air balloon which went up in 1783.

2. *Charles:* substituted hydrogen for air, and equipped his balloon with a valve; he and *Robert* sent up a balloon earlier with a basket; they made some rather lengthy (45 km.) voyages.

3. *Hertschel:* German organist settled in England, who discovered and studied Uranus.

4. *Cassini:* director of the Paris Observatory.

5. *Lalande:* astronomy professor at the Collège de France.

6. *Humblot:* Diderot's cousin, a bookseller.

7. *Blanchard:* collaborator of Charles.

8. *Pilâtre de Roziers:* died in an attempt to cross the Channel by air.

102 PASSENGER-BARGE INCIDENT

1. *Water-coaches*: large barges for passenger transportation; they were drawn by six horses walking tow-paths, and they held as many as a hundred persons.

2. *Gouvernailleur*: the name of this barge.

103 TUMULTS—OUTBURSTS

1. *The Parlements* were the High Courts of the land, the Paris Parlement ruling over all of them. The latter had banned *Émile*; it was confiscated and burned in 1762.

2. *Philosophes*: in the Age of Enlightenment, these were publicists, economists, political scientists, and social reformers.

104 THE POLITICAL CLUBHOUSE

1. *Le Caveau*: a club established on the Buci circle, dissolved in 1739, re-established in 1759; Pelletier, Marmontel, Crébillon were frequent visitors.

2. *Lansquenet*: card game introduced in France by German mercenary soldiers; faro and brelan: other card games.

105 THE IRREPARABLE LOSS

1. Since the Marquise was by all evidence a nonexistent figure, this chapter is pure fiction. It is offered in the selection to show the complexity of the *Nights*, wherein the romantic sometimes prevails over reportage.

2. The first was Madame Parangon, the wife of Restif's first employer at Auxerre (see Note 4 under THE CAFÉ).

3. Augé, his son-in-law.

4. *The layette-maker*, like the others of the little society, was one of the girls rescued and sheltered by the Marquise.

106 THE PLACE DAUPHINE

1. On August 25, 1788, Necker replaced the dismissed Calonne.

2. Historians agree that from the start of the unrest, the Palais-Royal, residence of Louis Philippe Joseph, Duke of Orléans, was a center of intrigue. This prince spent a fortune to assure his popularity; he voted for the death of his cousin Louis XVI, but was himself executed in 1793. King Louis Philippe, born 1773 and reigning from 1830 to 1848, was his son.

107 THE WALKS IN THE NEW PALAIS-ROYAL

1. This is September, 1788. There were demonstrations on the Pont Neuf before the statue of Henry IV there; the statue was broken August 13, 1792.

2. *Fanny*: Marie-Anne Touchard, 1738-1813, wife of Comte de Beauharnais, lived in a private house on rue de Tournon. She received her friends on Fridays, with some claim to holding a literary salon. Restif was introduced to her in 1787. She was an aunt, by marriage, of Josephine, Napoleon's future wife.

108 SUPPERS WITH FANNY

1. Restif's religious convictions: apparently deist, but anticlerical.

2. *Sébastien Mercier*: author of the *Tableau de Paris* (1781-1790) and the *Nouveau Paris* (1799-1800).

THE NIGHTS OF THE REVOLUTION

109 JULY 12, 1789

1. *Necker*, exiled on July 11, left for Switzerland; he was to be recalled five days later.

2. It was not *Foulon* who succeeded him but Breteuil.

3. He was charged with clearing the Place Louis-XV of the demonstrators mobbing there.

4. *Palais d'Orléans*: the Palais-Royal, then occupied by Philippe, Duke of Orléans.

5. *Saint-Florentin*, minister of State in 1791. *Sartine*, chief of police (1759); *Lenoir* succeeded him in 1774.

6. *Obscenity*: read each word backwards.

7. Restif's accounts for this period have been questioned by some historians, credited by others. His authority as an eyewitness cannot be extended to all these pages; he acknowledges this himself.

111 JULY 14, 1789

1. *Tableaux de la Vie*, the texts of Restif's *Monument du costume*, illustrated by Moreau the younger, republished under this title at Neuwied on the Rhine.

2. *Jacques de Flesselles*: merchant-provost of Paris. *Delaunai*: warden of the Bastille.

3. *Veterans and Swiss guards*: they were defending the monarchy, and the Bastille.

4. *Carrying-hood*: worn by the slaughterhouse workers and the butchers to carry quarters, sides of meat.

5. *Lampposts*: the victims were hanged from the bar of the lampposts by the rope that served to lower and hoist the lanterns.

6. *Delolme*: connected with the administration of the prison.

7. *Districts*: territory of electoral precincts in 1789. There were sixty of them; each bore the name of the principal church of the quarter; later, Paris was divided into sections.

8. *Augé*, his son-in-law, whom Restif calls a villain elsewhere; Restif was acquitted and Augé sent to the Force prison for four days.

9. *Marion*: his second daughter, married to a cousin, Edmond Restif, who worked at the printer's with Restif. She was left a widow with three daughters, and she apparently cared for Restif during his last years.

112 JULY 17, 1789

1. *D'Artois*: Louis' brother, and the future Charles X.

2. *Polignacs*: Jules de Polignac, and his wife, a very good friend of the Queen's, were most unpopular.

3. *Bailli*: mayor of Paris (July 15, 1789).

4. *Lafayette*: caused the adoption of the tricolor cockades, and organized the national guard.

5. Lafayette was "hero of two worlds," because he had returned from America in glory.

6. *Bailli* had written works on the history of astronomy.

7. *Viri*: Foulon's assassination at Viry-Châtillon.

8. Bertier's death at Compiègne. (He was Foulon's son-in-law, and Intendant of Paris.)

9. *Saint-Nicolas-du-Chardonnet*: church at the corner of rue Saint-Victor and rue des Bernardins; Restif belonged to that district.

113 JULY 22, 1789

1. *Foulon* or *Foullon*: councilor of State in 1789, one-time Intendant General of the Army. Name is unfortunate

because it also means wringer, crusher, or winepress, carrying implication of ruthless profiteering for money.

2. *The Abbaye:* the Abbey of Saint-Germain-des-Près owned an abbatial prison in one of its buildings, which in September, 1792 became one of the principal prisons for suspects.

3. *Croix-de-Saint-Louis:* a Saint-Louis Cross: a retired officer decorated with that medal, whose ribbon was red and wide.

4. The revolutionary cockade was red, white and blue.

5. "Be instructed, ye judges of the earth" (Psalms 2:10).

6. Cautery ulcer: an artificial ulcer maintained in a suppurating state in order to relieve and heal a natural ulcer.

114 OCTOBER 5 to 6, 1789

1. *Saint-Huruge:* Marquis de; godson to the King of Sardinia. Victim of a lettre de cachet and imprisoned for three years at Charenton, he fled to England and returned in 1789 to devote himself to revolutionary agitation. Arrested with others, then liberated, he turned away from politics.

2. *The costliness of bread:* attributed to speculation and various manipulations, the bad state of agriculture in general, and five years of poor harvests.

3. *The Salpêtrière:* large prison complex.

4. Aria from *Richard coeur de Lion,* light opera by Grétry.

5. Arriving late, Lafayette stopped the massacre of the bodyguards at Versailles and rescued the Queen.

6. *Estates General:* the legislative body of the government, which had not assembled since 1614, consisting of 1200 representatives of the Three Estates: nobility; clergy; and the Third Estate, i.e., about 95% of the population. However, they had all equal shares of representation.

TWENTY PARIS NIGHTS

115 FEDERATION, July 13 to 14, 1790

1. *Champ-de-Mars:* former (until 1773) drill ground for adjacent military school. *An Altar of the Nation* was erected

on it, where Lafayette and then the King pledged indissoluble fidelity to the nation, and Talleyrand, then bishop of Autun, celebrated a solemn mass there before two hundred thousand persons.

2. God's words to Moses (Exodus 3:14).

3. *Horatius:* from the famous battle fought between the three Horatii and the three Curiaces, as reported by Livy (Book I).

118 JUNE 20 to 21, 1791

1. *January 21, 1793:* date of Louis' death by guillotine.

2. *Café Manouri:* this celebrated café was near the church of Saint-Germain-l'Auxerrois. It was patronized by Diderot, Voltaire, Sébastien Mercier, Restif, and many other writers and journalists of the time.

3. *Stewards'-pantries:* the scullery in the Tuileries garden where the palace servants brought the tableware to be washed.

4. *Swiss guard:* since 1496, under Charles VIII, Swiss volunteers enrolled in a special corps serving as protection of the palace inhabited by the King of France. In the eighteenth century, the guard comprised six squads of fifteen men each. In addition, there was a regiment of Swiss guards who supported the French guards. Corps dissolved in 1792.

5. Presently *rue Gît-le-Coeur*. Originally named for Gilles Queux, the king's cook; the name underwent distortions through Gilles-Coeur to the very engaging Gît-le-Coeur of today.

6. *Abbess:* title given ironically to the madam of a brothel.

119 THE KING'S FLIGHT

1. *Section:* Paris had been divided into forty-eight sections, or wards.

2. *Monsieur* and *Madame:* the King's brother (future Louis XVIII) and his wife. *Madame Élisabeth:* Louis XVI's sister. *Madame* (Royale): his daughter.

3. *Sainte-Menehould* (Marne): the postmaster recognized the fugitives and they were apprehended at Varennes, the next stop, at midnight of June 21, 1791.

120 JUNE 23 to 24, 1791

1. *Convention:* an error by Restif; he is probably referring to the Constituent Assembly which did not end until October 1, 1791.

2. *Barnave:* young lawyer, deputy from Grenoble. After Louis' return from Varennes, he attempted to exert a moderating influence on the revolutionaries. He was guillotined in 1793.

3 *Pétion de Villeneuve:* named mayor of Paris in 1791. Committed suicide in 1794.

4. *Phélipeaux:* four branches of the family occupied high positions under the last three kings of the Old Régime: Pontchartrain, La Vrillière, Saint-Florentin, Maurepas.

5. This refers to the garden of Mme. de Pompadour's residence, the Elysée Palace.

6. *Distaffs:* sent to lingering aristocrats by those who had already emigrated, as a sign of mockery and reproach.

121 THE KING'S RETURN, June, 1791

1. *Charles* and *Alexandre de Lameth:* Charles emigrated early; Alexandre, first a revolutionary, later joined the monarchists.

2. *Barnave* (see above)

3. *Mirabeau:* eloquent representative of the Third Estate (Provence); he favored a constitutional monarchy; died in 1791.

4. *Pepin the Short:* (714-768) founder of the Carolingian dynasty.

124 AUGUST 9 to 10, 1792

1. *"Knights of the Dagger":* aristocratic conspirators, banished from the Tuileries by Louis XVI in February, 1791.

125 HOUSE INSPECTIONS, August 28 to 29, 1792

1. *Non-juring priests:* those who refused to take the civil oath prescribed by the Civil Constitution of the Clergy: that is, all the bishops but seven, and almost half of the clergy; the others were called *constitutional priests.*

126 MASSACRES, September 2 to 5, 1792

1. 25,000 bandits and looters from the provinces are said to have roamed the streets of Paris around this time.

2. *The Conciergerie*: residence of the *Concierge*, high magistrate of the Palais de Justice; it was the Queen's last prison.

3. *Montmorin de Saint-Hérem*: formerly minister of Foreign Affairs.

4. *Prince royal*: Louis XVII.

5. *Louise de Croÿ d'Havré de Tourzel*: the royal children's governess; she escaped the Terror.

6. *Sainte-Pélagie*: old charity institution, used as a prison during this time.

7. *Princess de Lamballe*: Marie Antoinette's closest friend.

8. *D'Angremont* and *Laporte*: they were both close to the court, and were victims of the massacres. *Durosoi*: wrote openly in defense of Louis.

9. *Roland*: minister of the Interior in 1792.

127 THE SALPÊTRIÈRE, September 3 to 4, 1792

1. *The* (grande) *Force*, different from the (petite) *Force* in rue Saint-Antoine; this one a part of the Salpêtrière complex. This *hôpital* contained incurable invalids and lunatics as well as indigents, with a prison in the center of the buildings, divided into four sections for men and women.

2. *Counterfeit paper currency*: issued for personal profit as well as to bankrupt the resources of the Revolutionary government. Real bank notes issued 1789 by government against Church property, which was to be sold as national.

3. *Desrues' wife*: imprisoned for poisoning.

4. *La Dixmerie*: author of *Contes philosophiques*, and studies on Spanish literature, in prison at the same time as the Desrues woman.

5. *Jeanne de La Motte*: with her husband, implicated in the famous Necklace Affair.

128 OCTOBER 5 to 6, 1792

1. *The Temple:* an old fortress where Louis and his family were held prisoner.

129 LOUIS' DEFENSE, December 25 to 26, 1792

1. *Convention:* the National Convention, legislative body (1792-1795). Its deputies were called Gironde (The Right), Plain (The Center), and Mountain (The Left).

2. *Malesherbes:* former minister of State; minister of Justice in 1792.

3. *Target:* former president of the Constituent Assembly; he refused, on grounds of insanity, to take part in Louis' defense.

4. *Tronchet:* delegate to the Estates General, and *Desèze*, attorney from Bordeaux and former counsel to the Queen, were the King's defense lawyers.

5. *1992:* As we have seen before, Restif likes to think about the future and to visualize the consequences of an event at which he is present.

131 NIGHT INSPECTION. THE PALAIS-L'ÉGA-LITÉ. January 27-28, 1793

1. On January 20 *Pâris*, a body guard, had assassinated Lepeletier for having voted for Louis' death.

132 LOOTING OF THE GROCERS, February 26 to 27, 1793

1. The National Assembly had abolished the guilds, tariffs and tolls, and banned strikes in June, 1791.

133 RAVAGES, February 28, 1793

1. *Vendée:* royalist revolt in this western province of France, 1793-96, which cost more than 50,000 lives.

2. *Federalists:* group at the Convention who, after May, 1793, opposed the Mountain party on pretext that the Paris delegations had too great an influence on the National Convention. They were forced to accede.

3. *Charles-Joseph Panckoucke:* editor of the *Moniteur*.

4. *Prudhomme:* wrote pamphlets and published an illustrated newspaper, *Les Révolutions de Paris*.

5. *Palais-Égalité:* name of the Palais-Royal after the

abolition of the monarchy. For this reason the Duke of Orléans, who lived there, took the name Philippe-Égalité.

SUPERNUMERARY NIGHTS

134   SETBACKS, April 2, 3, 4, 1793
1. Reference to *Charles François Dumouriez*, Girondin general, who deserted to the enemy.

135   MARAT'S TRIUMPH, April 24, 1793
1. *Ci-devant:* (actually *former*) was used as a noun to indicate a man who belonged to the Old Régime because of title, position, etc.
2. *Sans-culotte:* since 1789, revolutionaries had discarded elegant dresses and knee-breeches (*culottes*) which were a symbol of the privileged classes, and had substituted simple, peasantlike clothes.

136   MAY 6 and 23, 1793
1. *Vendée:* see Note 1 under RAVAGES.

139   DECLARATION OF THE AUTHOR'S POLITICAL BELIEFS
1. *Mountain party:* The radical Jacobin wing whose seats in the Convention were high up toward the rear.
2. Louis XVI was referred to as *"Citizen Louis Capet"* after his imprisonment and death.
3. *Jacques-Pierre Brissot:* Girondin leader who was executed in 1793.
4. *Committee of General Security:* a group of deputies, set up by the Convention, which supervised police activities.